Mathematics for Mechanical Technicians

BOOK 2

SI METRIC EDITION

by M. G. PAGE

*B.Sc.(Eng.) Hons., C.Eng., F.I.Mech.E.,
F.I.Prod.E., M.B.I.M., F.S.S.*

*Head of the Department of Production Engineering
at The Polytechnic, Wolverhampton*

*Chief Examiner in Mathematics and Science
to the City & Guilds of London Institute
for the Mechanical Engineering Technicians Course*

Author of

Mathematics for Mechanical Technicians Book 1
Science for Mechanical Technicians Books 1 and 2
Answers to Problems in Workshop Technology

LONDON

Cassell & Co. Ltd—an imprint of
CASSELL & COLLIER MACMILLAN PUBLISHERS LTD
35 Red Lion Square, London, WC1R 4SG
Sydney, Auckland
Toronto, Johannesburg
An affiliate of Macmillan Inc., New York

First published July 1964
Second edition July 1965
Third edition (in SI units) July 1970
Third edition, second impression May 1971
Third edition, third impression July 1972
Third edition, fourth impression July 1974
Third edition, fifth impression April 1977

I.S.B.N. 0 304 93580 8

This volume is dedicated to members of Advisory
Committees, who so readily give of their time and
experience without thought of reward

Typeset by Gloucester Typesetting Co. Ltd., Gloucester
and printed in Great Britain by The Camelot Press Ltd, Southampton

Preface to the Third Edition

The pleasant reception afforded to the previous editions of this textbook suggests that no significant changes are necessary in the presentation of the material. In particular, since the examiner at the Part II level is entitled to set questions on both the T3 and T4 stages of the course, the decision to provide one book only for the Part II syllabus has been proved correct, especially in view of the marked trend away from part-time toward continuous studies.

The most noticeable change is the presentation of problems in metric units instead of 'British' units, and the volume now conforms fully to the recommendations contained in

BS 1957 *Presentation of Numerical Values*
BS 1991 *Letter Symbols, Signs and Abbreviations*
BS 3763 *International System (SI) Units*

The problems have also been rearranged. Now that the course is firmly established, it is no longer necessary for the author to indicate his opinion of the level at which the examinations will be set. Consequently problems now appear at the end of each article instead of at the end of each chapter. The number of problems has been considerably increased with extra problems compiled by the author, many of which he has set in his capacity as the Chief Examiner for the subject. He wishes to place on record his appreciation of the kindly permission readily granted by the City and Guilds of London Institute to reproduce those questions. The metric conversions have been made by the author so as to retain the significance of the original values.

Certain minor changes in presentation have been made in response to most welcome comments from professional colleagues, to whom the author wishes to tender his sincere thanks. He earnestly trusts this attractive co-operation will continue with this and other works.

Finally, the author wishes to place on record his appreciation of the efficiency and patience of Mrs Dorothy Wilson in assisting with the preparation of the manuscript for the metric version.

M. G. PAGE
WOLVERHAMPTON
1970

Contents

Chapter 5 Mensuration

Chapter One

Calculations

1.1 Common Logarithms

1.1.1 LOGARITHMS

The basic rules of logarithmic computation are:
$$\log (abc) = \log a + \log b + \log c$$

$$\log\left(\frac{a}{b}\right) = \log a - \log b$$

$$\log (a)^n = n (\log a)$$

$$\log \sqrt[n]{a} = \frac{\log a}{n}$$

In the work of Part I, computation was restricted to calculations including simple powers and roots. We will proceed to calculations where powers and roots are fractional and/or negative.

By the laws of indices

$$a^{-n} = a^{(o-n)} = \frac{a^o}{a^n} = \frac{1}{a^n}$$

hence
$$a^{-3} = \frac{1}{a^3} \text{ and } a^{-\frac{1}{3}} = \frac{1}{a^{\frac{1}{3}}} = \frac{1}{\sqrt[3]{a}}$$

A common logarithm consists of two parts, *the mantissa always being positive*, the characteristic being either negative or positive. The application of a negative sign to a characteristic is shown by placing the sign above the characteristic.

Thus log 0·03 $= \bar{2}\cdot477\ 1$
which implies $-2+0\cdot477\ 1$

A clear distinction between the characteristic and the mantissa will considerably assist logarithmic computation. This will be demonstrated in the following examples. Once more the reader is urged to make rough checks to determine whether or not the answer is reasonable, to set the work out in an orderly manner, and not to use logarithms if fundamental arithmetical processes provide a quicker, easier, and often, more exact solution.

Example

Evaluate $^{1\cdot41}\sqrt{0\cdot067\ 14}$ to three significant figures.

$$\log {}^{1\cdot41}\sqrt{0\cdot067\ 14}=\frac{\log 0\cdot067\ 14}{1\cdot41}$$

$$=\frac{\bar{2}\cdot827\ 0}{1\cdot41}=\frac{-2+0\cdot827\ 0}{1\cdot41}=\frac{-2+(0\cdot82-0\cdot82)+0\cdot827\ 0}{1\cdot41}$$

$$=\frac{-2\cdot82+1\cdot647\ 0}{1\cdot41}=-2+1\cdot168\ 0=-1+0\cdot168\ 0$$

$$=\bar{1}\cdot168\ 0$$

Antilog $\bar{1}\cdot168\ 0=0\cdot147\ 2$

No.	Log
1·647 0	0·216 7
1·41	0·149 2
1·168	0·067 5

Rough check: Answer must lie between 0·067 14 and $\sqrt[2]{0\cdot067\ 14}$, between 0·067 and about 0·25.

Answer: $^{1\cdot41}\sqrt{0\cdot067\ 14}=0\cdot147\ 2$

Example

Find the value of $pv^{1\cdot3}$ when $p=14\cdot7$ and $v=0\cdot75$.

$$\log pv^{1\cdot3}=\log p+1\cdot3\log v$$
$$=\log 14\cdot7+1\cdot3\log 0\cdot75$$
$$=1\cdot167\ 3+1\cdot3\ (\bar{1}\cdot875\ 1)$$
$$=1\cdot167\ 3+1\cdot3(-1+0\cdot875\ 1)$$
$$=1\cdot167\ 3-1\cdot3+1\cdot137\ 63$$
$$=2\cdot304\ 93-1\cdot3$$
$$=1\cdot004\ 93$$
$$pv^{1\cdot3}=\text{antilog } 1\cdot004\ 93=10\cdot11$$

Rough check: Answer is roughly

$$15 \times \left(\frac{3}{4}\right)^{1\cdot3}, \text{ and } \left(\frac{3}{4}\right)^{1\cdot3} \text{ is between } \left(\frac{3}{4}\right)^{1} \text{ and } \left(\frac{3}{4}\right)^{2}$$

$$= 15 \left(\text{between } \frac{3}{4} \text{ and } \frac{9}{16} \right)$$

$$= \text{between about 12 and about 9}$$

Answer: $pv^{1\cdot3} = 10\cdot11$

Example

When a belt drives a pulley, the ratio of the tension T_T in the tight side of the belt to the tension T_S in the slack side of the belt is given by the formula $\frac{T_T}{T_S} = 2\cdot718^{\mu\theta}$, where μ is the coefficient of friction between the belt and the pulley and θ is the angle of lap in radians. Find T_T when $T_S = 80$ N, $\mu = 0\cdot4$ and $\theta = 150°$.

$$\theta = 150° = \frac{150}{360} \times 2\pi \text{ radians} = \frac{5\pi}{6} \text{ radians}$$

$$= \frac{15\cdot71}{6} \text{ radians} = 2\cdot618 \text{ radians}$$

$$\mu\theta = 0\cdot4 \times 2\cdot618 = 1\cdot047\,2$$

$$\frac{T_T}{T_S} = 2\cdot718^{1\cdot0472}, \log 2\cdot718^{1\cdot0472} = 1\cdot047\,2 \,(\log 2\cdot718)$$

$$= 1\cdot047\,2\,(0\cdot4343) = 0\cdot454\,7$$

$$\frac{T_T}{T_S} = \text{antilog } 0\cdot454\,7 = 2\cdot849$$

No.	Log
1·047 2	0·020 0
0·434 3	$\bar{1}$·637 8
0·454 7	$\bar{1}$·657 8

$$\frac{T_T}{80 \text{ N}} = 2\cdot849, \quad T_T = 80 \text{ N} \times 2\cdot849$$

$$= 227\cdot92 \text{ N}$$

Rough check: $\mu\theta = $ about 1

$2\cdot718^{1} = $ about 2·5

$T_T = $ roughly $2\cdot5 T_S = $ about 200

Answer: Tension in tight side = 228 N

Example

For a particular turning operation the tool life T in hours is connected with the cutting speed V in m/min by the relationship $VT^{0\cdot15} = $ a constant. It is known that a tool life of 1 hour is obtained

3

with a speed of 50 m/min. Calculate the value of the cutting speed to produce a tool life of (*a*) 2 hours, (*b*) 30 minutes.

$$VT^{0\cdot15}=\text{a constant}=50\times1^{0\cdot15}=50\times1=50$$

$$\therefore\ VT^{0\cdot15}=50\text{ and }V=\frac{50}{T^{0\cdot15}}$$

(*a*) $T=2$: $\log 2^{0\cdot15}=0\cdot15\log 2=0\cdot15\ (0\cdot301\ 0)$
$$=0\cdot045\ 15$$

$$\log\frac{50}{T^{0\cdot15}}=\log 50-\log 2^{0\cdot15}$$

$$=1\cdot699\ 0-0\cdot045\ 15$$
$$=1\cdot653\ 85=\log 45\cdot06$$

(*b*) $T=30$ min$=0\cdot5$ hour. $\log 0\cdot5^{0\cdot15}=0\cdot15\log 0\cdot5$
$$=0\cdot15(\bar{1}\cdot699\ 0)=0\cdot15(-1+0\cdot699\ 0)$$
$$=-0\cdot15+0\cdot104\ 85=-0\cdot15+(0\cdot85-0\cdot85)+0\cdot104\ 85$$
$$=-1+0\cdot954\ 85=\bar{1}\cdot954\ 85$$

$$\log\frac{50}{0\cdot5^{0\cdot15}}=\log 50-\log 0\cdot5^{0\cdot15}=1\cdot699\ 0-\bar{1}\cdot954\ 85$$

$$=1\cdot744\ 15=\log 55\cdot48$$

It is very difficult to apply rough checks to logarithmic computation involving 'awkward' powers and roots. In this particular question the rough check is whether or not the answers are reasonably practical. This does seem so, since a slower cutting speed would give a longer tool life and vice versa.

Answers: Cutting speed for 2 hour tool life$=45\cdot1$ m/min
Cutting speed for 30 min tool life$=55\cdot5$ m/min

Example

In a particular turning operation, machining steel with a cutting tool of H.S.S. and using a coolant, the surface speed for a tool life of 1 hour is given by the formula

$$S\text{ m/min}=\frac{55}{d^{0\cdot14}f^{0\cdot42}}$$

where d is the depth of cut in mm and f is the feed of the tool in mm/rev.

Find S when $d=3\cdot5$ and $f=0\cdot2$

$$S=\frac{15}{(3\cdot5)^{0\cdot14}(0\cdot2)^{0\cdot42}}$$

4

$\log 3 \cdot 5^{0 \cdot 14}$ $= 0 \cdot 14 \ (\log 3 \cdot 5) = 0 \cdot 14 \ (0 \cdot 544 \ 1)$
                 $= 0 \cdot 076 \ 2$

$\log 0 \cdot 2^{0 \cdot 42}$ $= 0 \cdot 42 \ (\log 0 \cdot 2) = 0 \cdot 42 \ (\bar{1} \cdot 301 \ 0)$
                 $= 0 \cdot 42 \ (-1 + 0 \cdot 301 \ 0)$
                 $= -0 \cdot 42 + 0 \cdot 126 \ 4 = -0 \cdot 293 \ 6$
                 $= -1 + 0 \cdot 706 \ 4 = \bar{1} \cdot 706 \ 4$

Alternatively, $0 \cdot 42 \ (\bar{1} \cdot 301 \ 0) = 0 \cdot 42 \ (-1 + 0 \cdot 301 \ 0)$
                 $= 0 \cdot 42 \ (-0 \cdot 699 \ 0) = -0 \cdot 293 \ 6$
                 $= \bar{1} \cdot 706 \ 4$, as before.

$\log$ denominator $= 0 \cdot 076 \ 2 + \bar{1} \cdot 706 \ 4 = \bar{1} \cdot 782 \ 6$

$\log$ answer $= \log$ numerator $- \log$ denominator
                 $= 1 \cdot 740 \ 4 - \bar{1} \cdot 782 \ 6$
                 $= 1 \cdot 957 \ 8$

Answer $=$ antilog $1 \cdot 957 \ 8 = 90 \cdot 74$

Answer: Surface speed $= 90 \cdot 7$ m/min

(Once more the check is whether or not the answer is reasonable. In this case 90 m/min is a reasonable value. Values of 9 m/min or 900 m/min would certainly be unreasonable.)

Problems 1.1

1. When an amount of money A is invested to obtain a profit of $r\%$ at compound interest, the amount at the end of n years is

$$A \left(1 + \frac{r}{100} \right)^n$$

Calculate the amount at the end of 4 years when £500 is invested at 6%.

2. The book value £V, of a particular industrial asset is calculated from the formula

$$V = 800(0 \cdot 7)^n$$

n being its life in years.
Find the magnitude of V when $n = 3\frac{1}{2}$ years.

3. The speed ratio R between the two portions of a universal joint is given by

$$R = \frac{\cos \alpha}{1 - \cos^2 \theta \sin^2 \alpha}$$

Find the value of R when $\theta = 15°$ and $\alpha = 30°$.

4. The radius of curvature ρ at any point on the curve $y=\dfrac{x^3}{3}$ is given

by the equation $$\rho=\frac{(1+x^4)^{1.5}}{2x}$$

Find the radius of curvature at the point where $x=0.8$.

5. When water is discharged over a $90°$ vee-notch, the rate of discharge Q m³/s is given by
$$Q=1.46\ H^{2.5}$$
where H is the height above the vee apex in *metres*.
Find Q when $H=400$ *millimetres*, giving the answer in litres/s.

6. If a quantity of a certain gas expands in a particular manner, its pressure and volume are connected by the law
$$PV^{1.3}=K$$
It is known that when $P=1$ bar, $V=0.01$ m³.
Calculate:
   (*a*) the numerical value of K
   (*b*) the value of P, in bars, when $V=0.001$ m³.

7. The discharge of water, Q m³/s, over a rectangular weir is given by the formula
$$Q=1.84\left(B-\frac{H}{5}\right)H^{1.5}$$
B being the breadth of the weir and H the depth of water over the weir.
Find Q when $B=5$ m and $H=0.6$ m.

8. The maximum efficiency of a four-stroke petrol engine is given by
$$1-\left(\frac{1}{r}\right)^{n-1}$$
where r is the compression ratio and n is a constant depending upon the fuel. Calculate the maximum efficiency when $r=7$ and $n=1.41$.

9. If a sample of ten items is extracted from a large consignment which contains 6% of defectives, the probability that the sample contains exactly two defectives is
$$45(0.94)^8(0.06)^2$$
Calculate this value.

10. The slope of a particular curve depends upon the value of x and is given by

$$3 \cdot 9 x^{0 \cdot 3}$$

Find the value of the slope:
   (*a*) when $x=5$
   (*b*) when $x=0 \cdot 5$.

11. The velocity of flow v metres per second of the water in an irrigation canal cut in earth is given by

$$v = \left(\frac{50}{1 + \dfrac{2 \cdot 4}{\sqrt{m}}} \right) \left(\sqrt{mi} \right)$$

where i is the gradient of the canal
and m depends upon the dimensions of the channel.
Find v when $m=0 \cdot 8$ and $i=0 \cdot 000\ 1$.

12. The equivalent length L_e of straight pipe when calculating friction losses round a pipe bend of length L is given under certain conditions by

$$L_e = 13L \left(\frac{r}{R} \right)^{0 \cdot 8}$$

Find L_e when $L=4$ m and the ratio $\dfrac{r}{R}$ is $0 \cdot 2$.

13. If a fixed mass of gas changes its condition so that no heat energy enters or leaves the gas, the pressure-temperature relationship can be represented by the formula

$$\frac{T_2}{T_1} = \left(\frac{P_2}{P_1} \right)^{\frac{n-1}{n}}$$

P being a pressure, T a temperature on the kelvin scale, and n depends on the gas.
Find T_2 when $T_1=273$ K, $P_2=8$ bars, $P_1=1 \cdot 05$ bars and $n=1 \cdot 4$.

14. Under certain metal-cutting conditions, the connection between the surface speed S m/min and the tool life T hours is given by the formula

$$ST^{0 \cdot 18} = \text{a constant}$$

If it is known that a surface speed of 80 m/min will give a tool life of one hour, calculate:
   (*a*) The surface speed to give a tool life of 54 minutes.
   (*b*) The tool life, in hours, obtained with a surface speed of 50 m/min.

15. The torque in newton metres needed to rotate a drill of diameter d mm with a feed of f mm/rev in a particular operation is given by

$$T = Kd^x f^y$$

(a) Find the value of T when $K = 0.1$, $d = 20$ mm, $x = 1.75$, $f = 0.2$ mm and $y = 0.8$.

(b) Find the power consumed when the drill rotates at 210 rev/min.

16. If water flows from a container of constant circular cross-section A m^2 through a circular orifice in the side of area a m^2, then the time taken t seconds for the water to fall from a height above the orifice of H_1 to a height of H_2 is given by

$$t = \frac{2A}{Ka\sqrt{(2g)}}(\sqrt{H_1} - \sqrt{H_2})$$

A circular tank has a cross-sectional area of 0.3 m^2 and the orifice has an area of $0.000\,5$ m^2. Originally the water is 1.5 m above the orifice. Taking K as 0.6 and g as 9.8 m/s^2, find the time taken for the water level to fall by 1 metre.

17. The maximum efficiency obtainable in a diesel engine is given by the formula

$$1 - \left(\frac{1}{r}\right)^{n-1}\left\{\frac{c^n - 1}{n(c-1)}\right\}$$

where r is the compression ratio
n is a constant depending on the fuel
and c is the fuel cut-off ratio.
Find the maximum efficiency when $r = 14$, $n = 1.4$ and $c = 1.75$.

18. A formula to give a tool life of approximately one hour when machining cast iron under certain conditions is

$$V = \frac{C}{d^{0.1}f^{0.3}}$$

where V is the surface speed in m/min
C is a constant depending on the tool material
d is the depth of cut in mm
and f is the feed in mm/rev.
Find V when $C = 20$, $d = 6$ and $f = 0.5$.

(C.G.L.I.)

19. A suggested relationship between the cutting speed S m/min and the life of a tool T is

$$ST^n = C$$

where n and C are constants.

(a) Find the value of C when $S=48.75$, $T=2$ and $n=0.2$.

(b) Under certain conditions the optimum cutting speed V m/min for minimum cost is given by

$$V = C \left\{ \frac{n}{R(1-n)} \right\}^n$$

where C and n are constants in $ST^n = C$ referred to in (a), and R depends on tooling.

Find the value of V if $C=56$, $n=0.2$ and $R=4$.

(C.G.L.I.)

20. An expression used in connection with metal cutting is 'metal removal factor' which is obtained by dividing the volume of metal removed in cubic millimetres by the energy consumed at the drill point. The torque required in newton metres is given by $0.10 \, d^{1.8} f^{0.8}$ where d is the drill diameter in mm and f is the feed rate in mm/rev.

(a) Obtain a formula for the metal removal factor in mm³/J in terms of d, f and a constant, and show that it is independent of the speed of the drill. The power can be assumed to be entirely due to torque.

(b) Find the metal removal factor when $d=16$ and $f=0.2$.

21. A unit-head is employed for drilling holes of diameter 20 mm in an alloy steel, using a feed of 0.25 mm/rev.

(a) The value of the torque, T newton metres, to drill a hole, can be obtained from the formula

$$T = 0.2 \, d^{1.8} f^{0.8}$$

d being the drill diameter in millimetres, and f being the feed in mm/rev.

Calculate the torque required to drill one hole.

(b) If the unit-head can be considered to be 60% efficient, calculate the minimum power (in kilowatts) of the motor to be fitted to the unit-head for the simultaneous drilling of ten holes, each drill revolving at 210 rev/min. (Power is $T\omega$ watts, T being in newton metres and ω being in rad/s.)

(C.G.L.I.)

Answers to problems 1.1

1. £631
2. £230
3. 1·13
4. 1·04
5. 148 litres/s/
6. (a) 0·002 51   (b) 20 bars
7. 4·17 m³/s
8. 55·0%
9. 0·098 7
10. (a) 6·32   (b) 3·17
11. 0·121 m/s
12. 14·4 m
13. 488 K
14. (a) 81·5 m/min   (b) 13·6 hours
15. (a) 5·22 Nm   (b) 115 W
16. 234 seconds
17. 60·6%
18. 20·6 m/min
19. (a) 56·0   (b) 32·2 m/min
20. (a) 1·25 $\sqrt[5]{(df)}$ (b) 1·58 mm³/J
21. (a) 14·5 Nm   (b) 5·32 kW

1.2   Naperian Logarithms and Further Work on the Slide Rule

1.2.1   NAPERIAN LOGARITHMS

When a calculation is involved concerning an amount of rotation, the unit usually associated with the angle is the degree. When analytical mathematics is involved, the more usual unit for the magnitude of an angle is the radian. A somewhat similar occurrence happens with logarithms. For calculations, it is extremely convenient to use common logarithms, having a base of 10. In analytical mathematics, the base usually involved is the number represented by the unending series

$$1 + \frac{1}{1} + \frac{1}{1 \times 2} + \frac{1}{1 \times 2 \times 3} + \frac{1}{1 \times 2 \times 3 \times 4} \cdots$$

To three decimal places this number is 2·718. Just as we recognise that π is the number 3·142 (to three decimal places), in a similar way we use the small letter e to represent the number given by the sum of the above series. The mathematical name given to the value of e is 'exponent'.

Logarithms to the base e were invented by Sir John Napier, and are referred to as Naperian logarithms. To distinguish between common logarithms and Naperian logarithms, the base is not quoted for common logarithms.

Thus   log 6 is the common logarithm of 6 to the base 10

but $\log_e$ 6 is the Naperian logarithm of 6 to the base 2·718

In some more advanced works on mathematics a Naperian logarithm is indicated by 'lon', being a 'shorthand' way of writing 'natural logarithm'.

Thus lon 7 is the Naperian logarithm of 7.

To distinguish Naperian logarithms distinctly from common logarithms in this book the convention $\log_e$ has been adopted.

A direct study of Naperian logarithms is not specifically requested in the Mechanical Engineering Technician's Course, but since the exponent occurs in many problems, such as with the tensions in a belt drive and with probability, and also forms the basis of further work on the slide rule, it is advisable to devote a little time to the study of Naperian logarithms.

Let us first establish the connection between the common logarithm of a number and the Naperian logarithm of the same number. The formal way of indicating a number, a base, and its associated logarithm is

$$\log_2 8 = 3,$$

which implies that $2^3 = 8.$

Now let N be any number and a and b two different bases.

Further let $N = b^x$, so that $\log_b N = x$

Now $$\log_a N = \log_a (b^x)$$
$$= x (\log_a b)$$
$$= \log_b N \times \log_a b$$

In particular, if a is the base e and b is the base 10,
$$\log_e N = \log_{10} N \times \log_e 10$$

The logarithm of 10 to the base e is 2·303, since $e^{2 \cdot 303} = 10$.
$$\therefore \log_e N = 2 \cdot 303 (\log N)$$

Hence to convert common logarithms to Naperian logarithms we multiply by 2·303. Conversely, to convert Naperian logarithms to common logarithms we divide by 2·303.

To assist rapidity of working, Castle's *Four-figure Tables* include the Naperian logarithms of numbers of 1 to 10. Furthermore, the very last table in the book includes some extremely useful values of e^x and e^{-x}. There are no tables of 'Naperian anti-logarithms', these are found by using the tables in reverse order. It is important to note that if a number lies between zero and unity, its Naperian logarithm is expressed as a completely negative number, and we must remind ourselves that with the common logarithm of a number between zero and unity, the characteristic is negative but the mantissa is positive.

Example

Find $\log_e 0.070\ 4$

$$
\begin{aligned}
\log_e 0.070\ 4 &= 2.303 \log 0.070\ 4 \\
&= 2.303\ (\bar{2}.847\ 6) \\
&= 2.303\ (-2+0.847\ 6) \\
&= 2.303\ (-1.152\ 4) \\
&= -2.654 \text{ (using four-figure logs)}
\end{aligned}
$$

Answer: $\log_e 0.070\ 4 = -2.654$

Second method

$$
\begin{aligned}
\log_e 0.070\ 4 &= \log_e\left(\frac{7.04}{100}\right) \\
&= \log_e 7.04 - \log_e 100 \\
&= 1.951\ 6 - 4.605\ 2 \\
&= -2.653\ 6
\end{aligned}
$$

Answer: $\log_e 0.070\ 4 = -2.653\ 6$

The discrepancy between the answers is due to the lack of accuracy of four-figure tables. The multiplier, to four decimal places, is $2.302\ 6$, but to round off for use with four-figure tables we take the value 2.303. It is therefore recommended that if accuracy is important, the second method be used.

Example

Find the number whose Naperian logarithm is $-0.472\ 4$ (i.e. find the value of $e^{-0.4724}$)

We will find the corresponding common logarithm.

$$
\frac{-0.472\ 4}{2.303} = -0.205\ 1 \text{ (using four-figure logs)} = -1+0.794\ 9
$$

$$
= \bar{1}.794\ 9
$$

Common antilog of $\bar{1}.794\ 9 = 0.623\ 6$

Answer: $e^{-0.4724} = 0.623\ 6$

Second method

Add 2·302 6 successively until a positive value occurs.

$$-0{\cdot}472\,4+2{\cdot}302\,6=1{\cdot}830\,2$$

Adding 2·302 6 once has the effect of multiplying the number by 10.

Naperian antilog of 1·830 2=6·235 (from tables)

$$\therefore\ e^{0{\cdot}4724}=\frac{6{\cdot}235}{10}=0{\cdot}623\,5$$

Answer: $e^{0{\cdot}4724}=0{\cdot}623\,5$

The author has considerable experience in observing the work of students on the Mechanical Engineering Technician's Course, and knows only too well the difficulties that students have with negative characteristics. These difficulties, plus the greater accuracy obtainable, lead him to suggest that the second method be used in each case.

Example

In one type of reciprocating engine, the work done W during a stroke is given by

$$W=PV\log_e r$$

where P =the initial pressure
V =the initial volume

and r =the compression ratio

Find W (in joules) when $P=0{\cdot}8\times10^6$ N/m², $V=0{\cdot}1$ m³ and $r=4$

$$W=PV\log_e r$$

$$=0{\cdot}8\times10^6\times0{\cdot}1\times\log_e 4\ \frac{\text{N}\times\text{m}^3}{\text{m}^2}$$

$$=0{\cdot}08\times10^6\times1{\cdot}386\,3\ \text{Nm}$$
$$=80\,000\times1{\cdot}386\,3\ \text{J (since 1 Nm=1J)}$$
$$=110\,904\ \text{J}$$

Answer: work done=111 000 J

Example

Evaluate

(a) $e^{\mu\theta}$ when $\mu=0{\cdot}25$ and $\theta=\dfrac{\pi}{2}$

(b) $50\ e^{\frac{-Rt}{L}}$ when $R=50$, $t=0{\cdot}1$ and $L=10$.

13

The answers to both these problems could be found by using common logarithms, taking the value of e as 2·718. However, the use of Naperian logarithms provides much more rapid solutions.

(a) If $y=e^{\mu\theta}$, then $\log_e y=\mu\theta$

$$\mu\theta=0\cdot25\times\frac{\pi}{2}=\frac{0\cdot25\times3\cdot141\ 6}{2}=\frac{3\cdot141\ 6}{8}$$

$$=0\cdot393\ 7$$

If $\log_e y=0\cdot393\ 7$,

then $y=$ the Naperian antilogarithm of $0\cdot393\ 7$.

Entering Castle's tables at page 36,

antilogarithm of $0\cdot393\ 7=1\cdot482$.

(b) If $y=50e^{\frac{-Rt}{L}}$

then $\log_e y=\log_e 50+\log_e e^{\frac{-Rt}{L}}$

$$=\log_e 50+\left(\frac{-Rt}{L}\right)$$

$$=\log_e(5\times10)-\frac{50\times0\cdot1}{10}$$

$$=\log_e 5+\log_e 10-0\cdot5$$

$$=1\cdot6094+2\cdot3026-0\cdot5$$

$$=3\cdot4120$$

We now require the Naperian antilogarithm of $3\cdot412\ 0$.

Proceeding as indicated earlier in this article,

Start with $3\cdot412\ 0$

Deduct $\quad2\cdot302\ 6=\log_e 10$

$\overline{\qquad1\cdot109\ 4\qquad}$

Naperian antilog of $1\cdot109\ 4=3\cdot032$

Naperian antilog of $3\cdot412\ 0=10\times3\cdot032=30\cdot32$

If it is appreciated that e raised to a power produces a convenient value in the index, an even quicker solution may be effected.

In this case $\quad e^{\frac{-Rt}{L}}$ is $e^{-0\cdot5}$

By direct reference to the table on page 50 of Castle's *Four-figure Tables*,

$$e^{-0\cdot5}=0\cdot606\ 5$$

Whence $\qquad y=50\times0\cdot606\ 5=30\cdot325$

Answers: (a) $1\cdot48$

(b) $30\cdot3$

1.2.2 FURTHER CALCULATIONS ON THE SLIDE RULE

In Book 1, the Appendix included information on the use of the *A*, *B*, *C* and *D* scales of the slide rule for multiplication, division, calculation of squares, calculation of square roots, and combinations of these computations. We will now proceed to the use of certain other scales on slide rules. The scales engraved on slide rules other than the *A*, *B*, *C* and *D* scales vary according to the use to be made of the rule, the manufacturer of the rule, and the price. On the majority of rules there will be a scale along the bottom of the stock, beneath the *D* scale, which ranges from about 2·5 to 10^5 ($=10\ 000$). These are the values of e^x when x is the value on the *D* scale immediately above. Certain values of e^x can therefore be directly read off the rule, as also can values of $\log_e N$. In the Appendix of Book 1 it was explained that the *A*, *B*, *C* and *D* scales were logarithmic scales, and since the *D* scale shows Naperian logarithms of numbers on the e^x scale, the e^x scale is often referred to as a log-log scale.

Example

Find $e^{2\cdot24}$

Move slide away from 2·24 on *D* scale.

Bring cursor line over 2·24 on *D* scale.

Read off answer under cursor line on e^x scale.

Answer: $e^{2\cdot24}=9\cdot40$

Example

Find $\log_e 100$

Bring cursor line over 100 on e^x scale.

Read off answer direct on *D* scale.

Answer: $\log_e 100=4\cdot60$

1.2.3 ROOTS AND POWERS OTHER THAN SQUARE ROOTS AND SQUARES

Let us consider the evaluation of $4^{1\cdot5}$ using Naperian logs. We should have to find the Naperian log of 4, multiply it by 1·5 and find its Naperian antilog. These operations can be performed using the e^x, *C* and *D* scales of the slide rule.

Example

Evaluate $4^{1\cdot5}$

Bring the cursor line over 4 on the e^x scale: the cursor line now lies over $\log_e 4$ on the D scale.

Move the slide to bring the 1 of the C scale under the cursor line, and then move the cursor to bring the cursor line over the 1·5 of the C scale.

1·5 ($\log_e 4$) now appears under the cursor line of the D scale, and without moving the cursor the Naperian antilog can be read off on the e^x scale.

Answer: $4^{1\cdot5} = 8\cdot0$

Example

Find $^{1\cdot5}\sqrt{27}$

Bring cursor line over 27 on e^x scale.
Move slide to bring 1·5 on C scale under cursor line.

Move cursor to bring cursor line over 1 on C scale. $\dfrac{\log_e 27}{1\cdot5}$ now appears under cursor line on the D scale, and without moving the cursor, the Naperian antilog can be read off on the e^x scale.

Answer: $^{1\cdot5}\sqrt{27} = 9\cdot0$

On many slide rules a further scale appears ranging from about 1·1 to about 3. This is sometimes found at the top opposite scale A and sometimes on the stock adjacent to the e^x scale. This scale, ranging from about 1·1 to about 3, is aligned with the D scale, giving the values of $e^{0\cdot1x}$ for various values of x on the D scale.

Example

Evaluate $e^{0\cdot8}$

Move slide away from 8 on D scale.
Bring cursor line over 8 on D scale. $(8 = 10 \times 0\cdot8)$
Read off answer on $e^{0\cdot1x}$ scale.

Answer: $e^{0\cdot8} = 2\cdot225$

Example

Evaluate $\sqrt[4]{2\cdot5}$

Bring cursor line over 2·5 on $e^{0\cdot1x}$ scale.
Move slide to bring 4 on C scale under cursor line.

Move cursor to bring cursor line over 1 on *C* scale.
Read off answer under cursor line on $e^{0 \cdot 1x}$ scale.

Answer: $\sqrt[4]{2 \cdot 5} = 1 \cdot 257$

A little practice will be necessary if the final answer comes 'off the rule'. The combined $e^{0 \cdot 1x}$ and e^x scales give a range of about $1 \cdot 1$ to about 100 000. It will be observed that the values at the end of the $e^{0 \cdot 1x}$ scale are the start of the e^x scale. If an answer comes 'off the rule' we can multiply or divide it to bring it 'on the rule' but read it against another scale.

Example

Evaluate $\sqrt[4]{10}$

Bring cursor line over 10 on e^x scale.
Move slide to bring 4 of *C* scale under cursor line.
Answer would be read off opposite 1 on *C* scale but this is 'off the rule'.
Move cursor to other end of *C* scale, but instead of reading off the answer on the e^x scale, read it off on the $e^{0 \cdot 1x}$ scale.

Answer: $\sqrt[4]{10} = 1 \cdot 78$

Example

Evaluate $1 \cdot 7^5$

Bring cursor line over $1 \cdot 7$ on $e^{0 \cdot 1x}$ scale.
Move slide to bring 1 of *C* scale under cursor line.
Answer would be read off opposite 5 on the *C* scale but this is 'off the rule'.
Move slide to bring 10 of *C* scale under cursor line.
Move cursor to bring cursor line over 5 on *C* scale.
Read off answer under the cursor line on the e^x scale.

Answer: $1 \cdot 7^5 = 14 \cdot 2$

1.2.4 COMBINING OPERATIONS

Considerable experience in the use of the slide rule is necessary before a calculation such as

$$\frac{452 \, e^{2 \cdot 4}}{26 \cdot 7 \, ^{0 \cdot 27} \sqrt{0 \cdot 05}}$$

can be performed with one sequence of slide rule operations. The student is strongly advised for the time being not to attempt such complicated calculations with one continued sequence. It is recommended that for present studies the computation should be split into parts, each being performed separately, followed by a simple combination of multiplication and division to produce the final result.

In the example quoted, a suitable sequence would be

$$\frac{452}{26\cdot7}=A,$$

$$e^{2\cdot4}=B$$

$$^{0\cdot27}\sqrt{0\cdot05}=C$$

the overall result being given by $\frac{AB}{C}$.

Problems 1.2

1. Find the Naperian logarithms of the following numbers:
   (a) 5   (d) 1·671   (g) 0·1
   (b) 8·46   (e) 16·71   (h) 0·567
   (c) 100   (f) 167·1   (j) $\frac{\pi}{4}$

2. Find the Naperian antilogarithms of the following numbers:
   (a) 1·386 3   (d) 1·298 4   (g) 3·718 4
   (b) 1·876 4   (e) 2·302 6   (h) −1·640 6
   (c) 0·616 8   (f) 4·605 2   (j) −4·017 2

3. Calculate the value of $\frac{e^x+e^{-x}}{2}$ when $x=0\cdot8$.

   (Be careful which set of tables you choose.)

4. If $y=e^{-\left(\frac{x^2}{2}\right)}$, find the value of x when $y=0\cdot5$.

5. The 'A-scale' of a slide rule, ranging from 1 to 100, has a length of 250 mm. Calculate the actual length, in millimetres, of the distance between the graduations marked:
   (a) 7·8 and 78
   (b) 6·6 and 43·2.

6. If a steady electromotive force of E volts is applied to a circuit of resistance R ohms containing an inductance of L henries, the current i amperes after t seconds is given by

$$i = \frac{E}{R}\left(1 - e^{\frac{-Rt}{L}}\right)$$

Find i when $E=60$, $R=5$, $t=1.5$ and $L=50$.

7. The frequency of occurrence f of a particular event is predicted by the formula

$$f = \frac{N}{\sqrt{(2\pi)}} e^{-\left(\frac{t^2}{2}\right)}$$

where N=the number of trials
and $\quad t$=the number of standard deviations.
Find, to the nearest whole number, the value of f when N remains constant at 50 and
   (a) $t=0$
   (b) $t=1$
   (c) $t=3$

8. The ratio between the tensions T_1 and T_2 in a belt drive is given by

$$\frac{T_1}{T_2} = e^{\mu\theta}$$

where θ is the angle of lap in radians
and μ is the coefficient of friction.
Find the value of T_1 if $T_2=500$ N, $\mu=0.3$ and $\theta=180°$.

9. When an angular vibration is damped, the amount of swing S degrees depends upon the time t, following the law

$$S = Ae^{-kt}$$

If $k=0.1$, what value of t will give a value of S of one half of that when $t=0$?

Answers to problems 1.2

1. (a) 1·609 4   (d) 0·513 4   (g) −2·302 6
   (b) 2·135 3   (e) 2·816 0   (h) −0·667 4
   (c) 4·605 2   (f) 5·118 6   (j) −0·241 6

2. (a) 4·000   (d) 3·663   (g) 41·20
   (b) 6·53   (e) 10·00   (h) 0·193 9
   (c) 1·853   (f) 100·0   (j) 0·018 0

3. 1·337 4
4. ±1·18
5. (a) 125 mm   (b) 102 mm
6. 1·67 amperes
7. (a) 20   (b) 12   (c) 0
8. 1 280 N
9. $t = 6·93$ seconds

1.3 Seven-figure Mathematical Tables

1.3.1 ACCURACY OF FOUR-FIGURE TABLES

While four-figure tables prove of considerable use in technical studies, it should be realised that the fourth significant figure is suspect. As a general guide, four-figure tables should only be used when an accuracy of three significant figures in the result is acceptable. In many cases, particularly in precision measurement, this degree of accuracy is not suitable.

Let us consider the co-ordinates y_1 and y_2 of the layout shown in Figure 1.1. Using the Theorem of Pythagoras:

$$y_1 = 36 - \sqrt{(36^2 - 2^2)}$$
$$= 36 - \sqrt{(1296 - 4)}$$
$$= 36 - \sqrt{1292}$$

Using four-figure tables, $\sqrt{1\,292} = 35·95$

$$y_1 = 36 - 35·95 = 0·05$$
$$y_2 = 36 - \sqrt{(36^2 - 4^2)}$$
$$= 36 - \sqrt{(1\,296 - 16)} = 36 - \sqrt{1\,280} = 36 - 35·78$$
$$= 0·22$$

If y_1 and y_2 were wanted for a purpose which required an accuracy of 0·0001, values of 0·05 and 0·22 are insufficiently accurate. For this particular problem, the values of $\sqrt{1\,292}$ and $\sqrt{1\,280}$ could be found by elementary arithmetic, but more complicated problems may involve the use of logarithms. The publication of seven-figure mathematical tables has relieved the problem of a higher degree of accuracy.

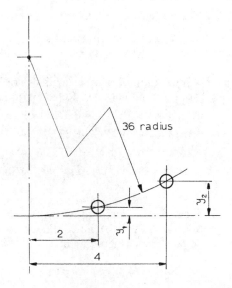

36 radius

FIG. 1.1

If these tables are used $\sqrt{1\ 292} = 35 \cdot 944\ 40$
and $\sqrt{1\ 280} = 35 \cdot 777\ 09$

More accurate values are $0 \cdot 055\ 60$ for y_1 instead of $0 \cdot 05$
and $0 \cdot 222\ 91$ for y_2 instead of $0 \cdot 22$

The proportionate error resulting from the use of four-figure tables in this problem is about 10% for y_1 and 1% for y_2.

Students are therefore recommended to use tables appropriate to the accuracy required in the final answer. Four-figure tables are invariably quite useful in the solution of problems in engineering science when an accuracy of three significant figures is acceptable, but problems in precise location will more often than not involve the use of seven-figure tables. When seven-figure tables should be used for questions in this volume, the fact is clearly implied in the question.

The seven-figure tables recommended for use with this volume are *Chambers's Seven-Figure Mathematical Tables*, edited by James Pryde, and published by Messrs W. & R. Chambers Ltd. An extract from these tables is printed on page 23 by kind permission of the publishers.

1.3.2 USE OF SEVEN-FIGURE LOGARITHM TABLES

The number of figures in logarithm tables has no effect on the rules for determining characteristics; they are found in the usual manner.

The mantissas of logarithms of numbers with five or less significant figures are read directly from the tables. Referring to page 23,

$$\text{mantissa of } 2 \cdot 35 \quad = 0 \cdot 371\ 067\ 9$$
$$\text{mantissa of } 0 \cdot 236\ 2 = 0 \cdot 373\ 279\ 9$$
$$\text{mantissa of } 23 \cdot 827 = 0 \cdot 377\ \overline{069}\ 4$$

(*Note the line above* 069 4 *to indicate that the first three figures are* 377 *and not* 376.)

If the mantissa of a number of six or seven significant figures is desired, the increment for the last one or two significant figures is obtained by proportion. It will be noted that a decimal point is implied previous to every seven-figure mantissa.

Example

Find the seven-figure log of 238·624 7

$$\text{mantissa for } 2\ 385\ 300 = 0 \cdot 377\ 725\ 0$$
$$\text{mantissa for } 2\ 386\ 200 = 0 \cdot 377\ 706\ 8$$

By subtraction, difference for 100 $\quad = \quad$ 18 2

Increment for $47 = \dfrac{47}{100} \times 182 = 86$ to nearest whole number.

$$\text{mantissa for } \quad 2\ 386\ 200 = 0 \cdot 377\ 706\ 8$$
$$\underline{\text{increment for} \qquad\quad 47 = \qquad\qquad 8\ 6}$$
$$\text{mantissa of} \quad 2\ 386\ 247 = 0 \cdot 377\ 715\ 4$$

The characteristic is 2

Answer: log 238·624 7 = 2·377 715 4

The determination of the increment for the last two significant figures can often be eased by the use of the difference tables in the extreme right-hand column of the tables.

The difference between logs of 23 863 and 23 862 has already been found to be 182. In the extreme right-hand column under 182, differences are shown in units of tens. We require 4·7 tens to be added, which by estimation is 86. (*An estimation may result in slight errors of the last figure, but on occasions the last figure need not be precise. If it must, the formal method of proportions by hundredths is recommended.*)

No.	0	1	2	3	4	5	6	7	8	9	Diff.
2350	371 0679	0863	1048	1233	1418	1603	1787	1972	2157	2342	
51	2526	2711	2896	3080	3265	3450	3635	3819	4004	4189	185
52	4373	4558	4742	4927	5112	5296	5481	5666	5850	6035	
53	6219	6404	6588	6773	6957	7142	7327	7511	7696	7880	
54	8065	8249	8434	8618	8802	8987	9171	9356	9540	9725	
55	9909	0094	0278	0462	0647	0831	1015	1200	1384	1569	
56	372 1753	1937	2122	2306	2490	2674	2859	3043	3227	3412	
57	3596	3780	3964	4149	4333	4517	4701	4885	5070	5254	
58	5438	5622	5806	5991	6175	6359	6543	6727	6911	7095	
59	7279	7464	7648	7832	8016	8200	8384	8568	8725	8936	
60	9120	9304	9488	9672	9856	0040	0224	0408	0592	0776	

Proportional parts (185): 1 19 · 2 37 · 3 56 · 4 74 · 5 93 · 6 111 · 7 130 · 8 148 · 9 167

No.	0	1	2	3	4	5	6	7	8	9	Diff.
2361	373 0960	1144	1328	1512	1696	1879	2063	2247	2431	2615	
62	2799	2983	3167	3350	3534	3718	3902	4086	4270	4453	184
63	4637	4821	5005	5189	5372	5556	5740	5924	6107	6291	
64	6475	6658	6842	7026	7210	7393	7577	7761	7944	8128	
65	8311	8495	8679	8862	9046	9230	9413	9597	9780	9964	
66	374 0147	0331	0515	0698	0882	1065	1249	1432	1616	1799	
67	1983	2166	2350	2533	2716	2900	3083	3267	3450	3634	
68	3817	4000	4184	4367	4551	4734	4917	5101	5284	5467	
69	5651	5834	6017	6201	6384	6567	6750	6934	7117	7300	
70	7483	7667	7850	8033	8216	8400	8583	8766	8949	9132	

Proportional parts (184): 1 18 · 2 37 · 3 55 · 4 74 · 5 92 · 6 110 · 7 129 · 8 147 · 9 166

No.	0	1	2	3	4	5	6	7	8	9	Diff.
2371	9316	9499	9682	9865	0048	0231	0414	0598	0781	0964	
72	375 1147	1330	1513	1696	1879	2062	2245	2428	2611	2794	183
73	2977	3160	3343	3526	3709	3892	4075	4258	4441	4624	
74	4807	4990	5173	5356	5539	5722	5905	6088	6270	6453	
75	6636	6819	7002	7185	7368	7550	7733	7916	8099	8282	
76	8464	8647	8830	9013	9195	9378	9561	9744	9926	0109	
77	376 0292	0475	0657	0840	1023	1205	1388	1571	1753	1936	
78	2119	2301	2484	2666	2849	3032	3214	3397	3579	3762	
79	3944	4127	4310	4492	4675	4857	5040	5222	5405	5587	
80	5770	5952	6135	6317	6499	6682	6864	7047	7229	7412	

Proportional parts (183): 1 18 · 2 37 · 3 55 · 4 73 · 5 92 · 6 110 · 7 128 · 8 146 · 9 165

No.	0	1	2	3	4	5	6	7	8	9	Diff.
2381	7594	7776	7959	8141	8323	8506	8688	8871	9053	9235	
82	9418	9600	9782	9965	0147	0329	0511	0694	0876	1058	
83	377 1240	1423	1605	1787	1969	2152	2334	2516	2698	2880	
84	3063	3245	3427	3609	3791	3973	4155	4338	4520	4702	
85	4884	5066	5248	5430	5612	5794	5976	6158	6340	6522	182
86	6704	6886	7068	7250	7432	7614	7796	7978	8160	8342	
87	8524	8706	8888	9070	9252	9434	9616	9798	9979	0161	
88	378 0343	0525	0707	0889	1071	1252	1434	1616	1798	1980	
89	2161	2343	2525	2707	2889	3070	3252	3434	3616	3797	
90	3979	4161	4342	4524	4706	4887	5069	5251	5432	5614	

Proportional parts (182): 1 18 · 2 36 · 3 55 · 4 73 · 5 91 · 6 109 · 7 127 · 8 146 · 9 164

No.	0	1	2	3	4	5	6	7	8	9	Diff.
2391	5796	5977	6159	6341	6522	6704	6885	7067	7249	7430	
92	7612	7793	7975	8156	8338	8519	8701	8882	9064	9245	
93	9427	9608	9790	9971	0153	0334	0516	0697	0879	1060	
94	379 1241	1423	1604	1786	1967	2148	2330	2511	2692	2874	
95	3055	3237	3418	3599	3780	3962	4143	4324	4506	4687	
96	4868	5049	5231	5412	5593	5774	5956	6137	6318	6499	
97	6680	6862	7043	7224	7405	7586	7767	7948	8130	8311	181
98	8492	8673	8854	9035	9216	9397	9578	9759	9940	0121	
99	380 0302	0484	0665	0846	1027	1208	1389	1570	1750	1931	
2400	2112	2293	2474	2655	2836	3017	3198	3379	3560	3741	

There are no separate tables of antilogarithms. An antilog is found by using the tables in the reverse order. If an accuracy of up to five significant figures is acceptable, antilogs can be read direct. Otherwise, proportion should be used.

Example

Find to five significant figures the antilog of $\bar{2}\cdot375\ 483\ 6$

Referring to the tables, the mantissa quoted lies between the mantissa of log 23 740 and the mantissa of log 23 741, being nearer the former. Noting the characteristic is $\bar{2}$, the number required is 0·023 740.

Answer: The antilog of $\bar{2}\cdot375\ 483\ 6$ is 0·023 740 (to five significant figures)

Example

Find the antilog of $1\cdot373\ 747\ 6$, as accurately as seven-figure tables allow.

Referring to the tables, and neglecting the characteristic, the number lies between 2 364 500 and 2 364 600.

mantissa of 2 364 600＝373 757 7
mantissa of 2 364 500＝373 739 3

By subtraction, difference＝ 18 4

Given mantissa＝373 747 6
mantissa of 2 364 500＝373 739 3

By subtraction, difference＝ 8 3

By proportion, $\dfrac{83}{184}\times100=45$ to nearest whole number.

Significant figures of answer are 2 364 500＋45＝2 364 545

The characteristic is 1

∴ The antilog of $1\cdot373\ 747\ 6$ is 23·645 45

Answer: The antilog of $1\cdot373\ 747\ 6$ is 23·645 45

Again, if acceptable, the difference table in the right-hand column can be used. The difference for 100 is 184, and we require a proportion of 100 represented by $\dfrac{83}{184}$; by estimation this is 4·5 tens or 45.

In addition to tables of logarithms, *Chambers's Seven-Figure Mathematical Tables* include trigonometric ratios, degrees to radians, logs of trigonometric ratios, and other tables primarily concerned with navigation. The use of other tables often referred to by engineers will now be demonstrated.

1.3.3 EXAMPLES OF THE USE OF OTHER SEVEN-FIGURE TABLES

Example

Express 37° 15′ 42″ as radians.

$$37° 15' \quad =0·650\ 135\ 1\ \text{rad}$$
$$42''=0·000\ 203\ 6\ \text{rad}$$

By addition 37° 15′ 42″=0·650 338 7 rad

Answer: 37° 15′ 42″=0·650 338 7 rad

Example

Find sin 83° 16′ 42″.

From 83° 16′ to 83° 17′, difference=341.

Increment for $42'' = \dfrac{42}{60} \times 341 = 239$ to nearest whole number.

$$\sin 83° 16' \quad =0·993\ 102\ 6$$
Increment for $\qquad 42''= \qquad 23\ 9$

By addition sin 83° 16′ 42″=0·993 126 5

Answer: sin 83° 16′ 42″=0·993 126 5

Example

Find cos 27° 37′ 45″.

With cosines, cosecants, and cotangents, differences have to be subtracted.

From cos 27° 37′ to cos 27° 38′, difference=1349

Decrement for $45'' = \dfrac{45}{60} \times 1349 = 1012$ to the nearest whole number

$$\cos 27° 37' \quad =0·886\ 068\ 8$$
Decrement for $\qquad 45''= \qquad 101\ 2$

By subtraction cos 27° 37′ 45″=0·885 967 6

Answer: cos 27° 37′ 45″=0·885 967 6

Example

Find tan 53° 16′ 25″.

$$
\begin{array}{ll}
\tan 53°\ 17' & = 1\cdot340\ 788\ 8 \\
\tan 53°\ 16' & = 1\cdot339\ 975\ 3
\end{array}
$$

Difference for	$60'' =$	813 5

Increment for $\qquad 25'' = \dfrac{25}{60} \times 813\ 5 = \dfrac{3389}{\text{whole number}}$ to nearest whole number

$$
\begin{array}{ll}
\tan 53°\ 16' & = 1\cdot339\ 975\ 3
\end{array}
$$

Increment for	$25'' =$	338 9

By addition $\tan 53°\ 16'\ 25'' = 1\cdot340\ 314\ 2$

Answer: $\tan 53°\ 16'\ 25'' = 1\cdot340\ 314\ 2$

Example

Find arcsin (sin⁻¹) 0·637 854 6 to the nearest second.

From inspection of the tables, the angle lies between 39° 37′ and 39° 38′.

$$
\begin{array}{ll}
\text{Value given} & = 0\cdot637\ 854\ 6 \\
\sin 39°\ 37' & = 0\cdot637\ 648\ 1
\end{array}
$$

By subtraction difference$=$ 206 5

From tables, difference between 39° 37′ and 39° 38′ is 2240.

$$
\therefore\ \text{Number of seconds} = \frac{2065}{2240} \times 60 = 55\cdot31
$$

Answer: arcsin 0·637 854 6 = 39° 37′ 55″ to nearest second

With the logarithms of trigonometrical ratios, 10 is added to the characteristic to avoid complications in printing 'bar' characteristics.

For instance, log sin 43° 15′ is printed as 9·835 806 6, the true value being $\bar{1}\cdot835\ 806\ 6$.

Furthermore, as with trigonometric ratios, the differences for log cos, log cot, and log cosec have to be subtracted.

Example

Find log cosec 35° 17′ 10″.

From inspecting the tables, difference between 35° 17′ and 35° 18′ is 178 4.

$$\therefore \text{ Difference for } 10'' = \frac{10}{60} \times 178\ 4$$

$$= 297 \text{ to the nearest whole number}$$

	log cosec 35° 17′	= 10·238 357 6
Decrement for	10″ =	29 7

By subtraction,   10·238 327 9

Subtract 10,   log cosec 35° 17′ 10″ =   0·238 327 9

Answer: log cosec 35° 17′ 10″ = 0·238 327 9

Example

Find the angle, to the nearest minute, whose logarithmic sine is $\bar{1}$·777 864 7.

Add 10, to give the value 9·777 864 7.

From inspection of the tables, the angle lies between 36° 50′ and 36° 51′, the corresponding difference being 168 6.

$$\text{Ratio given} = 9\cdot777\ 864\ 7$$

$$\log \tan 36° 50' = 9\cdot777\ 781\ 5$$

$$\text{Increment above } 36° 50' = \qquad 83\ 2$$

$$\therefore \text{ Number of seconds} = \frac{832}{1\ 686} \times 60 = 30 \text{ to nearest whole number}$$

Answer: Angle required = 36° 50′ 30″

Problems 1.3

1. If 25·4 mm = 1 in, calculate how many inches there are in a metre to five significant figures.

2. The co-ordinates, in millimetres, of the centres of two shafts in a machine frame are (0, 89) and (121·5, 173). Calculate the centre distance of the shafts to the nearest 0·01 mm.

3. Ten holes lie equally spaced on a pitch circle diameter of 84·375 mm. Calculate the chordal distance between two adjacent holes to the nearest 0·001 mm.

4. Calculate the distances A and B shown in Figure 1.2, correct to the nearest 0·001 mm.

5. What is the difference, to one significant figure, between the ratios $\frac{100}{193}$ and $\frac{143}{276}$?

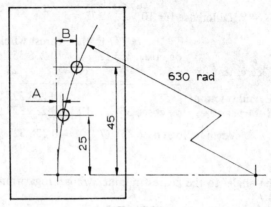

FIG. 1.2

6. Determine the co-ordinates *A* and *B* shown on Figure 1.3 accurate to the nearest 0·001 mm.

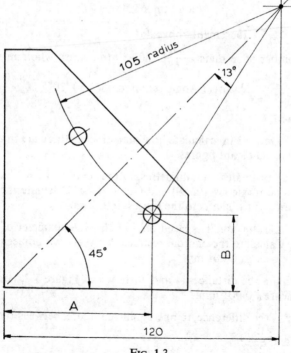

FIG. 1.3

7. A gear-wheel of 48 teeth, 10 mm metric module, meshes with a rack.

   (*a*) If the gear-wheel moves through 115°, find the linear movement of the rack to the nearest 0·01 mm. (Take π as 3·141 593.)

   (*b*) Find the angular rotation of the gear-wheel, to the nearest five seconds, if the rack moves 100 mm.

8. When using a sine-bar nominally of 200 mm centres the slip gauge pile had a height of 58·72 mm. Determine the angle of tilt, to the nearest five seconds.

9. In the definition of the metre it is stated that it corresponds to 1 650 763·73 wavelengths of a particular type of light. Legally, one yard is precisely equal to 0·914 4 metre. How many of the wavelengths correspond to one inch, to the nearest whole number?

10. Calculate, to the nearest 0·01 mm, the pitch circle diameter of a gear having 110 teeth of 5 mm module. (π=3·141 593)

11. Two gear centres are dimensioned by co-ordinates in millimetres. The first is nominally (10, 20), the second is (151, 83·8). If each of these four nominal dimensions is limited to ±0·01 mm, what is the tolerance on the gear centres, to the nearest 0·005 mm?

Answers to problems 1.3

1. 39·370 in
2. 147·71 mm
3. 26·073 mm
4. A=0·486 mm B=1·609 mm
5. 0·000 02
6. A=64·358 mm B=30·955 mm
7. (*a*) 481·71 mm   (*b*) 23° 52′ 25″
8. 17° 4′ 25″
9. 41 929
10. 175·07 mm
11. 0·055 mm

1.4 Continued Fractions

1.4.1 DETERMINATION OF PARTIAL QUOTIENTS

Any vulgar fraction *less than unity* can be put in the form

$$\cfrac{1}{A+\cfrac{1}{B+\cfrac{1}{C+\cfrac{1}{D+\cfrac{1}{E}}}}} \text{ etc.}$$

by the selection of appropriate values for A, B, C, D, E etc. A vulgar fraction in this form is termed a *continued fraction*. A, B, C, D, E, etc. are known as *partial quotients*, A being the first, B the second, C the third, and so on. For example, the fraction $\frac{4}{7}$ would have partial quotients of 1, 1, 2 and 1, since

$$\cfrac{1}{1+\cfrac{1}{1+\cfrac{1}{2+\cfrac{1}{1}}}} = \cfrac{1}{1+\cfrac{1}{1+\frac{1}{3}}} = \cfrac{1}{1+\cfrac{1}{1\frac{1}{3}}} = \frac{1}{1+\frac{3}{4}} = \frac{1}{1\frac{3}{4}} = \frac{1}{\frac{7}{4}} = \frac{4}{7}$$

We will now demonstrate the method of obtaining the partial quotients, by expressing the vulgar fraction $\dfrac{149}{195}$ as a continued fraction.

The first step is to divide the numerator into the denominator to establish the first partial quotient and a remainder, thus:

$$149 \enclose{updiagonalstrike}{\,\boxed{195}\,} \quad 1 = \text{first partial quotient}$$
$$\underline{149}$$
$$46 = \text{remainder}$$

The other partial quotients can be obtained in order by dividing the remainder into the previous divisor. Thus for the second partial quotient:

$$\text{remainder} \ldots 46 \,\boxed{149}\, \quad 3 \ldots \text{second partial quotient}$$
$$\underline{138}$$
$$11 \ldots \text{remainder}$$

and the third:

remainder ... 11 $\lceil\overline{46}\rceil$ 4 ... third partial quotient
44
$\overline{2}$ ... remainder

The whole sequence can be put down in the following form:

149 $\lceil\overline{195}\rceil$ 1
149
$\overline{46}\rceil$ 149 $\lceil\overline{3}$
138
$\overline{11}\rceil$ 46 $\lceil\overline{4}$
44
$\overline{2}\rceil$ 11 $\lceil\overline{5}$
10
$\overline{1}\rceil$ 2 $\lceil\overline{2}$
2

The partial quotients are 1, 3, 4, 5, 2,

and
$$\frac{149}{195}=\cfrac{1}{1+\cfrac{1}{3+\cfrac{1}{4+\cfrac{1}{5+\cfrac{1}{2}}}}}$$

It is convenient to express a continued fraction as a series by stating

the values of $\dfrac{1}{A}$, $\dfrac{1}{A+\dfrac{1}{B}}$, $\dfrac{1}{A+\dfrac{1}{B+\dfrac{1}{C}}}$

and so on.

These can be found by formal arithmetic, but there is a much quicker way which enables a check to be made on the accuracy of the partial quotients.

We erect the following table:

		1	3	4	5	2
$\dfrac{0}{1}$						

It will be noted that the partial quotients have been put down in the correct sequence, and the fraction $\frac{0}{1}$ has been inserted for use in future calculations. Under the first partial quotient we insert the reciprocal of the first partial quotient, in this case $\frac{1}{1}$.

(Irrespective of the value of the partial quotients, the fraction $\frac{0}{1}$ is always used, and the first fraction is always the reciprocal of the first partial quotient.)

So far, we have

		1	3
$\frac{0}{1}$		$\frac{1}{1}$	

The remaining fractions are established by a method common to them all.

Putting the table so far in the general form,

		A	B
$\frac{0}{1}$		$\frac{1}{A}$	

The fraction under B is $\dfrac{B \times 1 + 0}{B \times A + 1}$,

i.e. having obtained a fraction, the next fraction is

$$\frac{(\text{next partial quotient} \times \text{numerator}) + \text{previous numerator}}{(\text{next partial quotient} \times \text{denominator}) + \text{previous denominator}}$$

In this case $\qquad \dfrac{(3 \times 1) + 0}{(3 \times 1) + 1} = \dfrac{3}{4}$

The next will be $\qquad \dfrac{(4 \times 3) + 1}{(4 \times 4) + 1} = \dfrac{13}{17}$

Finally, the table is completed to give:

		1	3	4	5	2
$\frac{0}{1}$		$\frac{1}{1}$	$\frac{3}{4}$	$\frac{13}{17}$	$\frac{68}{89}$	$\frac{149}{195}$

If the calculations have been performed correctly, the last fraction will be the original fraction, or its equivalent by cancellation. For example, if $\frac{1\,000}{1\,535}$ were to be expressed as a continued fraction, the final fraction would be $\frac{200}{307}$. If the value $\frac{200}{357}$ had been obtained, it would be fairly safe to conclude that the partial quotients were correct, but that the calculations of the denominators were in error. If the final value produced an illogical value of say $\frac{176}{853}$, which shows no resemblance at all to $\frac{200}{357}$, it is highly probable that the partial quotients were incorrect.

Example

Find a continued fraction for $\frac{90}{127}$

```
    90 ⌈ 127 ⌉ 1
         90
         37 ⌉ 90 ⌈ 2
              74
             ⌈ 16 | 37 ⌈ 2
                    32
                    5 | 16 ⌈ 3
                        15
                        1 | 5 ⌈ 5
                            5
                            =
```

		1	2	2	3	5
$\frac{0}{1}$		$\frac{1}{1}$	$\frac{2}{3}$	$\frac{5}{7}$	$\frac{17}{24}$	$\frac{90}{127}$

Answer: $\frac{1}{1}, \frac{2}{3}, \frac{5}{7}, \frac{17}{24}, \frac{90}{127}$

A *proper fraction* is a fraction where the numerator is smaller than the denominator, e.g. $\frac{3}{4}$. Occasionally we find it convenient to express a ratio with the numerator greater than the denominator, e.g. $\frac{48}{25}$. Such a fraction is called an *improper fraction*. Its actual magnitude is greater than unity.

If a fraction is greater than unity, a continued fraction should be found for its reciprocal. Inversion of every fraction in the result produces the series desired. The proof of the validity of this procedure is not called for in the Part II syllabus.

Example

Taking π as 3·1416, find a continued fraction for π.

Since the ratio is greater than unity, we will find a continued fraction for its reciprocal, and finally invert all the fractions of the series.

$$\frac{1}{3\cdot141\,6} = \frac{10\,000}{31\,416}$$

```
10 000 | 31 416 | 3
         30 000
          1 416 | 10 000 | 7
                  9 912
                     88 | 1 416 | 16
                          1 408
                             8 | 88 | 11
                                 88
                                 ==
```

	3	7	16	11
$\frac{0}{1}$	$\frac{1}{3}$	$\frac{7}{22}$	$\frac{113}{355}$	$\frac{1\,250}{3\,927}$

$\left(= \frac{10\,000}{31\,416} \right)$

Inverting these fractions gives the desired result.

Answer: 3, $\frac{22}{7}$, $\frac{355}{113}$, $\frac{3\,927}{1\,250}$

1.4.2 THE CONVERGENCE OF A CONTINUED FRACTION

Let us refer back to the continued fraction for $\frac{149}{195}$.

To five places of decimals, the fraction $\frac{149}{195}$ is 0·764 10. We will tabulate the fractions which led to the result of $\frac{149}{195}$, with their differences from that value, to five places of decimals.

Order	Vulgar fraction	Decimal equivalent	Difference
First	$\frac{1}{1}$	1·000 00	0·235 90
Second	$\frac{3}{4}$	0·750 00	−0·114 10
Third	$\frac{13}{17}$	0·764 71	0·000 61
Fourth	$\frac{68}{89}$	0·764 04	−0·000 06
Fifth	$\frac{149}{195}$	0·764 10	0

It will be observed that the differences are alternately positive and negative, and that as the order grows, the numerical value of the difference decreases. The fractions *converge* on the original value.

This property is true of any continued fraction, and enables us to put to good use the evaluation of a continued fraction, since it will enable us to obtain a close approximation to a particular fraction using smaller numbers. For example, a particular gear ratio may prove to be unobtainable. Continued fractions will enable us to obtain a close approximation which may be acceptable.

Because of the converging property of a continued fraction, the fractions in the result are known as *convergents*. For $\frac{149}{195}$, $\frac{1}{1}$ is the *first convergent*, $\frac{3}{4}$ the *second convergent*, and so on. The higher the order of the convergent, the closer it is to the original fraction. Hence the approximation chosen for use should be the highest convergent possible to satisfy given conditions.

Example

A screw of lead 5 mm has to be cut on a lathe having a leadscrew of 0·25 in (=6·35 mm). A 127T gear-wheel is not available, but there are two sets of gears of 20T to 120T at 5T intervals. Evaluate an approximate compound train, and the resulting error, in millimetres, over a length of 10 leads, using the convergents established in a suitable continued fraction. Give the answer to two decimal places.

35

$$\frac{\text{drivers}}{\text{driven}} = \frac{\text{lead required}}{\text{lead of leadscrew}} = \frac{5 \text{ mm}}{6 \cdot 35 \text{ mm}} = \frac{100}{127}$$

```
100 | 127 | 1
      100
       27 | 100 | 3
             81
             19 | 27 | 1
                  19
                   8 | 19 | 2
                        16
                         3 | 8 | 2
                              6
                              2 | 3 | 1
                                   2
                                   1 | 2 | 2
                                        2
                                        =
```

	1	3	1	2	2	1	2
$\dfrac{0}{1}$	$\dfrac{1}{1}$	$\dfrac{3}{4}$	$\dfrac{4}{5}$	$\dfrac{11}{14}$	$\dfrac{26}{33}$	$\dfrac{37}{47}$	$\dfrac{100}{127}$

Noting that the highest convergent is the closest approximation, the ratio $\dfrac{26}{33}$ is most convenient $\left(\dfrac{37}{47}\right.$ cannot be accommodated by the gears. $\Big)$

$$\frac{26}{33} = \frac{5\,200}{6\,600} = \frac{80 \times 65}{110 \times 60}$$

10 leads should be 10×5 mm $= 50$ mm
10 leads cut using approximate gear train

$$= 10 \times \frac{26}{33} \times 6 \cdot 35 \text{ mm}$$

$$= 50 \cdot 030\,3 \text{ mm}$$

Error $= 50 \cdot 030\,3$ mm $- 50$ mm $= 0 \cdot 03$ mm to 2 decimal places

Answers: Compound train $= \dfrac{80 \times 65}{110 \times 60}$, or similar ratio

Error on 10 leads $= 0 \cdot 03$ mm

Example

Two spur gears have to mesh at a centre distance of 250 mm and provide a gear ratio close to 2·378. Determine, from a continued fraction, a convenient metric module and the numbers of teeth on the gears, with the actual ratio and the amount of error, each to five decimal places.

Since the ratio is greater than unity, we will first obtain a continued fraction for its reciprocal.

$$\frac{1}{2\cdot378} = \frac{1\,000}{2\,378} = \frac{500}{1\,189}$$

```
500 | 1189 | 2
      1000
       189 | 500 | 2
             378
             122 | 189 | 1
                   122
                    67 | 122 | 1
                         67
                         55 | 67 | 1
                              55
                              12 | 55 | 4
                                   48
                                    7 | 12 | 1
                                         7
                                         5 | 7 | 1
                                             5
                                             2 | 5 | 2
                                                 4
                                                 1 | 2 | 2
                                                     2
                                                     =
```

	2	2	1	1	1	4	1	1	2	2
$\frac{0}{1}$	$\frac{1}{2}$	$\frac{2}{5}$	$\frac{3}{7}$	$\frac{5}{12}$	$\frac{8}{19}$	$\frac{37}{88}$	$\frac{45}{107}$	$\frac{82}{195}$	$\frac{209}{497}$	$\frac{500}{1\,189}$

The centre distance C of spur gears having T_1 and T_2 teeth of metric module m is given by

$$C = \frac{m(T_1 + T_2)}{2}$$

T_1 and T_2 must be whole numbers, while m should be a convenient value (preferably a whole number) to avoid non-standard cutters. Totalling numerators and denominators of the continued fraction, we obtain values of

$$3 \quad 7 \quad 10 \quad 17 \quad 27 \quad 125 \quad 152 \quad 277 \quad 706 \quad 1689$$

Noticing that the highest order of convergent produces the closest approximation, the value of 125 when $T_1 = 88$ and $T_2 = 37$ will provide a convenient metric module.

$$125 = \frac{m(88 + 37)}{2}$$
$$250 = 125 \, m, \; m = 2$$

Since the error is required to five places of decimals, the ratio must be evaluated with seven-figure tables

$$\log 88 = 1 \cdot 944 \, 482 \, 7$$
$$\log 37 = 1 \cdot 568 \, 201 \, 7$$
$$\overline{\log 2 \cdot 378 \, 378 = 0 \cdot 376 \, 281 \, 0}$$

To five decimal places, ratio is 2·378 38,

an error of 0·000 38.

Answers: Module = 2 mm

Numbers of teeth = 88 and 37

Actual ratio = 2·378 38

Error = 0·000 38

(It should be noted that 4 mm, 176T and 74T, or similar relationships to 2 mm, 88, and 37 also suffice.)

Example

A dividing head has the standard ratio of 40 to 1, so that one turn of the operating handle rotates the workspindle through an angle of 9°. The index plate has hole circles from 30 to 60 inclusive at unit intervals.

(*a*) Calculate, by the method of continued fractions, the nearest indexing ratio to rotate the workspindle through 5·29°.

(*b*) Calculate the error, in degrees, to the first significant figure.

(C.G.L.I.)

$$\text{Number of turns} = \frac{\text{angle required}}{9°} = \frac{5 \cdot 29°}{9°} = \frac{529}{900}$$

```
529 │ 900 │ 1
      529
      371 │ 529 │ 1
            371
            158 │ 371 │ 2
                  316
                   55 │ 158 │ 2
                        110
                         48 │ 55 │ 1
                              48
                               7 │ 48 │ 6
                                   42
                                    6 │ 7 │ 1
                                        6
                                        1 │ 6 │ 6
                                            6
                                            =
```

$\frac{0}{1}$	1	1	2	2	1	6	1	6
$\frac{0}{1}$	$\frac{1}{1}$	$\frac{1}{2}$	$\frac{3}{5}$	$\frac{7}{12}$	$\frac{10}{17}$	$\frac{67}{114}$	$\frac{77}{131}$	$\frac{529}{900}$

The highest order of convergent which is convenient is $\frac{10}{17}$

$$\text{Indexing} = \frac{10}{17} = \frac{20 \text{ holes}}{34 \text{ circle}} \text{ or } \frac{30 \text{ holes}}{51 \text{ circle}}$$

$$\text{Actual turning} = \frac{10}{17} \times 9° = \frac{90°}{17}$$

$$= 5·294\ 1°$$

Error $= +0·004°$ to the first significant figure

Answers: (*a*) $\frac{10}{17}$ ratio, either $\frac{20 \text{ holes}}{34 \text{ circle}}$ or $\frac{30 \text{ holes}}{51 \text{ circle}}$

(*b*) Error $= +0·004°$

1.4.3 COMBINED FRACTIONS

The method of continued fractions is not the only method of obtaining a fraction which is approximately equal to a given ratio. A method which can rapidly produce a series of approximations, particularly if a calculating machine is available, is that of combined fractions.

If $\frac{A}{B}$ and $\frac{C}{D}$ are two fractions, $\frac{C}{D}$ being greater than $\frac{A}{B}$, then another fraction which is greater than $\frac{A}{B}$, is less than $\frac{C}{D}$, but which is not the arithmetical mean of $\frac{A}{B}$ and $\frac{C}{D}$, is $\frac{A+C}{B+D}$

Example

By combining the fractions $\frac{3}{5}$ and $\frac{5}{8}$, find a fraction that is within 0·0001 of 0·609 75.

$$\text{Combine } \frac{3}{5} \text{ with } \frac{5}{8}, \frac{3+5}{5+8} = \frac{8}{13} = 0.615\ 4$$

$\frac{3}{5}$ is too low, $\frac{8}{13}$ is too high.

$$\text{Combine } \frac{3}{5} \text{ with } \frac{8}{13}, \frac{3+8}{5+13} = \frac{11}{18} = 0.611\ 1$$

$\frac{3}{5}$ is too low, $\frac{11}{18}$ is too high.

$$\text{Combine } \frac{3}{5} \text{ with } \frac{11}{18}, \frac{3+11}{5+18} = \frac{14}{23} = 0.608\ 7$$

$\frac{14}{23}$ is too low, $\frac{11}{18}$ is too high.

$$\text{Combine } \frac{14}{23} \text{ with } \frac{11}{18}, \frac{14+11}{23+18} = \frac{5}{41} = 0.609\ 76$$

This answer is acceptable.

Answer: Fraction is $\frac{25}{41}$

(*It will be shown later that there is a multiplicity of other fractions, but $\frac{25}{41}$ was the first one revealed by the method.*)

1.4.4 INTERMEDIARY RATIOS IN A CONTINUED FRACTION

A continued fraction does not reveal all the simple fractions which may be suitable approximations for given conditions, especially so when a compound gear drive of the type $\dfrac{T_1 \times T_3}{T_2 \times T_4}$ is permissible.

It is possible to use the method of continued fractions followed by the method of combined fractions to obtain further approximate ratios which may be acceptable.

If we let the second convergent of a continued fraction be $\dfrac{p_2}{q_2}$ and the third convergent be $\dfrac{p_3}{q_3}$, then a fraction which lies between them is $\dfrac{p_2+p_3}{q_2+q_3}$.

It will be noted that this is the fourth convergent if the fourth partial quotient is unity.

A fraction which lies between

$$\frac{p_2}{q_2} \text{ and } \frac{p_2+p_3}{q_2+q_3} \text{ is } \frac{2p_2+p_3}{2q_2+q_3}$$

while a fraction which lies between

$$\frac{p_2+p_3}{q_2+q_3} \text{ and } \frac{p_3}{q_3} \text{ is } \frac{p_2+2p_3}{q_2+2q_3}$$

Further combinations could be made showing that there is an infinite number of fractions between $\dfrac{p_2}{q_2}$ and $\dfrac{p_3}{q_3}$ given by the general formula $\dfrac{Ap_2+Bp_3}{Aq_2+Bq_3}$. For convenience, A and B are taken as positive whole numbers which do not have a common factor. For example, let two fractions be $\dfrac{3}{4}$ and $\dfrac{4}{5}$, that is, 0·75 and 0·80. We can calculate a multiplicity of fractions which lie between these values by using various values of A and B.

With $A=1$ and $B=1$, $\dfrac{1(3)+1(4)}{1(4)+1(5)} = \dfrac{7}{9} = 0.777\,8$

With $A=2$ and $B=1$, $\dfrac{2(3)+1(4)}{2(4)+1(5)} = \dfrac{10}{13} = 0.769\,2$

With $A=1$ and $B=2$, $\dfrac{1(3)+2(4)}{1(4)+2(5)}=\dfrac{11}{14}=0\cdot785\ 7$

With $A=5$ and $B=2$, $\dfrac{5(3)+2(4)}{5(4)+2(5)}=\dfrac{23}{30}=0\cdot766\ 7$

With $A=5$ and $B=4$, $\dfrac{5(3)+4(4)}{5(4)+4(5)}=\dfrac{31}{40}=0\cdot775\ 0$

The process could be continued indefinitely. The selection of suitable values for A and B to produce a given degree of accuracy is a matter of trial. Certain problems give A and B and ask that a particular ratio be proved to be acceptable. If A and B are not given, their determination could be quite protracted. However, there is one property of a continued fraction which proves of considerable service. No other fraction in a continued fraction is closer to the desired ratio than the fraction which lies next to the desired ratio. Returning to the series obtained for $\dfrac{149}{195}$ by the method of continued fractions, viz. :

$$\frac{1}{1} \qquad \frac{3}{4} \qquad \frac{13}{17} \qquad \frac{68}{89} \qquad \frac{149}{195}$$

the nearest fraction to $\dfrac{149}{195}$ revealed by this method is $\dfrac{68}{89}$. If this fraction does not provide a sufficient degree of accuracy, then $\dfrac{68+149}{89+195}$ is even closer to $\dfrac{149}{195}$ than is $\dfrac{68}{89}$.

Further combinations may lead to a fraction providing a numerator and denominator which both factorize to produce a ratio of the type $\dfrac{T_1 \times T_3}{T_2 \times T_4}$. This could then be used in a compound gear train. We will demonstrate the use of combined and continued fractions in the following examples.

Example

A gear ratio of $\dfrac{80}{127}$ is required, accurate to within $0\cdot000\ 1$, without any gear-wheel having more than 100 teeth.

(a) Obtain by the method of continued fractions a series of fractions converging upon $\dfrac{80}{127}$.

(b) Show that the method does not reveal a fraction of sufficient accuracy.

(c) If the fifth convergent is represented by $\dfrac{p_5}{q_5}$ and the sixth convergent by $\dfrac{p_6}{q_6}$, show that $\dfrac{p_5+3p_6}{q_5+3q_6}$ provides an acceptable ratio which could be applied to a simple gear train.

(a)
$$\frac{80}{127}=0.629\,921\,3$$

```
80 │ 127 │ 1
     80
     47 │ 80 │ 1
          47
          33 │ 47 │ 1
               33
               14 │ 33 │ 2
                    28
                    5 │ 14 │ 2
                        10
                        4 │ 5 │ 1
                            4
                            1 │ 4 │ 4
                                4
                                =
```

		1	1	1	2	2	1	4
$\dfrac{0}{1}$	$\dfrac{1}{1}$	$\dfrac{1}{2}$	$\dfrac{2}{3}$	$\dfrac{5}{8}$	$\dfrac{12}{19}$	$\dfrac{17}{27}$	$\dfrac{80}{127}$

(b) The nearest approximation to $\dfrac{80}{127}$ produced by this series is $\dfrac{17}{27}$

$$\frac{80}{127}=0{\cdot}629\ 921\ 3$$

$$\frac{17}{27}=0{\cdot}629\ 629\ 6$$

Difference$=0{\cdot}000\ 291\ 7$, not acceptable

(c)

$$\frac{p_5}{q_5}=\frac{12}{19}\qquad\frac{p_6}{q_6}=\frac{17}{27}$$

$$\frac{p_5+3q_6}{q_5+3q_6}=\frac{12+3(17)}{19+3(27)}=\frac{63}{100}$$

No gear-wheel has to have more than 100 teeth, hence this ratio could be obtained with a simple gear train.

$$\frac{63}{100}=0{\cdot}630\ 000\ 0$$

$$\frac{80}{127}=0{\cdot}629\ 921\ 3$$

Error$=0{\cdot}000\ 078\ 7$, acceptable

Answers: (a) $\dfrac{1}{1}, \dfrac{1}{2}, \dfrac{2}{3}, \dfrac{5}{8}, \dfrac{12}{19}, \dfrac{17}{27}, \dfrac{80}{127}$

(b) $\dfrac{17}{27}$ is not of sufficient accuracy

(c) $\dfrac{63}{100}$ has an error of $0{\cdot}000\ 078\ 7$ which is acceptable.

Example

A ratio of $\dfrac{10}{19{\cdot}3}$ is required, accurate to within $0{\cdot}000\ 05$. Obtain by the method of continued fractions a series of fractions which converge upon $\dfrac{100}{193}$. Show that this method does not reveal a fraction of sufficient accuracy.

Combine the most accurate approximation revealed by the continued fraction with the original value of $\dfrac{100}{193}$ to provide a fraction which is sufficiently accurate, and show that the numerator and denominator of this latter fraction both factorize.

$$\frac{10}{19\cdot3}=\frac{100}{193}=0\cdot518\ 134\ 7$$

```
100 | 193 | 1
      100
       93 | 100 | 1
             93
              7 | 93 | 13
                   91
                    2 | 7 | 3
                        6 |
                        1 | 2 | 2
                            2
                           ===
```

0		1	1	13	3	2
1		1	1	14	43	100
		1	2	27	83	193

$$\frac{100}{193}=0\cdot518\ 134\ 7$$

$$\frac{43}{83}=0\cdot518\ 072\ 2$$

Error$=0\cdot000\ 062\ 5$ not acceptable

Combine $\frac{43}{83}$ with $\frac{100}{193}$

$$\frac{43+100}{83+193}=\frac{143}{276}$$

$$\frac{100}{193}=0\cdot518\ 134\ 7$$

$$\frac{143}{276}=0\cdot518\ 116\ 0$$

Error$=0\cdot000\ 018\ 7$ acceptable

$$\frac{143}{276}=\frac{11\times13}{12\times23}$$

Answers: Most accurate fraction, $\frac{43}{83}$, not acceptable

Combined fraction, $\frac{143}{276}=\frac{11\times13}{12\times23}$, acceptable

45

Problems 1.4

1. Express the following proper fractions as continued fractions and establish their convergents:

   (a) $\dfrac{14}{47}$ (b) $\dfrac{16}{41}$ (c) $\dfrac{187}{283}$ (d) $\dfrac{107}{363}$

2. Express the following improper fractions as continued fractions and establish their convergents as improper fractions:

   (a) $\dfrac{221}{42}$ (b) $\dfrac{1\,493}{306}$

3. Obtain, by the method of continued fractions, a series of ratios (which are improper fractions) converging upon $2\dfrac{9}{97}$.

4. Taking π as 3·142, establish by the method of continued fractions a set of improper fractions converging upon π.

5. The minor sector of a circle subtends an angle of 113°. Determine, by the method of continued fractions, a series of fractions converging upon the ratio represented by:

$$\frac{\text{area of minor sector}}{\text{area of major sector}}$$

6. When spiral milling on a particular horizontal milling machine, the gear train ratio is established from:

$$\frac{\text{drivers}}{\text{driven}} = \frac{200 \text{ mm}}{\text{lead required}}$$

   If a lead of 153 mm was required find the nearest ratio revealed by continued fractions subject to the limitation that the numerator must not exceed 20.

7. A dividing head has the usual 40 to 1 worm gear ratio so that one turn of the operating handle rotates the main spindle by 9 degrees. A particular setting requires the main spindle to rotate through an angle of 6° 33′. The dividing head index plate has every hole circle from 30 holes to 60 holes circle inclusive. Determine:

   (a) The nearest approximate hole spacing and hole circle that is revealed by the method of continued fractions.

   (b) The amount of error, to nearest whole number of seconds.

   (C.G.L.I.)

8. A lathe has a leadscrew of pitch 5 mm. It is to be used to cut a replacement leadscrew of pitch 0·25 in.

   (*a*) Taking 1 in=25·4 mm, determine the driver/driven relationship of the gear drive.

   (*b*) Obtain, by the method of continued fractions, a set of convergents for the ratio.

   (*c*) If there are two sets of gear wheels 5T to 100T at 5T intervals, select the most accurate combinations revealed by the method of continued fractions for:
   (i) a simple train involving two wheels
   (ii) a compound train involving four wheels.

9. A machine table is driven by a leadscrew of pitch 5 mm. The input to the leadscrew drive rotates at 20 rev/min. The table is required to move linearly at the rate of 86·1 mm/min. Calculate, by the method of continued fractions, the nearest $\dfrac{\text{driver}}{\text{driven}}$ ratio of the gear drive if the table is to be traversed at the rate of 86·1 mm/min, and neither the numerator nor denominator of the fraction is to exceed 100.

10. By combining the fractions $\dfrac{1}{2}$ and $\dfrac{4}{7}$, find the fraction with the lowest denominator which lies between 0·535 6 and 0·535 8.

11. A gear train is to provide the ratio $\dfrac{250}{433}$. Calculate a set of fractions converging upon this value. If the nth convergent is represented by $\dfrac{p_n}{q_n}$ $\left(\text{so that, for instance, the ratio } \dfrac{3}{5} \text{ is } \dfrac{p_3}{q_3}\right)$ show that $\dfrac{p_8+p_9}{q_8+q_9}$ gives a fraction whose numerator and denominator both factorize and give a convenient ratio for use on a hobbing machine.

12. A thread of pitch 0·5 in is to be cut on a lathe having a leadscrew of pitch 5 mm so that the gear ratio between the spindle and the leadscrew is $\dfrac{127}{50}$

   (*a*) Obtain a continued fraction for this ratio.

(b) No single wheel of the gear train has to have more than 100 teeth. If the nth convergent of the continued fraction is represented by $\dfrac{p_n}{q_n}$ $\left(\text{so that } \dfrac{p_6}{q_6}=\dfrac{127}{50}\right)$, show that $\dfrac{p_5+p_6}{q_5+q_6}$ gives a ratio whose numerator and denominator both factorize.

(c) If this latter ratio is used, what is the cumulative pitch error over a length of 100 pitches, to the nearest 0·01 of a millimetre?

13. When simple indexing, using a dividing head, every complete turn of the operating handle will rotate the main spindle by 9°. For a particular operation the main spindle has to rotate by 7·27°. It is found from mathematical tables that 727 is a prime number. Consequently an approximation has to be used. The dividing head has every hole circle from 30 holes to 60 holes. Find the nearest approximation available revealed by the method of continued fractions, and calculate the error, in degrees, to one significant figure.

14. A 1B.A. thread (pitch 0·9 mm) has to be cut on a special lathe with a leadscrew of 6 t.p.i. The lathe does not have a 127T gear, but a compound train can be used, using any combination of gears of 20T to 100T at intervals of 5T. The error of the gear train ratio must not exceed 0·0002.

(a) Obtain a fraction for the $\dfrac{\text{driver}}{\text{driven}}$ ratio of the compound train.

(b) Find the best available ratio using the method of continued fractions, and show that this method does not reveal a fraction of sufficient accuracy.

(c) There are five fractions in the series before $\dfrac{27}{127}$. Show that the fourth and fifth can be simply combined to give a ratio which is acceptable.

Answers to problems 1.4

1. (a) $\dfrac{1}{3}$ $\quad\dfrac{2}{7}$ $\quad\dfrac{3}{10}$ $\quad\dfrac{14}{47}$

   (b) $\dfrac{1}{2}$ $\quad\dfrac{1}{3}$ $\quad\dfrac{2}{5}$ $\quad\dfrac{7}{8}$ $\quad\dfrac{16}{41}$

(c) $\dfrac{1}{1}$ $\dfrac{1}{2}$ $\dfrac{2}{3}$ $\dfrac{37}{56}$ $\dfrac{187}{283}$

(d) $\dfrac{1}{3}$ $\dfrac{2}{7}$ $\dfrac{3}{10}$ $\dfrac{5}{17}$ $\dfrac{23}{78}$ $\dfrac{28}{95}$ $\dfrac{107}{363}$

2. (a) $\dfrac{5}{1}$ $\dfrac{16}{3}$ $\dfrac{21}{4}$ $\dfrac{100}{19}$ $\dfrac{221}{42}$

   (b) $\dfrac{4}{1}$ $\dfrac{5}{1}$ $\dfrac{39}{8}$ $\dfrac{122}{25}$ $\dfrac{161}{33}$ $\dfrac{444}{91}$ $\dfrac{1\,049}{215}$ $\dfrac{1\,493}{306}$

3. $\dfrac{2}{1}$ $\dfrac{21}{20}$ $\dfrac{23}{11}$ $\dfrac{90}{43}$ $\dfrac{203}{97}$

4. $\dfrac{3}{1}$ $\dfrac{22}{7}$ $\dfrac{509}{162}$ $\dfrac{531}{169}$ $\dfrac{1\,571}{500}$

   $\left(\text{The last fraction is equal to } \dfrac{3\,142}{1\,000}\right)$

5. $\dfrac{1}{2}$ $\dfrac{5}{11}$ $\dfrac{11}{24}$ $\dfrac{16}{35}$ $\dfrac{27}{59}$ $\dfrac{43}{94}$ $\dfrac{113}{247}$

6. $\dfrac{17}{13}$

7. (a) Any $\dfrac{8}{11}$ ratio, e.g. $\dfrac{24 \text{ holes}}{33 \text{ circle}}$

   (b) 16 seconds

8. (a) $\dfrac{127}{100}$

   (b) $\dfrac{1}{1}$ $\dfrac{4}{3}$ $\dfrac{5}{4}$ $\dfrac{14}{11}$ $\dfrac{33}{26}$ $\dfrac{80}{63}$ $\dfrac{127}{100}$

   (c) (i) 70 driver, 55 driven

   (ii) the $\dfrac{33}{26}$ ratio, giving $\dfrac{11}{13}\times\dfrac{3}{2}$,

   i.e. 55 driver with 65 driven
   with any 3/2 ratio such as 60 driver, 40 driven

9. $\dfrac{31}{36}$

10. $\dfrac{15}{28}$

11. $\dfrac{56+97}{97+168}=\dfrac{153}{265}=\dfrac{3\times51}{5\times53}$

12. (a) $\dfrac{2}{1} \quad \dfrac{3}{1} \quad \dfrac{5}{2} \quad \dfrac{28}{11} \quad \dfrac{33}{13} \quad \dfrac{127}{50}$

    (b) $\dfrac{33+127}{13+50}=\dfrac{160}{63}=\dfrac{8\times20}{7\times9}$ ratio

    (c) 0·16 mm

13. 42 holes on 52 circle, error is 0·0008°

14. (a) $\dfrac{27}{127}$

    (b) $\dfrac{27}{127}=0.212\ 598\ 4,\quad \dfrac{7}{33}=0.212\ 121\ 2$, insufficiently accurate

    (c) $\dfrac{7+10}{33+47}=\dfrac{17}{80}$, gear train $\dfrac{85\times20}{80\times100}$,

    $\dfrac{17}{80}=0.212\ 500\ 0$, acceptable

1.5 Progressions

1.5.1 ARITHMETICAL PROGRESSIONS

Consider the series of numbers:

$$3, \quad 10, \quad 17, \quad 24, \quad 31.$$

It will be observed that each number is 7 more than the previous number. Any similar series can be made to fit the pattern:

$$a, a+d, a+2d, a+3d \ldots$$

by using appropriate value for the *first term a* and the *common difference d*. A series of this type is called an *arithmetical progression*.

The first term is a, which can be written as $a+0d$.
The second term is $a+d$, which can be written as $a+1d$.
The third term is $(a+d)+d$, which can be written as $a+2d$.
The fourth term is $(a+2d)+d$, which can be written as $a+3d$.
It can be deduced that the nth term of an arithmetical progression is $a+d(n-1)$.

Let S represent the sum of n terms of an arithmetical progression of first term a and common difference d, and let the last term be l.

$$S=(a)+(a+d)+(a+2d) \ldots +(l-d)+(l).$$

Writing the series in the reverse order,

$$S=(l)+(l-d)+(l-2d)\ldots+(a+d)+(a).$$

Adding the above equations,

$$2S=(a+l)+(a+l)+(a+l)\ldots(a+l)+(a+l)$$
$$=(a+l) \text{ to } n \text{ terms}=n(a+l)$$

Now $l=a+d(n-1)$

$$\therefore\ 2S=n\{a+a+d(n-1)\}$$
$$\therefore\ 2S=n\{2a+d(n-1)\}$$

$$\therefore\ S=\frac{n}{2}\left\{2a+d(n-1)\right\}$$

Example

A body falling freely from rest without resistance falls 4·9 m in the first second, 14·7 m in the second second, 24·5 m in the third second, and so on.

(a) How far does it fall in the tenth second?
(b) How far has it fallen altogether in 10 seconds?
(c) How long will it take to fall 122·5 m?
The series is 4·9, 14·7, 24·5 . . ., which is an arithmetical progression with $a=4\cdot9$ and $d=9\cdot8$

(a) n^{th} term$=a+d(n-1)$
 10th term$=4\cdot9+9\cdot8(10-1)=4\cdot9+9\cdot8(9)$
 $\qquad\qquad=4\cdot9+88\cdot2=93\cdot1$ m

(b) $S=\dfrac{n}{2}\left\{2a+d(n-1)\right\}=\dfrac{10}{2}\left\{9\cdot8+9\cdot8(9)\right\}$
 $\qquad=5\{9\cdot8+88\cdot2\}=5\{98\}=490$ m

(c) $\qquad S=\dfrac{n}{2}\left\{2a+d(n-1)\right\}$

$$122\cdot5=\frac{n}{2}\left\{9\cdot8+9\cdot8(n-1)\right\}$$

$$122\cdot5=\frac{n}{2}\left\{9\cdot8+9\cdot8n-9\cdot8\right\}$$

$$=\frac{n}{2}\left\{9\cdot8n\right\}$$

$$122\cdot5=4\cdot9n^2$$

$$n^2 = \frac{122 \cdot 5}{4 \cdot 9} = 25$$

$$n = \sqrt{25} = \pm 5$$

$\therefore$ $n = 5$ since $n = -5$ is illogical

Answers: (*a*) Distance in 10th second $= 93 \cdot 1$ m
(*b*) Distance in 10 seconds $= 490$ m
(*c*) Time to fall $122 \cdot 5$ m $\quad = 5$ s

1.5.2 GEOMETRIC PROGRESSIONS

Let us consider the series:

$$2, \quad 4, \quad 8, \quad 16, \quad 32, \quad 64, \quad \text{etc.}$$

It will be observed that each number is twice the value of the preceding number. Any similar series can be made to fit the general form.

$$a, \quad ar, \quad ar^2, \quad ar^3, \quad ar^4, \quad ar^5, \quad \text{etc.,}$$

by the use of appropriate values for the *first term a* and the *common ratio r*. A series of this type is called *geometric progression*.

The first term is a, which can be written as $ar^0 = ar^{1-1}$
The second term is ar, which can be written as $ar^1 = ar^{2-1}$
In a similar way, the third term is ar^{3-1}, the fourth term is ar^{4-1}, and the nth term is ar^{n-1}.

Let the nth term of a geometric progression be b.

Then
$$b = ar^{n-1}$$

$$r^{n-1} = \frac{b}{a}$$

and
$$r = \sqrt[n-1]{\left(\frac{b}{a}\right)}$$

By taking logs of each side

$$\log r = \frac{\log b - \log a}{n-1}$$

$$\therefore \quad n - 1 = \frac{\log b - \log a}{\log r}$$

and
$$n = \left(\frac{\log b - \log a}{\log r}\right) + 1$$

The intermediary values between b and a are termed *geometric means*. For the special case of one geometric mean, there will be three terms in all, viz. :

$$a, \quad x, \quad b$$

where x is the single geometric mean.

From the standard pattern of a geometric progression

$$\frac{x}{a} = \frac{b}{x}$$

$$\therefore \ x^2 = ab, \text{ and } x = \sqrt{(ab)}$$

1.5.3 THE SUM OF A GEOMETRIC SERIES

Let S be the sum of the first n terms of a geometric series of first term a and common ratio r.

$$S = a + ar + ar^2 + ar^3 \ldots + ar^{n-1}$$

$$\therefore \ Sr = \quad ar + ar^2 + ar^3 + ar^4 \ldots + ar^{n-1} + ar^n$$

By subtraction of these equations,

$$Sr - S = ar^n - a$$

$$\therefore \ S(r-1) = a(r^n - 1)$$

$$\therefore \ S = \frac{a(r^n - 1)}{r-1} \qquad \ldots (1)$$

Alternatively, since $Sr - S = ar^n - a$,

multiplying through by -1,

$$S - Sr = a - ar^n$$

$$S(1-r) = a(1-r^n)$$

$$\therefore \ S = \frac{a(1-r^n)}{1-r} \qquad \ldots (2)$$

Formula (1) should be used if $|r|$ is greater than unity, and formula (2) should be used if $|r|$ is less than unity. Let us consider particularly the case when $|r|$ is less than unity.

$$S = \frac{a(1-r^n)}{1-r}$$

As n approaches infinity, $|r^n|$ approaches zero.

In which case

$$S \text{ approaches } \frac{a(1-0)}{1-r} = \frac{a}{1-r}$$

This is the *limiting value* which is never actually reached, but as n gets larger, the sum gets closer to this value. From the original proviso, it will be noted that for there to be a limiting value, the common ratio must lie between unity and minus unity.

Example

An instrument needle is oscillating about a particular value. The first reading is 26°, the next is 11°, the third is 21°. If the differences from the final steady reading form a geometric series, find the final steady reading.

Let the final reading be x

First difference $=26-x$

Second difference$=11-x$

Third difference $=21-x$

These differences are in geometric progression.

$$\therefore \frac{26-x}{11-x}=\frac{11-x}{21-x}$$

$$\therefore (26-x)(21-x)=(11-x)(11-x)$$
$$546-47x+x^2=121-22x+x^2$$
$$-47x+22x=121-546$$
$$-25x=-425$$
$$x=\frac{-425}{-25}=17$$

Answer: Final reading$=17°$

Example

A sphere of metal falls vertically on to a flat surface from a height of 10 m. The sphere after an impact rebounds to a height of 0·8 of the distance from which it falls. Determine the theoretical distance of travel in coming to rest.

The distance is

$$10 \ + \ 8+ \ \ 8 \ \ +6·4+ \ 6·4 \ +5·12+ \ 5·12 \ ...$$
down up down up down up down

$=10+2$ (limiting sum of a geometric progression of first term 8 and common ratio 0·8)

$$=10+2\left(\frac{a}{1-r}\right)=10+2\left(\frac{8}{1-0·8}\right)$$

$$=10+2\left(\frac{8}{0·2}\right)=10+2(40)=90$$

Answer: Theoretical total travel$=90$ m

(*The sphere never quite travels this distance, since theoretically it never stops bouncing.*)

Example

A factory commences production of a certain article at the rate of 400 articles per week. If every week production rises by 5%, what is the minimum number of complete weeks required for the total production to exceed 5000 articles? What is the production rate in the last week, and how many articles are made in all if production continues to the end of the final week?

The production rates form a geometric progression of common ratio $1+5\%$, i.e. $1 \cdot 05$. The first term is 400. Let the number of weeks be n.

$$S = \frac{a(r^n - 1)}{r - 1}$$

$$\therefore \ 5\,000 = \frac{400(1 \cdot 05^n - 1)}{1 \cdot 05 - 1}$$

$$\therefore \ \frac{5\,000 \times 0 \cdot 05}{400} = 1 \cdot 05^n - 1$$

$$\therefore \ 1 \cdot 05^n - 1 = \frac{250}{400} = 0 \cdot 625$$

$$1 \cdot 05^n = 1 \cdot 625$$

$$n \log 1 \cdot 05 = \log 1 \cdot 625$$

$$n = \frac{\log 1 \cdot 625}{\log 1 \cdot 05} = \frac{0 \cdot 210\ 9}{0 \cdot 021\ 2} = \text{over 9 but less than 10}$$

Hence 10 weeks are required.

The production rate is the 10th term of 400, 420, 441, etc.
i.e. $400(1 \cdot 05)^{10-1} = 400(1 \cdot 05)^9 = 620 \cdot 7$

No.	Log
400	0·602 1
9 log 1·05	0·190 8
620·7	0·792 9

$$S = \frac{a(r^n - 1)}{r - 1}$$

$$= \frac{400(1 \cdot 05^{10} - 1)}{1 \cdot 05 - 1}$$

$$= 8\,000(1 \cdot 05^{10} - 1)$$

$$= 8\,000(1 \cdot 629 - 1)$$

$$= 8\,000 \times 0 \cdot 629 = 5\,032$$

The final answer checks itself:

it should be a little over 5 000

Answers: Length of run = 10 weeks
Final production rate = 621 per week
Total production = 5 030 articles

One particular use of a geometric progression is in connection with the selection of intermediary speeds between a maximum and a minimum, such as the spindle speeds of a machine tool. Designers seek to obtain a geometric progression of spindle speeds so that a change from one speed to the next has equal practical significance throughout the range. If the speeds were in arithmetical progression a speed change at the lower speeds may be too great to be of practical use, while at the higher speeds the values of the spindle speeds would be so close together that there would be no really significant difference between them. What is desired in a speed change is not a constant numerical amount of change in the spindle speed, but a constant ratio, so the next highest speed is always the same ratio faster, irrespective of the speed. While a range of speeds in geometric progression is desirable, it is virtually impossible to achieve this in an all-geared headstock, since the numbers of teeth on the gears must be whole numbers, and ratios of whole numbers rarely fit exactly to multiples of the common ratio. For example, suppose that the centre distance of two parallel shafts in an all-geared headstock was 240 mm and gears of 4 mm module were to connect the shafts.

Representing the number of teeth on the gears by T_1 and T_2,

$$T_1 + T_2 = 120$$

Suppose the gear ratio to provide a geometric progression were 1·313, then

$$\frac{T_1}{T_2} = 1\text{·}313 \quad \text{or} \quad T_1 = 1\text{·}313 T_2$$

By substitution, $\qquad 1\text{·}313 T_2 + T_2 = 120,$

$$2\text{·}313 T_2 = 120, \quad T_2 = \frac{120}{2\text{·}313} = 51\text{·}88$$

Now T_2 must be a whole number, hence a drive of $T_2 = 52$ and $T_1 = 68$ could be used, though perhaps continued fractions could reveal a closer approximation with a change of module.

$$\frac{68}{52}(=1\text{·}308)$$

is very close to the desired ratio of 1·313, but it is not exact. Small variations from a true geometric progression of lathe speeds are unavoidable with an all-geared headstock, unless the common ratio is a simple value such as 1·5, 1·2, 1·25, etc.

Example

A lathe is to be designed so that its maximum spindle speed will occur when turning material of diameter 17·5 mm at 33 m/min and its minimum speed in screwing material of diameter 87·5 mm at 6·6 m/min. The lathe is to have seven intermediary speeds. Determine the theoretical values of all nine speeds assuming they form a geometric progression. Take π as $\frac{22}{7}$.

$$S=\pi dN, \quad \therefore \quad N=\frac{S}{\pi d}.$$

The linear units of S and d must be identical.

33 m/min=33 000 mm/min   6·6 m/min=6 600 mm/min

Highest speed$=\dfrac{33\ 000\times\ 7}{22\ \ \times17\cdot5}=600$ rev/min

Lowest speed$=\dfrac{6\ 600\times\ 7}{22\ \ \times87\cdot5}=24$ rev/min

$$b=ar^{n-1}, \quad r=\sqrt[n-1]{\left(\frac{b}{a}\right)}=\sqrt[9-1]{\left(\frac{600}{24}\right)}=\sqrt[8]{25}$$

$$\log r=\frac{\log 25}{8}=\frac{1\cdot397\ 9}{8}=0\cdot174\ 74$$

Speed No.	Value	Log
1	24	1·380 2
		0·174 74
2	35·88	1·554 94
		0·174 74
3	53·65	1·729 68
		0·174 74
4	80·24	1·904 42
		0·174 74
5	120·0	2·079 16
		0·174 74
6	179·5	2·253 90
		0·174 74
7	268·3	2·428 64
		0·174 74
8	401·3	2·603 38
		0·174 74
9	599·9	2·778 12

The logarithmic table for a, ar, ar^2 is shown alongside.

Although 'five decimal places' are used to correct minor variations in the fourth decimal place, four-figure tables are used.

Answer: Spindle speeds in rev/min are 24, 35·9, 53·6, 80·2, 120, 180, 268, 410, and 600

Mathematics for Mechanical Technicians 2

Problems 1.5

1. A set of spacers, each of different length, commence with the shortest of length 16 mm, and each succeeding spacer increases by 3 mm. Determine, using the formula for the sum of an arithmetical progression, the overall length of the smallest seven spacers.

2. The cost of excavating the first metre of a well is £4, and thereafter every succeeding metre costs a further £1·50. Find the total cost of excavating a well of depth 15 m.

3. Find a formula for the sum of the first n whole numbers (exclude zero).

4. Obtain, to three significant figures, a series of eleven numbers, the first being unity, the last being 10, which increase in geometric progression.

5. Show that the sum of the series 5, 11, 19, 31, 51, 87, etc., is the sum of an arithmetical progression of first term 3 and common difference 4, plus the sum of a geometric progression. Hence determine the sum of the first eight terms of the series.

6. The seventh term of a geometric progression is 1 458 and the fourth term is 54.
   Calculate:
   (a) The common ratio.
   (b) The first term.
   (c) The sum of the first six terms.

7. A machine tool has a maximum spindle speed of 400 rev/min and a minimum spindle speed of 20 rev/min. If there are twetve spindle speeds in all, calculate the theoretical values of the len intermediate speeds to nearest whole numbers, assuming that the speeds form a geometric series.

8. A factory decides to terminate a production line by successively reducing its output by 20% per week. At the time the decision is made, the output from the line was 500 articles per week. The production in the first week of reducing production was therefore 400 articles. It was further decided that production would terminate after the week in which the rate of production first fell below 100 articles per week.

Determine:

(*a*) The number of weeks that reducing production occurs.
(*b*) The number of articles made during this period.
(*c*) The production rate in the final week.

9. A four-speed change gearing is to connect two shafts at a centre distance of 120 mm, the metric module of all four simple gear trains being 2 mm. The minimum gear ratio is 2 to 1 and the maximum is 4 to 1. The four ratios are to approximately conform to a geometric progression. Calculate the numbers of teeth on each of the intermediary simple trains.

10. An article whose book value at installation is £600 is to be depreciated by deducting a fixed percentage after every year from its present book value. The percentage deduction is to be arranged so that the book value after ten years (i.e. after ten deductions) is £200.

(*a*) Calculate the actual rate of percentage deduction.
(*b*) Calculate the book value after five years, to the nearest pound sterling.

11. An indicator needle oscillates about its final position, the variations from its final position forming a geometric progression. Three successive readings are 26°, 2°, and 14°. Each swing, such as 26° to 2° and 2° to 14° takes 0·4 seconds.
Determine:

(*a*) The final steady reading of the indicator needle.
(*b*) The time, after indicating 26°, that the ncedle takes to continually indicate a reading within 1° of its final steady reading.
(*c*) The theoretical total amount of movement of the needle, in degrees, when it reaches its final steady position.

12. A block of metal is being manipulated by rolling. Every pass of the rolls reduces its thickness by 10 %. The block originally has a thickness of 60 mm.

(*a*) How many complete passes are necessary to reduce the thickness to 40 mm?
(*b*) What is the thickness after the third pass?

13. An indicator needle is oscillating about its final steady reading. The deviations from the final steady reading at the end of each swing form a geometric progression. At the end of the first,

c

second, and third swings the readings are 27°, 12°, and 22°. Find the final steady reading and the readings after the fourth and fifth swings, the latter to the nearest minute.

(C.G.L.I.)

14. A factory commences the production of an article at the rate of 500 per week. If the weekly production rate rises successively by 5%,
    (*a*) how many complete weeks are necessary for the production of a minimum of 6000 articles,
    (*b*) how many are actually produced in this complete number of weeks,
    (*c*) how many articles are produced in the last week?

(C.G.L.I.)

15. (*a*) A drilling machine is to be designed around a nominal cutting speed of 11 m/min and a range of drill diameters from 7 mm to 35 mm. Taking π as $\frac{22}{7}$ find the maximum and minimum spindle speeds.
    (*b*) The gearbox is to provide a total of six spindle speeds approximating to a geometric progression. Determine the four intermediate speeds to the nearest whole numbers.
    (*c*) Which of these speeds most nearly corresponds to the nominal speed for drilling a hole of diameter 14 mm?

(C.G.L.I.)

16. (*a*) Find, to an accuracy of two decimal places, a series of five numbers, the first being 1, the last being 10, the series conforming to a geometric progression.
    (*b*) A firm manufacturing cast yacht anchors at present offers two models, of similar dimensional and structural design, of masses 50 kg and 500 kg. The smallest is 400 mm overall and includes in its design a flat surface of area 50 mm². The firm now wishes to introduce an intermediary size between its existing models so that the *masses* form a geometric progression. For the intermediary size, calculate:
    (i) the mass
    (ii) the overall dimension
    (iii) the size of the flat surface.

(C.G.L.I.)

Answers to problems 1.5

1. 175 mm
2. £217·50
3. $S=\dfrac{n^2+n}{2}$ or $\dfrac{n(n+1)}{2}$
4. 1   1·26 1·59 2·00 2·51
   3·16 3·98 5·01 6·31 7·94 10
5. 646
6. (a) 3   (b) 2   (c) 728
7. 26   34   45   59   78
   102 135 177 232 305
8. (a) 8 weeks   (b) 1664   (c) 84/week
9. 86T to 34T, 91T to 29T
10. (a) 10·4%   (b) £350
11. (a) 10°   (b) 1·6 s   (c) 32°
12. (a) 4 passes   (b) 43·7 mm
13. 18°, 15° 20′, 19° 47′
14. (a) 10 weeks   (b) 6 290   (c) 776
15. (a) 500 rev/min, 100 rev/min
   (b) 138, 190, 263, and 362
   (c) 263 rev/min
16. (a) 158 kg ($50 \times 3·16$)
   (b) 587 mm ($400 \times \sqrt[3]{3·16}$)
   (c) 108 mm² ($50 \times {}^{1·5}\sqrt{3·16}$)
   (Mass and area are proportional to the cube and square of linear dimensions.)

1.6 Arithmetical Mean and Standard Deviation

1.6.1 DETERMINATION OF AN ARITHMETICAL MEAN

Numerical data can often be expressed in tabular form by stating a value and the number of times the value occurs; that is, by quoting a *variate* and the *frequency* of that variate. In Book 1, article 1.6, it was stated that the arithmetical mean $\bar{x}$ of a total of N items of variates x with associated frequencies f was given by the formula

$$\bar{x}=\frac{\Sigma(fx)}{N} \quad \text{where } N=\Sigma f$$

It is common practice to use simply the word *mean* when referring to the arithmetical mean.

Calculations can be expedited by selecting a fictitious mean A and establishing a correcting value d, so that $\bar{x}=A+d$. An inspection of the data will reveal a variate A which is close to the mean. The symbol given to the original variate is x.

Suppose we now use new variates of $(x-A)$ and retain the original frequencies. Let us further obtain the mean of the new data; that is,

the value of $\dfrac{\Sigma f(x-A)}{N}$.

We shall now prove that $\dfrac{\Sigma f(x-A)}{N}$ is the correcting value d.

$$\frac{\Sigma f(x-A)}{N} = \frac{\Sigma(fx)}{N} - \frac{\Sigma(fA)}{N}, \text{ by expansion}$$

Let $\qquad \dfrac{\Sigma f(x-A)}{Nx} = d$

Now $\qquad \dfrac{\Sigma(fN}{(} = \bar{x}$, by definition

and $\dfrac{\Sigma(fA)}{N} = A$, because if A is a constant, Σf cancels with N.

$$\therefore \quad d = \bar{x} - A$$
and $\qquad\qquad \bar{x} = A + d$

Example

A traffic survey was made of the number of vehicles passing along a road. Fifty different five-minute observations produced the following data:

Number of vehicles	7	8	9	10	11
Frequency occurring	6	12	18	9	5

Determine the mean number of vehicles passing in a five-minute period. The mean number of vehicles passing is in the vicinity of 9.

Let $A=9$

f	x	$(x-A)$	$f(x-A)$
6	7	−2	−12
12	8	−1	−12
18	9	0	0
9	10	1	9
5	11	2	10
$\Sigma f = 50 = N$			$\Sigma f(x-A)$ $=19-24$ $=\ -5$

$$d = \frac{\Sigma f(x-A)}{N} = \frac{-5}{50} = -0\cdot1$$
$$\bar{x} = A + d = 9 + (-0\cdot1) = 8\cdot9$$

Answer: Mean number of vehicles passing = 8·9

It may seem that no time is saved by the method used, when compared with the use of $\bar{x} = \frac{\Sigma(fx)}{N}$, *but in view of the work which follows, this procedure is usually followed in the determination of a mean value in statistical method.*

1.6.2 STANDARD DEVIATION

An arithmetical mean, by itself, gives no measure of the uniformity of the items under consideration. For instance, four bars of lengths 24 mm, 23 mm, 26 mm, and 27 mm have a mean length of 25 mm. Four bars of lengths 6 mm, 37 mm, 34 mm, and 23 mm also have a mean length of 25 mm. It is obvious that the first four, as a group, show more uniformity than the latter four. Much more information can be provided if, together with the mean, an indication is given of how closely the items are distributed with reference to the mean.

Figure 1.4 shows a pictorial representation of ten items with a line indicating the position of the arithmetical mean. Each individual item differs from the mean by $x - \bar{x}$.

We cannot use the mean of the $(x - \bar{x})$ values as a measure of uniformity because the value of the mean was chosen so that $\Sigma(x - \bar{x}) = 0$. This point should be borne in mind, as we shall use it a little later in this section. We could take the mean of the $(x - \bar{x})$ values irrespective of their arithmetical sign, but in view of later work in statistics we

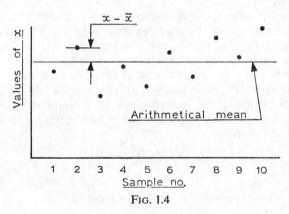

FIG. 1.4

find a more useful indication is a particular average called a *root mean square* of the $(x-\bar{x})$ values.

A root mean square of a set of values, as its name implies, is the square root of the mean of the squares of those values. For our particular case we require the root mean square of the $(x-\bar{x})$ values. The sum of the squares is given by $\Sigma f(x-\bar{x})^2$.

The mean of the squares is given by $\dfrac{\Sigma f(x-\bar{x})^2}{N}$.

The root mean square value is therefore $\sqrt{\left(\dfrac{\Sigma f(x-\bar{x})^2}{N}\right)}$.

In statistical method this particular root mean square value is so important that it carries the special name *standard deviation* and when extracted from a set of data is given the symbol *s*.

The reader should note the phrase 'when extracted from a set of data'. A set of data usually applies to a *sample* extracted from a much larger number of items. This larger number of items, in statistical method, is called a *population*. The mean and standard deviation of a sample are given the symbols $\bar{x}$ and *s* respectively. The mean and standard deviation of the population from which the sample is drawn are given the symbols μ and σ respectively.

As a formal definition, the standard deviation *s* of a set of values of variates *x* and frequencies *f* having an arithmetical mean $\bar{x}$ is given by the formula

$$s=\sqrt{\left(\frac{\Sigma f(x-\bar{x})^2}{N}\right)}, \quad \text{where } N=\Sigma f$$

In most practical cases, $\bar{x}$ is usually an awkward number, and the resulting calculation of standard deviation using this formula can be quite lengthy. It will be recalled that the calculation of the arithmetical mean was facilitated by the selection of a fictitious mean *A* and the application of a correcting value of *d*. In a statistical analysis it is usual to calculate the mean together with the standard deviation, and in a somewhat similar way to correcting a fictitious mean it is possible to calculate a fictitious standard deviation *S* and correct it to the true standard deviation *s*.

$$\text{Let } S=\sqrt{\left(\frac{\Sigma f(x-A)^2}{N}\right)}$$

that is, by using the fictitious mean *A* instead of the true mean $\bar{x}$.

Squaring and transposing,
$$NS^2=\Sigma f(x-A)^2$$
$$=\Sigma f(x-\bar{x}+\bar{x}-A)^2$$
$$=\Sigma f\{(x-\bar{x})+(\bar{x}-A)\}^2$$
$$=\Sigma f\{(x-\bar{x})+d\}^2, \quad \text{since } \bar{x}-A=d$$
$$=\Sigma f(x-\bar{x})^2+\Sigma fd^2+2\{\Sigma f(x-\bar{x})(d)\}$$
$$\therefore \ S^2=\frac{\Sigma f(x-\bar{x})^2}{N}+\frac{\Sigma fd^2}{N}+\frac{2\Sigma f(x-\bar{x})(d)}{N}$$

Now $\quad \dfrac{\Sigma f(x-\bar{x})^2}{N}=s^2$, by definition,

while $\quad \dfrac{\Sigma fd^2}{N}=d^2$, since d is a constant and Σf cancels with N,

and $\quad \dfrac{2\Sigma f(x-\bar{x})(d)}{N}=0$, since $\Sigma(x-\bar{x})=0$ (see page 63)

$$\therefore \ S^2=s^2+d^2$$
and $\qquad\qquad s^2=S^2-d^2$

It should be noted that a fictitious standard deviation is always greater than the true standard deviation.

The calculations required to establish a mean and a standard deviation are therefore as follows:

(*a*) Select a fictitious mean A.

(*b*) Retabulate, with new variates $(x-A)$.

(*c*) Establish a correction $d=\dfrac{\Sigma f(x-A)}{N}$ where $N=\Sigma f$.

(*d*) The mean $\bar{x}$ is $A+d$.

(*e*) Establish a square of a fictitious standard deviation
$$S^2=\frac{\Sigma f(x-A)^2}{N}$$

(*f*) The true standard deviation s is $\sqrt{(S^2-d^2)}$

A tabular layout assists the calculation, as demonstrated in the example which follows.

Example

100 batches of goods were inspected, and records were kept of the number of defectives in the batches, resulting in the data:

Number of defectives	0	1	2	3	4	5
Occasions	6	23	36	19	12	4

Calculate the mean and the standard deviation of these results.

The mean is in the vicinity of 2 defectives.

Let $A=2$

f	x	$(x-A)$	$f(x-A)$	$(x-A)^2$	$f(x-A)^2$
6	0	-2	-12	4	24
23	1	-1	-23	1	23
36	2	0	0	0	0
19	3	1	19	1	19
12	4	2	24	4	48
4	5	3	12	9	36

$$\Sigma f = 100 = N \qquad \begin{aligned}\Sigma f(x-A) &= 55-35 \\ &= 20\end{aligned} \qquad \Sigma f(x-A)^2 = 150$$

$$d = \frac{\Sigma f(x-A)}{N} = \frac{20}{100} = 0\cdot2$$

$$\bar{x} = A + d = 2 + 0\cdot2 = 2\cdot2$$

$$S^2 = \frac{\Sigma f(x-A)^2}{N} = \frac{150}{100} = 1\cdot5$$

$$\begin{aligned}s &= \sqrt{(S^2 - d^2)} \\ &= \sqrt{\{1\cdot5 - (0\cdot2)^2\}} \\ &= \sqrt{(1\cdot5 - 0\cdot04)} = \sqrt{1\cdot46} = 1\cdot208\end{aligned}$$

Answers: Mean value $= 2\cdot2$ defectives
Standard deviation $= 1\cdot208$ defectives
$= 1\cdot21$ to 3 sig. figs.

It will be noted from the solution that by selecting one of the original variates as the fictitious mean, a row of zeros occurred in the tabular solution, eliminating some of the calculations. Hence the fictitious mean A should always be one of the original variates.

The problem was set on discrete variates; that is to say, the variate jumped from one value to another. If the statistical data referred to continuous variates, it would be necessary to indicate boundaries. For instance, for lengths, the variates could be 5 m to 6 m, 6 m to 7 m, 7 m to 8 m, and so on. In such cases it is sufficiently accurate for the present studies in the determination of the mean and standard deviation to use the methods demonstrated with discontinuous variates, using the means of the boundaries as variates in the calculations. For 5 m to 6 m the value of the variate would be 5·5, for 6 m to 7 m it would be 6·5 m, and so on. As a check on the value obtained for standard deviation, it will be shown later, in the work on probability, that if the distribution is reasonably symmetrical, the whole range of values should roughly fall within the range of (mean plus three standard deviations) to (mean minus three standard deviations). For instance, in the problem previously solved the 100 values should roughly lie between {2·2+3(1·21)} and {2·2−3(1·21)}, i.e. between about 5·8 and −1·4 defectives. Hence the standard deviation found seems reasonable.

If the $(x−A)$ values are less than unity, it may be preferred to work in units such as 0·1, 0·01, or 0·001 in order to perform calculations in the table with whole numbers. The use of small units and continuous variates, with the *three standard deviations rough check*, is demonstrated in the next example.

Example

A sample of 50 bars were measured on a length nominally 50 mm ±0·1 mm and put into cells as follows:

Length x mm	49·90–49·94	49·94–49·98	49·98–50·02	50·02–50·06	50·06–50·10
Frequency f	6	13	19	9	3

Determine the mean and standard deviation of these results.

The variates are continuous, hence a new tabulation will be made using mid-boundaries of cells, a basic dimension of 49·90 mm and units of 0·01 mm.

The first cell takes the variate 49·92 mm, and using a basis of 49·90 mm the value to be used is 0·02 mm or 2 units. The next cell is 49·96 mm or 6 units.

The tabulation we shall operate on therefore becomes:

x	2	6	10	14	18
f	6	13	19	9	3

Fictitious mean $A = 10$.

f	x	$(x-A)$	$f(x-A)$	$(x-A)^2$	$f(x-A)^2$
6	2	−8	−48	64	384
13	6	−4	−52	16	208
19	10	0	0	0	0
9	14	4	36	16	144
3	18	8	24	64	192

$\Sigma f = 50 = N$ $\begin{aligned}\Sigma f(x-A) \\ = 60-100 \\ = -40\end{aligned}$ $\begin{aligned}\Sigma f(x-A)^2 \\ = 928\end{aligned}$

$$d = \frac{\Sigma f(x-A)}{N} = \frac{-40}{50} = -0.8$$

$$\bar{x} = A + d = 10 + (-0.8) = 9.2 \text{ units}$$

$$S^2 = \frac{\Sigma f(x-A)^2}{N} = \frac{928}{50} = 18.56$$

$$s^2 = \sqrt{(S^2 - d^2)} = \sqrt{(18.56 - 0.64)} = \sqrt{17.92} = 4.23 \text{ units}$$

$\bar{x} = 9.2$, and using the basis of 49.90 and units of 0.01,

$$\bar{x} = 49.90 + 9.2 \, (0.01 \text{ mm})$$
$$= 49.992 \text{ mm}$$

Standard deviation = 4.23 units = 0.0423 mm
Rough check: Values should lie within $49.992 \pm 3(0.0423)$,
i.e. about 50 ± 0.13 mm
Values seem reasonable.

Answers: Mean length = 49.92 mm
Standard deviation = 0.0423 mm

If the mean comes out as a very simple value, such as a whole number, calculations can be further simplified.
Let us return to $\bar{x} = A + d$
and $s^2 = S^2 - d^2$.

Now let $A = 0$,   so that $\bar{x} = d$.

Now since $S^2 = \dfrac{\Sigma f(x-A)^2}{N}$ and $A = 0$,

then, in this case $S^2 = \dfrac{\Sigma f(x^2)}{N}$

and $d^2 = (\bar{x})^2$

whence
$$s^2 = \frac{\Sigma f(x)^2}{N} - (\bar{x})^2$$

and
$$s = \sqrt{\left(\frac{\Sigma f(x)^2}{N} - (\bar{x})^2 \right)}$$

However, the number of occasions on which this method provides a quicker result are rare, and furthermore it calls on the student to commit to memory another quite involved formula. The author strongly recommends the student to adhere to one method, i.e. using a fictitious mean and, if necessary, adjusting a basic datum and the cell interval so as to work in convenient whole numbers.

Problems 1.6

1. The output from 10 successive shifts was 63, 61, 59, 77, 72, 53, 64, 71, 66, and 54 articles respectively. Determine the arithmetical mean and standard deviation of these results.

2. The number of marks obtained by a group of 30 students for a particular task was as follows:

Mark	0	1	2	3	4	5	6	7	8	9	10
Frequency	0	0	0	0	1	2	5	9	7	4	2

Determine the arithmetical mean and standard deviation of these results.

3. The following data give the masses of 50 castings. By assuming a value for the variates of the mean of the cell boundaries, determine the arithmetical mean and the standard deviation.

Mass (kg)	5–5·2	5·2–5·4	5·4–5·6	5·6–5·8	5·8–6·0
Frequency	5	12	16	13	4

4. Forty samples of a material were tested in a Hardness Testing Machine, yielding the following data:

Hardness value	200–220	220–240	240–260	260–280	280–300
Frequency	5	9	15	8	3

Determine the mean and the standard deviation of these results.

5. One hundred 2 mm feeler gauges were tested for thickness, yielding the following data:

Thickness	1·990 to 1·994	1·994 to 1·998	1·998 to 2·002	2·002 to 2·006	2·006 to 2·010
Frequency	8	24	46	18	4

Determine the mean and standard deviation of these results.

6. The following data represents two different samples, each of fifty items, of the number of defectives found when inspecting by sampling large batches of equal size.

Defectives	0	1	2	3
Frequency	9	18	17	6

Defectives	0	1	2	3
Frequency	6	16	20	8

Determine the mean and standard deviation of these results:
(a) $\bar{x}$, and s_1 from the first set,
(b) $\bar{x}_2$ and s_2 from the second set, and
(c) $\bar{x}_3$ and s_3 from both sets combined.

Answers to problems 1.6

1. Mean=64, standard deviation=7·36
2. Mean=7·3, standard deviation=1·42
3. Mean=5·496 kg, standard deviation=0·221 kg
4. Mean=247·5, standard deviation=22·0
5. Mean=1·999 44 mm, standard deviation=0·003 75 mm
6. (a) $\bar{x}_1=1·4$, $s_1=0·916\ 5$
   (b) $\bar{x}_2=1·6$, $s_2=0·894\ 4$
   (c) $\bar{x}_3=1·5$, $s_3=0·911\ 0$

Chapter Two

Algebra

2.1 Equations Solved with the Aid of Logarithms

2.1.1 EQUATIONS SOLVED WITH COMMON LOGARITHMS

If an equation has to be solved and an unknown appears in the index, a solution can often be effected with the aid of logarithms. We have already met this when dealing with geometrical progressions. If a geometric progression has a first term of a, and n^{th} term of b, the common ratio being r,

then
$$r = \sqrt[n-1]{\left(\frac{b}{a}\right)}$$

Supposing that r, b, and a, were all known, and we had to find the value of n, then by taking logarithms

$$\log r = \frac{\log b - \log a}{n-1}$$

$$n-1 = \frac{\log b - \log a}{\log r}$$

whence
$$n = \left(\frac{\log b - \log a}{\log r}\right) + 1$$

Substituting the known values of r, b, and a will give a simple equation from which the value of n can be found.

Let us now extend the work to the formation of simultaneous equations. Suppose we have a formula of the type

$$y = ax^n$$

where a and n are constants,

and we are asked to determine the values of a and n. One of the unknowns appears as an index, so let us take logarithms, and obtain

$$\log y = \log a + n \log x$$

If we now have two pairs of values of y and x which satisfy the equation, then a pair of simultaneous equations can be formed which will enable us to determine the values of a and of n.

Example

As a liquid was cooling, its temperature $T°C$ was noted t minutes after a datum time, and it is known that T and t are connected by the formula

$$T=at^n$$

a and t being constants.

It was found that T was 40°C when t was 4 minutes, and T was 20°C when t was 16 minutes.

Determine:

    (a) The values of the constants a and n.
    (b) The value of T when $t=6\cdot25$ minutes.
    (c) The value of t when $T=16$°C.

(a) $T=at^n$

    Taking logs, $\log T=\log a+n\log t$
    Using 40, 4 $\log 40=\log a+n(\log 4)$
    Using 20, 16 $\log 20=\log a+n(\log 16)$
    Inserting values, $1\cdot602\ 1=\log a+0\cdot602\ 1n$
                          $1\cdot301\ 0=\log a+1\cdot204\ 1n$
    By subtraction $\overline{0\cdot301\ 1=\ \ \ \ \ \ \ -0\cdot602\ 0n}$

$$n=\frac{0\cdot301\ 1}{-0\cdot602\ 0}=-\frac{1}{2}$$

    Substituting $1\cdot602\ 1=\log a+(0\cdot602\ 1)(-0\cdot5)$
                  $1\cdot602\ 1=\log a-0\cdot301\ 05$
                 $\log a=1\cdot602\ 1+0\cdot301\ 05$
                         $=1\cdot903\ 15$

If the log of a is $1\cdot903\ 15$, then a is the antilog of $1\cdot903\ 15$, which is 80

Hence $a=80$ and $n=-0\cdot5$

(b) The formula is

$$T=80t^{-0\cdot5}$$

Now $-0\cdot5=-\frac{1}{2}$ and $t^{-\frac{1}{2}}=\frac{1}{t^{\frac{1}{2}}}=\frac{1}{\sqrt{t}}$

and the formula can be written as

$$T=\frac{80}{\sqrt{t}}$$

When $t=6\cdot25,\ T=\frac{80}{\sqrt{6\cdot25}}=\frac{80}{2\cdot5}=32$

(c) When $T=16°C$,

$$16=\frac{80}{\sqrt{t}}$$

$$\sqrt{t}=\frac{80}{16}=5$$

Squaring $\qquad t=25$

Answers: (a) $a=80°C$, $n=-0\cdot5$
(b) $T=32°C$ when $t=6\cdot25$ min
(c) $t=25$ min when $T=16°C$

2.1.2 EQUATIONS SOLVED WITH NAPERIAN LOGARITHMS

If the original formula includes e, the base of Naperian logarithms, the substitution of $2\cdot718$ for e and the taking of common logarithms is still valid for certain formulae, but a quicker solution can often be effected by taking Naperian logarithms.

For instance, if the formula is of the type

$$y=ae^{bx}$$

then by taking Naperian logarithms

$$\log_e y=\log_e a+bx \log_e e$$

which reduces to

$$\log_e y=\log_e a+bx$$

(because the log of e to the base of e is unity)

Example

If $\frac{T_1}{T_2}=e^{\mu\theta}$, and $T_1=480$ N when $T_2=20$ N and $\mu=0\cdot2$, find the value of θ.

$$e^{\mu\theta}=\frac{T_1}{T_2}=\frac{480\text{ N}}{20\text{ N}}=24$$

$$e^{\mu\theta}=24$$

Taking Naperian logs $\qquad \mu\theta=\log_e 24$
$$=\log_e(2\cdot4\times10)$$
$$=\log_e 2\cdot4+\log_e 10$$
$$=0\cdot875\ 5+2\cdot302\ 6$$
$$=3\cdot178\ 1$$

$$\theta=\frac{3\cdot178\ 1}{\mu}=\frac{3\cdot178\ 1}{0\cdot2}=15\cdot890\ 5$$

Answer: $\theta=15\cdot9$

Example

From an experiment conducted to establish the relationship between two variables, y and x, the following were typical results:

$$y = 46 \cdot 2 \quad \text{when} \quad x = 5$$

and $\qquad\qquad y = 36 \cdot 3 \quad \text{when} \quad x = 20.$

If y and x are connected by the formula $y = ae^{bx}$, find the values of the constants a and b, each to two significant figures.

$$y = ae^{bx}$$

Taking Naperian logs,

$$\log_e y = \log_e a + bx$$

Using 5, 46·2: $\qquad \log_e 46 \cdot 2 = \log_e a + 5b$

Using 20, 36·3: $\qquad \log_e 36 \cdot 3 = \log_e a + 20b$

$$\log_e 46 \cdot 2 = \log_e (4 \cdot 62 \times 10) = \log_e 4 \cdot 62 + \log_e 10$$
$$= 1 \cdot 530\ 4 + 2 \cdot 302\ 6 = 3 \cdot 833\ 0$$
$$\log_e 36 \cdot 3 = \log_e 3 \cdot 63 + \log_e 10$$
$$= 1 \cdot 289\ 2 + 2 \cdot 302\ 6 = 3 \cdot 591\ 8$$

Substituting $\qquad\qquad 3 \cdot 833\ 0 = \log_e a + 5b$

$$\underline{3 \cdot 591\ 8 = \log_e a + 20b}$$

Subtracting $\qquad\qquad 0 \cdot 241\ 2 \qquad\qquad -15b$

$$b = \frac{0 \cdot 241\ 2}{-15} = -0 \cdot 016\ 08$$

Substituting $\qquad\qquad 3 \cdot 833\ 0 = \log_e a + 5(-0 \cdot 016\ 08)$

$$3 \cdot 833\ 0 = \log_e a + -0 \cdot 0804$$
$$\log_e a = 3 \cdot 833\ 0 + 0 \cdot 080\ 4 = 3 \cdot 913\ 4$$

If $\log_e a = 3 \cdot 913\ 4$, a is the Naperian antilog of $3 \cdot 913\ 4$

Starting with $\qquad\qquad 3 \cdot 913\ 4$

Deduct $\qquad\qquad\qquad \underline{2 \cdot 302\ 6} = \log_e 10$

$$\overline{1 \cdot 610\ 8}$$

Naperian antilog of $1 \cdot 610\ 8$ is $5 \cdot 007$

$\therefore$ Naperian antilog of $(1 \cdot 610\ 8 + 2 \cdot 302\ 6)$ is $5 \cdot 007 \times 10$

$$= 50 \cdot 07$$

Rounding off to two significant figures

$$b = -0 \cdot 016, \quad a = 50$$

Answers: $a = 50$, $b = -0 \cdot 016$

Problems 2.1

1. A centre lathe has to have a total of eight spindle speeds ranging from 20 rev/min to 400 rev/min. If an ideal geometric progression is sought between these values determine the common ratio.

2. The connection between the absolute pressure P and the volume V of a gas is given by $PV^n = C$. If it is known that when $P=8$ units and $V=2$ units the value of C is 21·1 units, calculate the value of the index n.

3. Find the value of n if $Q=KH^n$ and $Q=12·25$ and $K=2·6$ when H is 0·74.

4. The ideal efficiency η of a certain internal combustion engine cycle is given by

$$\eta = 1 - \frac{1^{n-1}}{r}$$

n being the compression ratio.

Find the minimum value of r so that the efficiency will not be less than 50% when $n=1·4$.

5. Find the value of n if $\left(\dfrac{P_1}{P_2}\right)^{\frac{n-1}{n}} = 0·82$

and $P_1=2$ when $P_2=4$.

6. When experimenting with the flow of water Q over a vee-notch, the height H above the notch was recorded. It was known that $Q=KH^n$. If Q was 4·1 units when H was 1·2 units and Q was 9·65 when H was 1·7 units, find by a mathematical method the values of K and of H, each to two significant figures.

7. If a fixed mass of gas changes its conditions so that no heat enters or leaves that gas, the connection between the absolute pressure P and the volume V is given by the law $PV^n = K$.

If $P=8$ units when $V=2$ units and $P=3·03$ units when $V=4$ units, find by a mathematical method the values of n and K.

8. When circular shafts are made of a certain material, the safe torque T newton metres that can be transmitted depends upon the diameter d millimetres, following the law $T=Kd^n$, where K and n are constants.

If $T=80$ when $d=20$ and $T=640$ when $d=40$, find by a mathematical method values for the constants K and d.

9. The outside diameter D of a certain screw thread is connected with the pitch p by a relationship $D=Kp^n$, K and n being constants.

   If $D=6$ mm when $p=1$ mm, and $D=2\cdot8$ mm when $p=0\cdot53$ mm, find by a mathematical method values for the constants K and n, and hence deduce a value for p when $D=2\cdot2$. All answers are to be given to two significant figures.

10. Two variables are connected by the formula $V=Pe^{kt}$. If $V=500$ when $t=0$ and $V=824$ when $t=7$, find by a mathematical method values of the constants P and k.

11. When conducting a test on an item of electrical equipment, two variables i and t were investigated which are connected by the formula $i=Ie^{kt}$. It was found that i was $6\cdot703$ when $t=2$ and i was $0\cdot82$ when $t=12\cdot5$. Find by a mathematical method the values of the constants I and k.

12. An experiment was conducted on belt friction to obtain a coefficient of friction μ. The formula investigated was $\dfrac{T_1}{T_2}=e^{\mu\theta}$. If T_1 was 136 N when θ was 4 units, and T_1 was 370 N when θ was 8 units, find by a mathematical method the value of the constant T_2 and the coefficient of friction μ.

Answers to problems 2.1

1. $1\cdot53$
2. $1\cdot40$
3. $2\cdot50$
4. $5\cdot66$
5. $1\cdot40$
6. $K=2\cdot6$, $n=2\cdot5$
7. $n=1\cdot40$, $K=21\cdot1$
8. $K=0\cdot01$, $n=3\cdot00$
9. $K=6\cdot0$, $n=1\cdot2$; $0\cdot43$ mm
10. $P=500$, $k=0\cdot10$
11. $I=10$, $k=-0\cdot20$
12. $T_2=50$ N, $\mu=0\cdot25$

2.2 Quadratic Equations

2.2.1 SOLUTION OF QUADRATIC EQUATIONS

Any quadratic equation can be put in the form

$$ax^2+bx+c=0$$

by substituting appropriate values for x, a, b, and c.

Quadratic equations can be solved analytically by one of two general methods. In solution by factors, the original equation is modified if necessary to leave zero on the right-hand side, and the left-hand side is then factorized. Each factor in turn is equated to zero to obtain the roots of the equation.

In solution by formula, the original equation is put in the form:

$$ax^2+bx+c=0$$

then
$$x=\frac{-b\pm\sqrt{(b^2-4ac)}}{2a}$$

If the roots of a quadratic equation are p and q, then

$$p+q=\frac{-b}{a} \text{ and } pq=\frac{c}{a}$$

A quadratic equation has two roots and in some solutions one root has to be discarded, being inappropriate for the conditions stated. In isolated circumstances, when $b^2=4ac$, the roots are equal.

Example

If a body passes a datum with a velocity of u, with constant acceleration a, the distance s from the datum after a time t is given by the formula:

$$s=ut+\frac{at^2}{2}$$

Find t when $s=96$ m, $u=10$ m/s, and $a=2$ m/s^2

$$s=ut+\frac{at^2}{2}$$

Working in units of metres and seconds,

$$96=10t+\frac{2t^2}{2}$$

$$96=10t+t^2$$

$$t^2+10t-96=0$$

$$(t+16)(t-6)=0$$

$\therefore$ Either $t+16=0$, $t=-16$ (root inadmissible)

or $t-6=0$, $t=6$

$$\text{Check: } 96 = 10(6) + \frac{2(6)^2}{2}$$
$$96 = 60 + 36$$
$$96 = 96$$

Answer: Time taken = 6 seconds

Example

A template is in the form of a rectangle with a semicircle on one end. The maximum overall length from the side of the rectangle to the 'nose' of the radius is 5 mm and the area is 18 mm². Denoting the radius of the semicircle by r, show that r is a root of the equation

$$r^2(4-\pi) - 20r + 36 = 0$$

Take π as 3·142, and find a logical value for r.

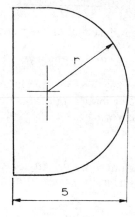

Fig. 2.1

The template is shown diagrammatically in Figure 2.1. Working in mm units:

Area of rectangle + area of semicircle = 18

$$2r(5-r) + \frac{\pi r^2}{2} = 18$$

$$10r - 2r^2 + \frac{\pi r^2}{2} = 18$$

Multiplying by 2, $\qquad\qquad 20r + 4r^2 + \pi r^2 \qquad = 36$

Multiplying by -1, and rearranging $\quad 4r^2 - \pi r^2 - 20r + 36 = \ 0$

$$r^2(4-\pi) - 20r + 36 = \ 0$$

With π as 3·142, $\qquad r^2(4-3\cdot142)-20r+36=0$
$$0\cdot858r^2-20r+36=0$$

$$r=\frac{-(-20)\pm\sqrt{\{20^2-4(0\cdot858)(36)\}}}{2(0\cdot858)}$$

$$=\frac{20\pm\sqrt{(400-123\cdot6)}}{1\cdot716}$$

$$=\frac{20\pm\sqrt{276\cdot4}}{1\cdot716}=\frac{20\pm16\cdot62}{1\cdot716}$$

$$=\frac{36\cdot62 \text{ or } 3\cdot38}{1\cdot716}=21\cdot34 \text{ or } 1\cdot970$$

The first root is inadmissible; $r=1\cdot97$ to two decimal places.

Check: Sum of roots $=\dfrac{-b}{a}$

$$21\cdot34+1\cdot97=\frac{20}{0\cdot858}$$

$$23\cdot31=23\cdot31$$

Product of roots $=\dfrac{c}{a}$

$$(21\cdot34)(1\cdot97)=\frac{36}{0\cdot858}$$

$$42\cdot04=41\cdot96 \text{ (Error due to}$$
$$\text{four-fig tables)}$$

Another check is to evaluate the area of the figure.

Area of semicircle (from tables) $=\dfrac{12\cdot192}{2}$

$$=6\cdot096 \text{ mm}^2$$

Area of rectangle $=3\cdot94\times3\cdot03=11\cdot94 \text{ mm}^2$

$$\text{Total}=18\cdot036 \text{ mm}^2$$

Answer: Radius of semicircle $=1\cdot97$ mm

The normal unit for a linear dimension in engineering is the millimetre. In some problems which eventually proceed to the solving of a quadratic equation the figures quoted in the problem can often produce very large numbers in the resulting quadratic equation. This tends to increase the possibility of error. The reader, wherever possible, is advised to 'scale down' the values of a problem so that the manipulation of figures deals with the lowest reasonable quantities, preferably whole numbers. However, care is needed with areas and volumes. If one unit of length is 10 mm, then one unit of area is 10 mm $\times$ 10 mm $=$ 100 mm^2 and one unit of volume is 1 000 mm^3. For example, if a problem contains a length of 60 mm, an area of 400 mm^2, and a volume of 7 500 mm^3, then working in units of a linear length of 10 mm, the length is 6 units, the area is 4 units and the volume is 7·5 units.

Example

A rectangular plate has a length which is 60 mm longer than its breadth. It is pierced by a rectangular hole so as to leave a margin of 30 mm all round. The area remaining is three-quarters that of the original plate. Find the dimensions of the original plate.

The working will be in units of 10 mm, so that 60 mm $=$ 6 units and 30 mm $=$ 3 units.

Let the original length $= x$
Then the original breadth $= x - 6$
Margin is 3 units wide.

$\therefore$ Length of pierced hole $= x - 6$
and breadth of pierced hole $= (x - 6) - 6 = x - 12$
Original area $= x(x - 6) = x^2 - 6x$
Area of pierced hole $= (x - 6)(x - 12) = x^2 - 18x + 72$
Area remaining $= (x^2 - 6x) - (x^2 - 18x + 72)$
$= x^2 - 6x - x^2 + 18x - 72$
$= 12x - 72$

$\therefore \dfrac{12x - 72}{x^2 - 6x} = \dfrac{3}{4}$

By cross multiplication,

$$48x - 288 = 3x^2 - 18x$$
$$3x^2 - 18x - 48x + 288 = 0$$
$$3x^2 - 66x + 288 = 0$$
$$x^2 - 22x + 96 = 0$$
$$(x - 16)(x - 6) = 0$$
$\therefore$ Either $x - 16 = 0$, $x = 16$
or $x - 6 = 0$, $x = 6$

The value $x = 6$ is illogical as it will not allow for a pierced hole and must be discounted; hence $x = 16$.

Length $= 16$ units $= 160$ mm
Width $= (16 - 6)$ units $= 10$ units $= 100$ mm

Check : Original area $=160\times100=16\,000$ mm²
Pierced hole $=100\times40=4\,000$ mm²
By subtraction, area remaining $=12\,000$ mm²

and
$$\frac{12\,000}{16\,000}=\frac{3}{4}$$

Answer: Plate is 160 mm × 100 mm

2.2.2 EQUATIONS REDUCIBLE TO QUADRATICS

Many equations which apparently are not quadratics are reducible to quadratics by a suitable substitution. The guide to most substitutions can be obtained by modifying the equation so that zero is on the right-hand side. The terms on the left-hand side should then be arranged as a series of descending powers. The standard quadratic form is

$$ax^2+bx+c=0$$

and the substitution is made by putting another symbol, say z, for the central term, neglecting its coefficient. This method will be demonstrated by typical examples.

Example

Solve the equation $\dfrac{1}{y^2}+\dfrac{3}{y}=10$ by means of a suitable substitution.

Rewriting as
$$\frac{1}{y^2}+\frac{3}{y}-10=0$$

The central term on the left-hand side is $3\left(\dfrac{1}{y}\right)$, so let $z=\dfrac{1}{y}$

$$\frac{1}{y^2}=z^2,\ \frac{3}{y}=3z$$

$$\therefore\ z^2+3z-10=0$$

and
$$(z+5)(z-2)=0$$

Either $\qquad z+5=0,\ z=-5$

or $\qquad z-2=0,\ z=2$

If $\qquad z=\dfrac{1}{y},\ y=\dfrac{1}{z}$

When $\qquad z=2,\ y=\frac{1}{2}$ and when $z=-5,\ y=-\frac{1}{5}$

Check : $\dfrac{1}{(\frac{1}{2})^2}+\dfrac{3}{\frac{1}{2}}=10,\quad 4+6=10,\ 10=10$

$$\frac{1}{(-\frac{1}{5})^2}+\frac{3}{-\frac{1}{5}}=10,\ 25-15=10,\ 10=10$$

Answer: $y=\frac{1}{2}$ or $-\frac{1}{5}$

The question particularly requested a solution by substitution. Another method would be to multiply all through by y^2, producing the equation $1+3y=10y^2$, or $10y^2-3y-1=0$. If, in an examination, a particular method is requested, then the candidate must offer that method. If no method is specified, the candidate has discretion to use any correct method which provides a reasonable degree of accuracy.

Example

Solve the equation $\qquad 3^{2x}=5(3^x)-6$.

Rewriting as $\qquad\qquad 3^{2x}-5(3^x)+6=0$

The central term on the left-hand side is $-5(3^x)$, so let $z=3^x$

$$3^{2x}=3^{x+x}=(3^x)(3^x)=z^2$$

$$-5(3^x)=-5z$$

$$\therefore\ z^2-5z+6=0$$

and $\qquad\qquad (z-2)(z-3)=0$

Either $\qquad z-2=0,\ z=2;$ or $z-3=0,\ z=3$

Now $z=3^x$, so by taking logs of each side,

$$\log z=x\log 3,\ \ x=\frac{\log z}{\log 3}$$

When $\qquad z=2,\ x=\dfrac{\log 2}{\log 3}=\dfrac{0\cdot301\ 0}{0\cdot477\ 1}=0\cdot630\ 9$

When $\qquad z=3,\ x=\dfrac{\log 3}{\log 3}=1$

Check: $x=0\cdot630\ 9$ $\quad 3^{1\cdot2618}=5(3)^{0\cdot6309}-6$

$$4\qquad =5(2)\qquad -6$$

$$4\qquad =10-6=4$$

$$x=1\qquad\qquad 3^2\qquad =5(3)-6$$

$$9\qquad =15-6=9$$

Answer: $x=0\cdot6309\ (0\cdot631)$ or 1

Example

Find the angles between zero and $180°$ which satisfy the equation

$$8\cos^2\theta=5+2\sin\theta$$

Rewrite as $\qquad 8 \cos^2 \theta - 2 \sin \theta - 5 = 0$

The central term on the left-hand side is $-2 \sin \theta$, so let $z = \sin \theta$

$$\sin^2 \theta + \cos^2 \theta = 1$$
$$\therefore \cos^2 \theta = 1 - \sin^2 \theta = 1 - z^2$$
$$-2 \sin \theta = -2z$$
$$\therefore 8(1 - z^2) - 2z - 5 = 0$$
$$8 - 8z^2 - 2z - 5 = 0$$
$$-8z^2 - 2z + 3 = 0$$
$$8z^2 + 2z - 3 = 0$$
$$(4z + 3)(2z - 1) = 0$$

Either $\qquad 4z + 3 = 0, \ 4z = -3, \ z = -\frac{3}{4}$

or $\qquad 2z - 1 = 0, \ 2z = 1, \ z = \frac{1}{2}$

Now $\qquad z = \sin \theta, \ \theta = \arcsin z.$

Between 0 and 180°, when $z = 0.5$, arcsin $0.5 = 30°$ or 150°. Between 0 and 180°, when $z = -0.75$, $\sin^{-1} -0.75$ is *not* admissible, since sin is positive between 0 and 180°.

$$\text{Check}: \ \theta = 30°, \ \sin \theta = 0.5, \ \cos \theta = 0.866$$
$$8(0.866)^2 = 5 + 2(0.5)$$
$$8(0.75) = 5 + 1$$
$$6 = 6$$

$$\theta = 150°, \ \sin \theta = 0.5, \ \cos \theta = -0.866$$
$$8(-0.866)^2 = 5 + 2(0.5)$$
$$8(+0.75) = 5 + 1$$
$$6 = 6$$

Answer: $\theta = 30°$ or $150°$

Example

Find the co-ordinates of the points at which the straight line $4y = 3x + 2$ intersects the circle $x^2 - 4x + y^2 - 4y = 17$.

At the intersection points, the (x, y) values satsify both the law of straight line and the law of the circle.

$$\text{If } 4y = 3x + 2, \text{ then } y = \frac{3x + 2}{4}$$

Substitute this value of y in the law of the circle.

$$x^2 - 4x + \left(\frac{3x + 2}{4}\right)^2 - 4\left(\frac{3x + 2}{4}\right) = 17$$

$$x^2-4x+\frac{9x^2+12x+4}{16}-3x-2=17$$

Multiply all through by 16

$$16x^2-64x+9x^2+12x+4-48x-32=272$$
$$16x^2+9x^2-64x+12x-48x+4-32-272=0$$
$$25x^2-100x-300=0$$
$$x^2-4x-12=0$$
$$(x-6)(x+2)=0$$
$$\therefore \text{ Either } x-6=0, \ x=6 \text{ or } x+2=0, \ x=-2$$

When $\qquad x=6, \ y=\dfrac{3x+2}{4}=\dfrac{18+2}{4}=\dfrac{20}{4}=5$

When $\qquad x=-2, \ y=\dfrac{-6+2}{4}=\dfrac{-4}{4}=-1$

The values which simultaneously satisfy both laws are

$$x=6, \ y=5, \text{ and } x=-2, \ y=-1$$

Check: Using (6, 5) $4y=3x+2, \ 20=18+2, \ 20=20$
$x^2-4x+y^2-4y=17, \ 36-24+25-20=17, \ 17=17$
Using $(-2, -1)$ $4y=3x-2, \ -8=-6-2, \ -8=-8$
$x^2-4x+y^2-4y=17, \ 4+8+1+4=17, \ 17=17$

Answer: Points of intersection are (6, 5) and $(-2, -1)$

Problems 2.2

1. Find the smallest number so that the sum of the number and its reciprocal is 2·4.

2. Find the co-ordinates of the points at which the straight line $x-y=3$ intersects the hyperbola $xy=18$.

3. By making the substitution $z=\cos\theta$, find all the angles between zero and 360° which satisfy the equation
$$3\cos^2\theta+4\cos\theta=2\cdot75$$

4. If $z=\sin\theta$, express $\cos^2\theta$ as a function of z. Hence find all the angles between zero and 360° which satisfy the equation
$$4\cos^2\theta-3\sin\theta=1\cdot5$$

5. A square hole is cut in a square plate so that the border all round the hole is of width 4 mm. The area of the hole is one-quarter of the area of the original plate. Find the length of side of the original plate.

6. A disc of diameter D has a circular hole removed from it, concentric with the outside diameter, so that the width of the resulting annulus is W. Show that the ratio of the final area to the original area is given by

$$\frac{4WD - 4W^2}{D^2}$$

If $D=8$ mm, find the value of W so that the above ratio is $\frac{3}{4}$.

7. The perimeter of a right-angled triangle is 40 mm and the hypotenuse has a length of 17 mm. Find the lengths of the other two sides.

8. A solid cylinder has a length of 50 mm. The total surface area is 18 700 mm². Calculate the radius.
   (*Note*: If you work in units of 10 mm, i.e. centimetres, the length is 5 units but the unit of area is 10 mm × 10 mm = 100 mm², and the area is 187 units.)

9. The diagonal of a rectangle has a length of 170 mm. The area is 12 000 mm². Calculate the lengths of the sides.
   (Note the same point as in the previous question. Taking the diagonal as 17 units, the area is 120 units.)

10. A flat of width W is machined on a circular steel shaft of diameter D, as shown in Figure 2.2. Show that the depth of cut d is related to W and D by the equation

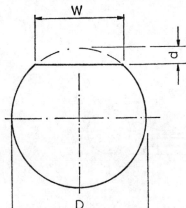

$$d^2 - dD + \frac{W^2}{4} = 0$$

Find d when $D=20$ mm and $W=5$ mm

Fig. 2.2

11. The roots of the equation $(x-a)(x-b)(x-c)=0$ are $x=a$, $x=b$, and $x=c$. One of the roots of the equation $x^3-4x^2+x+6=0$ is $x=2$. Find the other two roots.

12. One of the roots of the equation
$$x^3+3x^2-8x-32=0$$
is in the vicinity of $x=3$.

By putting $x=3+h$ in the original equation and discounting the term which includes h^3, solve the resulting quadratic to obtain a value of h. Hence find the value of the root in the vicinity of $x=3$ to three significant figures.

13. With the aid of the substitutions given, solve the following equations for x:

(a) $5(2 \cdot 718^x)-2 \cdot 718^{2x}=6 \cdot 2$, using $z=2 \cdot 718^x$.

(b) $5^x(5^x-4)+3=0$, using $z=5^x$.

14. Figure 2.3 shows a method of checking a large radius with the aid of rollers, a straight edge, and a slip gauge pile. The formula connecting R, C, d, and h is:
$$R=\frac{C^2}{8(d-h)}-\frac{h}{2}$$
Find the value of h when $R=100$ mm, $C=100$ mm and $d=20$ mm.

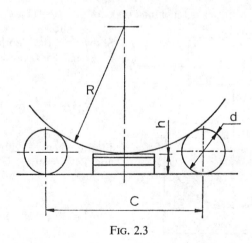

FIG. 2.3

15. Figure 2.4 shows a metal plate whose area is 1776 mm². Find the value of x.

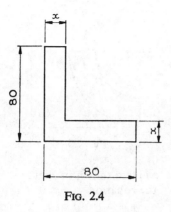

FIG. 2.4

16. When a body is projected vertically upwards with a velocity of 50 m/s, the height h metres above the point of release after t seconds can be obtained from the formula

$$h = 50t - 4 \cdot 9t^2$$

Find the values of t when $h = 100$ m.

17. A 'reverse-bend' of piping for a heat-exchanger system is shown in Figure 2.5. The *outer* diameter of the bend is 3 m and the *outer surface area* is to be 5 m².

Denoting the outer diameter of the pipe cross-section by d metres, show that

$$d^2 - 3d + \frac{10}{\pi^2} = 0$$

Taking $\pi = 3 \cdot 142$, solve this equation for d to two decimal places.

(C.G.L.I.)

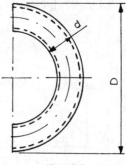

FIG. 2.5

18. The area of the template shown in Figure 2.6 is 66 mm². Show that r is a root of the equation

$$\frac{\pi r^2}{4} - 11r + 38 \cdot 5 = 0$$

Taking π as $\frac{22}{7}$, solve this equation to find a logical value for r.

(C.G.L.I.)

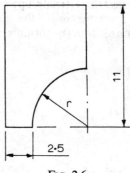

FIG. 2.6

19. (a) Show that the area A of the template shown in Figure 2.7 is given by the formula

$$A = \frac{R}{2}(3\pi R + 4L)$$

(b) If $A = 20$ mm² when $L = 3$ mm, take π as $\frac{22}{7}$ and show that

$$33R^2 + 42R - 140 = 0$$

(*c*) Solve this equation to find a logical value for *R*, giving the answer to two decimal places. (The left-hand side of the equation does not factorize.)

(C.G.L.I.)

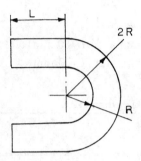

FIG. 2.7

20. (*a*) In plan view, two conveyor tracks cross at right-angles. At a certain instant, components A and B occupy the positions shown in Figure 2.8. They each travel along their individual tracks at the rate of 1 metre per minute. Show that their distance apart, in metres, after a further *t* minutes is given by

$$\sqrt{(41-18t+2t^2)}$$

(*b*) An assembly operation can be performed provided that the components are within 5 m of each other when viewed in plan. By putting the above expression equal to 5 and solving for *t* show that the time available for an assembly is 7 minutes.

(C.G.L.I.)

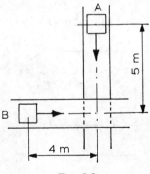

FIG. 2.8

21. The thin-walled container shown in Figure 2.9 is spun from a circular blank of diameter B. Assuming that the surface area of the container is equal to the surface area of the blank, show that

$$5R^2 + 2RH - \frac{B^2}{4} = 0$$

Find the value of R

(a) when $B = 180$ mm and $H = 60$ mm

(b) when $B = 100$ mm and $H = 20$ mm

(C.G.L.I.)

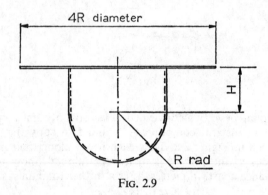

4R diameter

H

R rad

Fig. 2.9

22. A small pressure vessel has a cylindrical body with one hemi-spherical end and one flat end (Figure 2.10). The total surface area is 4 m² and the overall length is 2 m. If r is the radius of the cylinder and the hemisphere, in metres, show that

$$r^2 + 4r - \frac{4}{\pi} = 0$$

Taking $\frac{4}{\pi}$ as 1·275, find the value of r to two places of decimals.

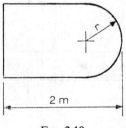

2 m

Fig. 2.10

23. The shaded area shown in Figure 2.11 has a cross-sectional area of 770 mm².

    (a) Show that $\pi(t^2-28t)-44t+770=0$

    (b) By letting $\pi=\dfrac{22}{7}$, show that this equation can be expressed as
    $$t^2-42t+245=0$$

    (c) Solve the equation and hence find a logical value for t.

    (C.G.L.I.)

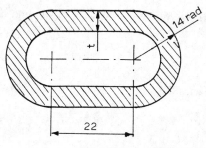

FIG. 2.11

24. A cylindrical canister, with an open top, is to be constructed of thin sheet metal of mass 10 kg/m². The height of the vessel is 0·25 m and its mass is 5 kg.

    (a) If r is the radius of the canister in metres, take π as $\dfrac{22}{7}$ and show that
    $$44r^2+22r-7=0$$

    (b) Solve the equation to find the radius of the canister as a fraction of a metre. (C.G.L.I.)

25. A pressure vessel of overall length 10 m has a cylindrical body with two hemispherical ends and a capacity of 25 m³. For these conditions, if r is the common radius then
    $$r^3-15r^2+12=0$$
    This *cubic* equation has a root in the vicinity of $r=1$. By substituting $(1+h)$ for r in the above equation, and then neglecting the h^3 term, form the quadratic equation
    $$12h^2+27h+2=0$$
    Solve this equation and hence determine a value of r to two decimal places. (C.G.L.I.)

D

Mathematics for Mechanical Technicians 2

26. In computing the probability of a particular event occurring from a sample of five items, it was found that the overall probability was a combination of probabilities. It was required to find when the overall probability reached a level of 55%.

The following equation was deduced from the above circumstances

$$5e^{2t}+5e^t=0{\cdot}55$$

By letting $x=e^t$, show that this equation can be transformed to

$$100x^2+100x-11=0$$

Solve this equation for x, and since $x=e^t$, find the value of t.

(C.G.L.I.)

Answers to problems 2.2

1. $0{\cdot}536$
2. $(6, 3)$ and $(-3, -6)$
3. $60°$ and $300°$
4. $\cos^2 \theta=1-z^2$, $\theta=30°$ or $150°$
5. 16 mm
6. 2 mm
7. 8 mm and 15 mm
8. 35 mm
9. 80 mm$\times$150 mm
10. $0{\cdot}32$ mm
11. $x=3$ and $x=-1$
12. $x=3{\cdot}05$
13. (a) 1 or $0{\cdot}823$ (b) 0 or $0{\cdot}683$
14. 8 mm
15. 12 mm
16. $2{\cdot}73$ s and $7{\cdot}47$ s
17. $0{\cdot}39$ m
18. $r=7$ mm
19. $1{\cdot}52$ mm
20. $t=1$ min or $t=8$ min, giving 7 min for assembly
21. (a) $R=30$ mm   (b) $R=18{\cdot}7$ mm
22. $0{\cdot}30$ m
23. 7 mm
24. $0{\cdot}221$ m
25. $0{\cdot}92$ m
26. $-2{\cdot}30$

2.3 Binomial Expansions

2.3.1 THE BINOMIAL EXPANSION FOR A POSITIVE WHOLE NUMBER INDEX

Using the standard method for the multiplication of algebraic expressions, the reader can readily prove for himself the validity of the following statements:

$$(1+x)^2=1+2x+x^2$$
$$(1+x)^3=1+3x+3x^2+x^3$$
$$(1+x)^4=1+4x+6x^2+4x^3+x^4$$
$$(1+x)^5=1+5x+10x^2+10x^3+5x^4+x^5$$
$$(1+x)^6=1+6x+15x^2+20x^3+15x^4+6x^5+x^6$$

The expression $(1+x)$, being an algebraic expression of two terms, is known as a *binomial*, while the series obtained for $(1+x)^n$ is known as a *binomial expansion*.

Some pertinent information regarding the expansion of $(1+x)^n$, where n is a positive whole number, can be deduced by considering the expansions which introduced this article.

(*a*) The first term is always unity.

(*b*) The expansion consists of a sum of positive terms of ascending powers of x, terminating with x^n.

(*c*) The second term is nx.

(*d*) The series terminates after $(n+1)$ terms.

The only other item which has to be deduced in order to write down any expansion of $(1+x)^n$, when n is a positive whole number, is a method of determining the coefficients of x^2, x^3, x^4, etc., up to x^{n-1}. The reader must accept without proof that the coefficient of x^r is:

$$\frac{n(n-1)(n-2), \text{etc., to } r \text{ terms}}{1 \times 2 \times 3, \text{etc., to } r \text{ numbers}}$$

The product of the first n natural numbers is known as *factorial n*, and is written as $n!$ Hence 5! is read as 'factorial 5' and is evaluated as $1 \times 2 \times 3 \times 4 \times 5 = 120$. We now can write down a general formula for the expansion of $(1+x)^n$, viz.:

$$(1+x)^n=1+nx+\frac{(n)(n-1)}{2!}x^2+\frac{(n)(n-1)(n-2)}{3!}x^3 \ldots x^n$$

If n is a positive whole number, this expansion terminates after $(n+1)$ terms and is true for any value of x.

The first term in the binomial expressions so far has been unity. Any binomial expression can be put in a form suitable for expansion using the formula above, by taking the first term out as a common factor.

For example:

$$(a+b)^n = \left\{ a\left(1+\frac{b}{a}\right)\right\}^n = a^n\left(1+\frac{b}{a}\right)^n$$

$$(2x+3y)^n = \left\{ 2x\left(1+\frac{3y}{2x}\right)\right\}^n = (2x)^n\left(1+\frac{3y}{2x}\right)^n$$

$$(3a-4b)^n = \left\{ 3a\left(1-\frac{4b}{3a}\right)\right\}^n = (3a)^n\left\{1+\left(-\frac{4b}{3a}\right)\right\}^n$$

Example

Find the expansion of $(1+x)^4$ and use the expansion to find the values of

(a) $2\cdot5^4$

(b) $(2a+3b)^4$

(c) $(a-2b)^4$

$$(1+x)^4 = 1+4x+\frac{4\times3}{1\times2}x^2+\frac{4\times3\times2}{1\times2\times3}x^3+\frac{4\times3\times2\times1}{1\times2\times3\times4}x^4$$

$$= 1+4x+6x^2+4x^3+x^4$$

(a) $2\cdot5^4$ can be written as $(1+1\cdot5)^4$

Let x in the expansion of $(1+x)^4$ be $1\cdot5$

$$(1+1\cdot5)^4 = 1+4(1\cdot5)+6(1\cdot5)^2+4(1\cdot5)^3+(1\cdot5)^4$$
$$= 1+6\cdot0+6(2\cdot25)+4(3\cdot375)+(5\cdot062\ 5)$$
$$= 1+6\cdot0+13\cdot50+13\cdot50+5\cdot062\ 5$$
$$= 39\cdot062\ 5$$

(b) $(2a+3b)^4$ can be written as $\left\{ 2a\left(1+\frac{3b}{2a}\right)\right\}^4$

$$\left\{ 2a\left(1+\frac{3b}{2a}\right)\right\}^4 = (2a)^4\left(1+\frac{3b}{2a}\right)^4 = 16a^4\left(1+\frac{3b}{2a}\right)^4$$

Let x in the expansion of $(1+x)^4$ be $\frac{3b}{2a}$

$$\left(1+\frac{3b}{2a}\right)^4 = 1+4\left(\frac{3b}{2a}\right)+6\left(\frac{3b}{2a}\right)^2+4\left(\frac{3b}{2a}\right)^3+\left(\frac{3b}{2a}\right)^4$$

$$= 1+\frac{6b}{a}+\frac{27b^2}{2a^2}+\frac{27b^3}{2a^3}+\frac{81b^4}{16a^4}$$

$$(2a+3b)^4=16a^4\left(1+\frac{3b}{2a}\right)^4$$

$$=16a^4\left(1+\frac{6b}{a}+\frac{27b^2}{2a^2}+\frac{27b^3}{2a^3}+\frac{81b^4}{16a^4}\right)$$

$$=16a^4+96a^3b+216a^2b^2+216ab^3+81b^4$$

(c) $(a-2b)^4$ can be written as $\left\{a\left(1-\frac{2b}{a}\right)\right\}^4=a^4\left(1-\frac{2b}{a}\right)^4$

Let x in the expansion of $(1+x)^4$ be $\left(\dfrac{-2b}{a}\right)$

(*Note carefully the inclusion of the minus sign.*)

$$\left(1-\frac{2b}{a}\right)^4=1+4\left(\frac{-2b}{a}\right)+6\left(\frac{-2b}{a}\right)^2+4\left(\frac{-2b}{a}\right)^3+\left(\frac{-2b}{a}\right)^4$$

$$=1-\frac{8b}{a}+\frac{24b^2}{a^2}-\frac{32b^3}{a^3}+\frac{16b^4}{a^4}$$

$$(a-2b)^4=a^4\left(1-\frac{2b}{a}\right)^4$$

$$=a^4-8a^3b+24a^2b^2-32ab^3+16b^4$$

Checks: (*a*) $2\cdot5^4=\left(\dfrac{5}{2}\right)^4=\dfrac{5^4}{2^4}=\dfrac{625}{16}=39\cdot062\ 5$

(*b*) Put *a* and *b* equal to 1
   $(2a+3b)^4=5^4=625$
   a^4, a^3b, a^2b^2, etc., are all equal to unity
   Sum of coefficients$=16+96+216+216+81=625$

(*c*) Put *a* and *b* equal to 1
   $(a-2b)^4=(-1)^4=1$
   a^4, a^3b, a^2b^2, etc., are all equal to unity
   Sum of coefficients$=1-8+24-32+16$
   $\qquad\qquad\qquad\quad=41-40=1$

Answers: $(1+x)^4=1+4x+6x^2+4x^3+x^4$
(*a*) $2\cdot5^4=39\cdot0625$
(*b*) $(2a+3b)^4=16a^4+96a^3b+216a^2b^2+216ab^3+81b^4$
(*c*) $(a-2b)^4=a^4-8a^3b+24a^2b^2-32ab^3+16b^4$

Before proceeding further, the reader should note from the above problem that if *n is a positive whole number*:

(*a*) When the binomial to be expanded consists of positive terms, all the signs of the expansion are positive.

(b) When the binomial to be expanded is a positive term followed by a negative term, after the first positive term of the expansion the signs are alternately negative and positive.

(c) The use of the coefficients of the expansion as a rough check.

2.3.2 THE BINOMIAL EXPANSION FOR AN INDEX OTHER THAN A POSITIVE WHOLE NUMBER

If we evaluate $(1+x)^{-1}$ by determining $\dfrac{1}{1+x}$ by long division, we would find that we would always be left with a remainder. In fact, the expansion would be

$$1-x+x^2-x^3+x^4-x^5, \text{ etc.}$$

and would continue indefinitely.

Using the binomial expansion formula in the previous article,

$$(1+x)^{-1}=1+(-1)x+\frac{(-1)(-2)}{2!}x^2+\frac{(-1)(-2)(-3)}{3!}x^3 \ldots$$

$$=1-x+x^2-x^3 \ldots$$

It seems, at first glance, that the expansion is still valid. However, let us attempt to evaluate $\dfrac{1}{3}$ by putting $x=2$, i.e.

$$\frac{1}{3}=(3)^{-1}=(1+2)^{-1}$$

$$=1-2+4-8+16-32, \text{ etc.}$$

Depending upon whether or not we considered an even or an odd number of terms, we would have a negative or positive result, which would certainly not be in the vicinity of $\dfrac{1}{3}$.

Let us try evaluating $\dfrac{1}{2}$, i.e. 2^{-1} or $(1+1)^{-1}$, by putting $x=1$

$$\frac{1}{2}=1-1+1-1+1-1 \text{ etc.}=0 \text{ or } 1$$

depending upon whether or not we considered an even or an odd number of terms.

Let us try evaluating $\dfrac{5}{6}$, i.e. $\dfrac{1}{1\cdot2}=1\cdot2^{-1}=(1+0\cdot2)^{-1}$, by putting $x=0\cdot2$.

$$(1+0\cdot2)^{-1}=1-0\cdot2+0\cdot04-0\cdot008+0\cdot001\ 6+0\cdot000\ 32, \text{ etc.}$$

Sum of first two terms $=0.8$
Sum of first three terms $=0.84$
Sum of first four terms $=0.832$
Sum of first five terms $=0.833\ 6$
Sum of first six terms $=0.833\ 28$

It will be observed that the more terms we take, the closer does the final value become to the accurate value of $\frac{5}{6}$.

From the preceding calculations, we note that when we use the expansion of $(1+x)^{-1}$ the expansion is not valid when x is equal to or greater than unity. The reader must accept without proof that this can be extended to cases where n is any negative whole number, or a fraction, whether it be a positive or a negative fraction.

Summarising the preceding articles on the binomial expansion,

$$(1+x)^n = 1 + nx + \frac{(n)(n-1)}{2!}x^2 + \frac{(n)(n-1)(n-2)}{3!}x^3 \ldots$$

(a) *If n be a positive whole number, the series terminates after (n+1) terms, and is valid for any value of x.*

(b) *If n be any number other than a positive whole number, the series never terminates, and is valid only if the value of x lies between 1 and −1.*

Example

Expand fully $(a-2b)^3$ and comment on the validity of the series obtained.

The expansion will be true for all values of a and b since n is a positive whole number. The series terminates after four terms.

$$(a-2b)^3 = \left\{ a\left(1-\frac{2b}{a}\right)\right\}^3 = a^3\left(1-\frac{2b}{a}\right)^3$$

$$(1+x)^n = 1 + nx + \frac{(n)(n-1)}{2!}x^2 + \frac{(n)(n-1)(n-2)}{3!}x^3 \ldots \text{etc.}$$

$$x = \frac{-2b}{a}, \quad n=3$$

$$\therefore \left(1-\frac{2b}{a}\right)^3 = 1 + (3)\left(\frac{-2b}{a}\right) + \frac{(3)(2)}{(1)(2)}\left(\frac{-2b}{a}\right)^2 + \frac{(3)(2)(1)}{(1)(2)(3)}\left(\frac{-2b}{a}\right)^3$$

$$= 1 - \frac{6b}{a} + \frac{12b^2}{a^2} - \frac{8b^3}{a^3}$$

$$a^3\left(1-\frac{2b}{a}\right)^3 = a^3\left(1-\frac{6b}{a}+\frac{12b^2}{a^2}-\frac{8b^3}{a^3}\right)$$

$$=a^3-6a^2b+12ab^2-8b^3$$

Rough check: Put a and $b=1$, $a-2b=-1$, $-1^3=-1$

Sum of coefficients$=-1$

Answer: $(a-2b)^3=a^3-6a^2b+12ab^2-8b^3$

and is true for any values of a and b

Example

Find the first four terms of a series for $\sqrt{(1+x)}$ when x lies between -1 and $+1$, and use the series to find $\sqrt{1\cdot4}$ to two places of decimals.

$$\sqrt{(1+x)}=(1+x)^{\frac{1}{2}}$$

$$(1+x)^n=1+nx+\frac{(n)(n-1)}{2!}x^2+\frac{(n)(n-1)(n-2)}{3!}x^3, \text{ to four terms}$$

$$(1+x)^{\frac{1}{2}}=1+(\tfrac{1}{2})(x)+\frac{(\tfrac{1}{2})(-\tfrac{1}{2})}{(1)(2)}x^2+\frac{(\tfrac{1}{2})(-\tfrac{1}{2})(-\tfrac{3}{2})}{(1)(2)(3)}x^3, \text{ to four terms}$$

$$=1+\frac{x}{2}-\frac{x^2}{8}+\frac{x^3}{16}, \text{ to four terms}$$

If $(1+x)=1\cdot4$, then $x=0\cdot4$

$$\sqrt{1\cdot4}=1+\frac{0\cdot4}{2}-\frac{0\cdot16}{8}+\frac{0\cdot064}{16}$$

$$=1+0\cdot2-0\cdot02+0\cdot004$$

$$=1\cdot184$$

Answers: $\sqrt{(1+x)}=1+\frac{x}{2}-\frac{x^2}{8}+\frac{x^3}{16}$ to four terms

$\sqrt{1\cdot4}=1\cdot18$ to two decimal places

Example

Find, using the Binomial Theorem, $\sqrt{98}$ to four decimal places.

We first have to put $\sqrt{98}$ in a form suitable for expansion.

$$(a+b)^n=\left\{a\left(1+\frac{b}{a}\right)\right\}^n=a^n\left(1+\frac{b}{a}\right)^n$$

We will have to choose a and b so that a^n can be easily evaluated, while $\frac{b}{a}$ is a small quantity compared with unity.

Writing 98 as $(100-2)$, $a=100$ and $\sqrt{100}=10$, while $\dfrac{b}{a}=\dfrac{-2}{100}=-0.02$

$$\sqrt{98}=98^{\frac{1}{2}}=(100-2)^{\frac{1}{2}}=\{100(1-0.02)\}^{\frac{1}{2}}$$
$$=100^{\frac{1}{2}}(1-0.02)^{\frac{1}{2}}=10(1-0.02)^{\frac{1}{2}}$$

Four terms of the expansion will suffice; this will give more than six decimal places in the expansion of $(1-0.02)^n$ and more than five decimal places when the result is multiplied by 10. The answer can then be rounded off to four decimal places.

$$(1+x)^n=1+nx+\frac{n(n-1)}{2!}x^2+\frac{(n)(n-1)(n-2)}{3!}x^3 \text{ to four terms}$$

$$(1-0.02)^{\frac{1}{2}}=1+(\tfrac{1}{2})(-0.02)+\frac{(\tfrac{1}{2})(-\tfrac{1}{2})}{(1)(2)}(-0.02)^2+\frac{(\tfrac{1}{2})(-\tfrac{1}{2})(-\tfrac{3}{2})}{(1)(2)(3)}(-0.02)^3$$

$$=1-\frac{0.02}{2}-\frac{0.000\,4}{8}-\frac{0.000\,008}{16}$$
$$=1-0.01-0.000\,05-0.000\,000\,5$$
$$=1-0.010\,050\,5$$
$$=0.989\,949\,5$$
$$\sqrt{98}=10(0.989\,949\,5)=9.899\,495$$

Answer: $\sqrt{98}=9.899\,5$ to four decimal places

2.3.3 APPROXIMATIONS

If x is so small when compared with unity that the effect of x^2, x^3, x^4 and higher powers of x can be discounted, then the first two terms of the binomial expansion lead to

$$(1+x)^n=1+nx \ (approximately)$$

Example

Find approximate values for

(a) $(1.03)^2$; (b) $\sqrt[3]{0.997}$; (c) $\sqrt[3]{1006}$; (d) $\dfrac{1}{0.995}$.

$$(1+x)^n=1+nx, \text{ approximately}$$

(a) $(1.03)^2=(1+0.03)^2 \ =1+(2)(0.03)$ approx
                                    $=1.06$ approx

(b) $\sqrt[3]{0.997}=(1-0.003)^{\frac{1}{3}}=1+(\tfrac{1}{3})(-0.003)$ approx
                                    $=0.999$ approx

(c) $\sqrt[3]{1\,006}=(1\,000+6)^{\frac{1}{3}}=\{1\,000(1+0\cdot006)\}^{\frac{1}{3}}$
$=1\,000^{\frac{1}{3}}(1+0\cdot006)^{\frac{1}{3}}$
$=10(1+0\cdot006)^{\frac{1}{3}}$
$=10\{1+(\tfrac{1}{3})(0\cdot006)\}$ approx
$=10(1\cdot002)$ approx$=10\cdot02$ approx

(d) $\dfrac{1}{0\cdot995}=(0\cdot995)^{-1}=(1-0\cdot005)^{-1}$

$=1+(-1)(-0\cdot005)$ approx
$=1+0\cdot005$ approx$=1\cdot005$ approx

Answers: (a) $1\cdot06$ approx
(b) $0\cdot999$ approx
(c) $10\cdot02$ approx
(d) $1\cdot005$ approx

2.3.4 APPROXIMATIONS OF PRODUCTS AND QUOTIENTS

$(1+a)^b(1+c)^d=(1+ab)(1+cd)$ approximately
$=1+ab+cd+abcd$ approximately

The above approximation assumed that a and c were small compared with unity. If a and c are small, then $abcd$ is very small, and if it is so very small that its effect can be discounted, then

$(1+a)^b(1+c)^d=1+ab+cd$ approximately

Hence $\dfrac{(1+a)^b}{(1+e)^f}=(1+a)^b(1+e)^{-f}$ approximately

$=1+ab-ef$ approximately

The process of approximation can be continued for several expressions in the numerator and denominator; for example,

$\dfrac{(1+a)^b(1-c)^d}{(1+e)^f(1-g)^h}=1+ab-cd-ef+gh$ approximately.

Example

Find the approximate percentage change in the volume of a cylinder when its diameter increases by 3% and its length decreases by 2%.

$$V=\frac{\pi D^2 H}{4}$$

New value of $D=D+3\%$ of $D=D+\dfrac{3D}{100}=D(1+0\cdot03)$

New value of $H=H-2\%$ of $H=H-\dfrac{2H}{100}=H(1-0\cdot02)$

New volume $=\dfrac{\pi}{4}\{D(1+0\cdot03)\}^2\{H(1-0\cdot02)\}$

$\quad\quad=\dfrac{\pi D^2 H}{4}(1+0\cdot03)^2(1-0\cdot02)^1$

$\quad\quad=\dfrac{\pi D^2 H}{4}\{1+2(0\cdot03)+1(-0\cdot02)\}$ approx

$\quad\quad=\dfrac{\pi D^2 H}{4}(1+0\cdot06-0\cdot02)=1\cdot04\dfrac{\pi D^2 H}{4}$ approx

Percentage change $=\dfrac{\text{new volume}-\text{original volume}}{\text{original volume}}\times100\%$

$\quad\quad=\left(\dfrac{1\cdot04\left(\dfrac{\pi D^2 H}{4}\right)-\dfrac{\pi D^2 H}{4}}{\dfrac{\pi D^2 H}{4}}\right)\times100\%$

$\quad\quad=\left(\dfrac{1\cdot04-1}{1}\right)\times100\%$

$\quad\quad=(0\cdot04)(100\%)=4\%$

Answer: Volume increases by 4% approximately

Example

Show that if terms of x^3 and higher powers of x can be neglected

$$\dfrac{(1+x)^3}{\sqrt{(1-x)}}=1+\dfrac{7x}{2}+\dfrac{39x^2}{8}\text{ approximately}$$

Hence, find $\dfrac{1\cdot02^3}{\sqrt{0\cdot98}}$ to four decimal places.

In this problem, note that x^2 terms must be included, and the approximation $(1+x)^n=1+nx$ cannot be applied.

$$(1+x)^n=1+nx+\dfrac{(n)(n-1)x^2}{2!},$$

if x^3 and higher powers of x are neglected.

$$\dfrac{(1+x)^3}{\sqrt{(1-x)}}=(1+x)^3(1-x)^{-\frac{1}{2}}$$

$$(1+x)^3=1+(3)(x)+\dfrac{(3)(2)}{(1)(2)}x^2=1+3x+3x^2$$

$$(1-x)^{-\frac{1}{2}}=1+(-\tfrac{1}{2})(-x)+\dfrac{(-\tfrac{1}{2})(-\tfrac{3}{2})}{(1)(2)}(-x)^2=1+\dfrac{x}{2}+\dfrac{3x^2}{8},$$

if x^3 and higher powers of x are neglected.

$$(1+x)^3(1-x)^{-\frac{1}{2}}=(1+3x+3x^2)\left(1+\frac{x}{2}+\frac{3x^2}{8}\right)$$

$$=\left(1+\frac{x}{2}+\frac{3x^2}{8}\right)+\left(3x+\frac{3x^2}{2}\right)+3x^2$$

(if x^3 and higher powers of x are neglected)

$$=1+\frac{7x}{2}+\frac{39x^2}{8}$$

If $x=0.02$, $1+\dfrac{7x}{2}+\dfrac{39x^2}{8}=1+0.07+0.001\ 95$

$$=1.071\ 95$$

Answer: $\dfrac{1.02^3}{\sqrt{0.98}}=1.0720$

Example

The intensity of illumination provided at a particular point by a light source varies inversely as the square of the distance from the point to the light source.

A particular point is 10 m from a light source. If the light source is moved a distance x m nearer to the point, where x is small compared with 10 m, show that the intensity of illumination is increased by approximately $20x\%$.

If I=intensity of illumination and d=distance from light source then

$$I\propto\frac{1}{d^2},\ I=\frac{K}{d^2}$$

Original intensity of illumination$=\dfrac{K}{10^2}=\dfrac{K}{100}$

New intensity of illumination $=\dfrac{K}{(10-x)^2}$

$$=\frac{K}{\left\{10\left(1-\dfrac{x}{10}\right)\right\}^2}=\frac{K}{100}\left(1-\frac{x}{10}\right)^{-2}$$

If x is small, then $(1+x)^n=1+nx$ approx

$$\therefore\ \left(1-\frac{x}{10}\right)^{-2}=1+(-2)\left(-\frac{x}{10}\right)\text{approx}=1+\frac{x}{5}\text{ approx}$$

$$\therefore \text{ New intensity} = \frac{K}{100}\left(1+\frac{x}{5}\right) = \frac{K}{100} + \frac{Kx}{500}$$

$$\text{Increase in intensity} = \frac{K}{100} + \frac{Kx}{500} - \frac{K}{100} = \frac{Kx}{500}$$

$$\text{Percentage increase} = \frac{\text{increase in intensity}}{\text{original intensity}} \times 100\%$$

$$= \left(\frac{Kx}{500} \div \frac{K}{100}\right) \times 100\%$$

$$= \frac{Kx}{500} \times \frac{100}{K} \times 100\% = 20x\%$$

Problems 2.3

1. Find the first four terms of the expansions of

(a) $\dfrac{1}{1+x}$ (b) $\sqrt{(1+x)}$

(c) $\sqrt{(1-2x)}$ (d) $\dfrac{1}{(1+x)^2}$

2. Expand fully $(2x+y)^4$ and $(3x-5y)^3$

3. Find the first four terms of

$\dfrac{1}{(1+2x)^4}$ and $\dfrac{1}{3-2x}$

in each case stating for which values of x the series is true.

4. Simplify $\left(1+\dfrac{1}{x}\right)^4 - \left(1-\dfrac{1}{x}\right)^4$

5. Find the first three terms of the expansion of $(x-y)^{\frac{1}{2}}$ and by putting $x=4$ and $y=0\cdot1$ use the expansion to find $\sqrt{3\cdot9}$ to five places of decimals.

6. An error of $1\cdot5\%$ was made in measuring the diameter of a circle. What was the resulting approximate percentage error in the determination of the area?

7. If x is so small that x^2 and higher powers of x can be disregarded, find a value for $\dfrac{1}{\sqrt[3]{(1-x)}}-1$

8. Find the first three terms of a series in ascending powers of x for $\sqrt{(9-x)}$ and state for which values of x the series is true.

9. If x is so small that x^3 and higher powers of x can be disregarded show that $1-\sqrt{(1+x)}=\dfrac{x^2}{8}-\dfrac{x}{2}$

10. Find the cube root of 126 to four places of decimals.

11. Find values of $\sqrt{98}$,
    (a) correct to two decimal places,
    (b) correct to four decimal places.

12. Find approximate values for
    (a) $\sqrt{1\cdot002}$ (b) $\sqrt[3]{0\cdot994}$
    (c) $\sqrt{27}$
    (d) $\dfrac{1}{\sqrt[3]{1\,006}}$

13. The periodic time T for one complete swing of a simple pendulum is given by the formula $T=2\pi\sqrt{\left(\dfrac{L}{g}\right)}$.
    (a) Rearrange the formula to give an expression for g.
    (b) If in a particular experiment, the value of L was $0\cdot5\%$ too large and the value of T was 2% too small, what is the approximate percentage error of the value of g?

14. (a) Use the Binomial Theorem to find the first four terms of the expansion of $\left(2-\dfrac{x}{2}\right)^7$ in ascending powers of x.
    (b) If x is so small that x^4 and higher powers can be neglected, show that $\dfrac{\sqrt{(1+2x)}}{1-x}=1+2x+\dfrac{3x^2}{2}+2x^3$. Use this result to find $\dfrac{\sqrt{1\cdot06}}{0\cdot97}$ to four decimal places.

15. If a cylinder of outside radius R and inside radius r contains gas having a pressure of p, the maximum tensile stress in the cylinder f is given by the formula

$$\frac{f}{p} = \frac{R^2 + r^2}{R^2 - r^2}$$

If t is the wall thickness (i.e. $r = R - t$), find an expression for f in terms of t and R and show that if t is small when compared with R, then $\frac{f}{p} = \frac{R}{t} - 1$ approximately.

16. A straight horizontal wire joins two points whose distance apart is L. If the centre of the wire is displaced vertically by a distance x, where x is small compared with L, show that the wire extends by an amount approximately equal to $\frac{2x^2}{L}$.

17. A ladder of length 12·5 m rests against a vertical wall, the top of the ladder being 12 m above the ground, the ground-level being horizontal. If the foot of the ladder is pulled away from the wall by a small amount x, show that the top of the ladder moves down the wall by an amount approximately equal to $\frac{7x}{24}$.

18. A tube of outside diameter $2D$ and inside diameter D is being turned and bored on a centre lathe. A cut of depth t is taken off the outside and inside so that the new diameters are $(2D - 2t)$ and $(D + 2t)$. Find an expression for the percentage of metal removed.

19. If $F_1 = \dfrac{k}{(d-x)^2}$ and $F_2 = \dfrac{k}{(d+x)^2}$ and x is so small when compared with d that terms containing x^2 and higher powers of x can be neglected, find a value for $F_1 - F_2$.

20. (a) Find the first four terms of the expansion of

$$\frac{1}{\sqrt{(1-x)}}$$

(b) If $x = 0.04$, show that

$$\frac{1}{\sqrt{(1-x)}} = \frac{5\sqrt{6}}{12}$$

and using the series obtained in (a), find $\sqrt{6}$ to five places of decimals.

105

Answers to problems 2.3

1. (a) $1-x+x^2-x^3$

   (b) $1+\dfrac{x}{2}-\dfrac{x^2}{8}+\dfrac{x^3}{16}$

   (c) $1-x-\dfrac{x^2}{2}-\dfrac{x^3}{2}$

   (d) $1-2x+3x^2-4x^3$

2. (a) $16x^4+32x^3y+24x^2y^2+8xy^3+y^4$
   (b) $27x^3-135x^2y+225xy^2-125y^3$

3. (a) $1-8x+40x^2-160x^3$, x must lie between $\frac{1}{2}$ and $-\frac{1}{2}$

   (b) $\dfrac{1}{3}+\dfrac{2x}{9}+\dfrac{4x^2}{27}+\dfrac{8x^3}{81}$, x must lie between $1\frac{1}{2}$ and $-1\frac{1}{2}$

4. $\dfrac{8}{x}+\dfrac{8}{x^3}$

5. $x^{\frac{1}{2}}\left(1-\dfrac{y}{2x}-\dfrac{y^2}{x^28}\right)$, $1\cdot974\,84$

6. 3%

7. $\dfrac{x}{3}$

8. $3-\dfrac{x}{6}-\dfrac{x^2}{216}$, true if x lies between 9 and -9

10. $5\cdot013\,3$

11. (a) $9\cdot90$ (b) $9\cdot899\,5$

12. (a) $1\cdot001$ (b) $0\cdot998$
    (c) $5\cdot2$ (d) $0\cdot099\,8$

13. (a) $g=\dfrac{4\pi^2L}{T^2}$ (b) $4\cdot5\%$ too large

14. (a) $128-224x+168x^2-70x^3$ (b) $1\cdot061\,4$

15. $f=p\left(\dfrac{2R^2-2Rt+t^2}{2Rt-t^2}\right)$

18. $\dfrac{400t}{D}\%$

19. $\dfrac{4kx}{d^3}$

20. (a) $1+\dfrac{x}{2}+\dfrac{3x^2}{8}+\dfrac{5x^3}{16}$ (b) $2\cdot449\,45$

2.4 Probability

2.4.1 DEFINITION OF PROBABILITY

One particular dictionary meaning of probability is that it is something which, by present evidence, is likely to be true, to exist, or to happen. If this meaning is accepted, it will lead to expressions of the type 'very likely' or 'highly probable'. Engineering science must be more exact, and in order to obtain a practical scale of probability the dictionary meaning is adjusted to fit the problems encountered.

If there is a group of m mutually exclusive and equally likely events which contains a sub-group of n events, the mathematical probability of any one of the sub-group occurring is measured by the fraction n/m.

Hence the scale of probability ranges from zero to unity, indicating impossibility to certainty.

A symbol commonly used to denote probability is p.

Example

What is the probability of cutting (*a*) the king of spades, (*b*) any king, from a pack of cards?

(*a*) The sub-group here consists of one card only, the king of spades, hence $n=1$. There are 52 different cards in all, each one equally likely to occur in a cut, hence $m=52$.

$$\therefore \ p = \frac{n}{m} = \frac{1}{52}$$

(*b*) Here $n=4$, since *any* king will do, and there are *four* kings. m remains at 52.

$$\therefore \ p = \frac{n}{m} = \frac{4}{52} = \frac{1}{13}$$

Answers: Probability of the king of spades $= \dfrac{1}{52}$

Probability of any king $\qquad = \dfrac{1}{13}$

Example

What is the probability of throwing a total of 18 in a single throw of three dice?

Mathematics for Mechanical Technicians 2

18 can only be obtained in one way, by throwing three sixes,

$$\therefore\ n=1$$

Since any one of the faces of the first die can be associated with any one of the faces of the second die, there are $6\times6=36$ possible combinations of two dice. Each of these 36 combinations can be associated with any of the six faces of the third die, hence the overall number of equally likely totals is $36\times6=216$, hence $m=216$.

$$\therefore\ p=\frac{n}{m}=\frac{1}{216}$$

Answer: Probability of a throw of 18 is $\dfrac{1}{216}$

2.4.2 ODDS AGAINST AN EVENT OCCURRING

'Odds against' differs slightly from probability although the same reasoning applies. The odds against an event occurring is usually defined as the proportion of 'unsuccessful' events to 'successful' events. In the previous example the odds against throwing 18 can be considered as 215 to 1 against. The chance of drawing a king of spades from a pack of cards is 51 to 1 against.

2.4.3 THE ADDITION LAW

If an event can occur one way with a probability of p_1, a second way with a probability of p_2, a third way with a probability of p_3 and so on, the probability of the event occurring in a single trial is $p_1+p_2+p_3$, etc.

A particularly important case of the addition law is that if P is the probability of an event happening, and Q the probability of it not happening, then $P+Q=1$, since an event must either happen or not happen.

Example

What is the probability of tossing two heads and a tail in a simultaneous toss of three coins?

$$m=2\times2\times2=8$$

Let us investigate the combinations of two heads and a tail by writing down all the possible combinations, and this will enable us to check $m=8$:

H	H	H	T	T	T
H	H	T	T	T	H
H	T	H	T	H	T
H	T	T	T	H	H

Each of these combinations has a probability of $\frac{1}{8}$, and there are three of them which produce two heads and a tail,

$$\therefore\ p=\frac{1}{8}+\frac{1}{8}+\frac{1}{8}=\frac{3}{8}$$

Answer: Probability of two heads and a tail $=\frac{3}{8}$

2.4.4 THE MULTIPLICATION LAW

If a first event has a probability of p_1, a second event a probability of p_2, a third event a probability of p_3, and so on, the probability of those events occurring in sequence is $p_1p_2p_3$, etc.

Example

If between A and B there are six ferry-boats in constant use, what is the probability of using the same ferry-boat in an outward journey one day and a return journey another day?

$$p_1=1,\ \ p_2=\frac{1}{6},\ \ p=p_1p_2=1\times\frac{1}{6}=\frac{1}{6}$$

Answer: Probability of the same boat $=\frac{1}{6}$

(It will be observed that on the outward journey ANY boat would do. It is only the return journey that it is essential to travel on a specific boat. If the question had stated the probability of using a particular ferry-boat for both journeys, the probability would have been $\frac{1}{6}\times\frac{1}{6}=\frac{1}{36}$.

2.4.5 EMPIRICAL DETERMINATION OF PROBABILITY

Let us now put probability into perspective. If there are n trials and the probability of success is p, then the expected number of successful events is np. This does not mean that the expectation *must* occur; it is what we *expect* to occur over a large number of trials. There must be variations; statisticians are just as wary of results which are 'too good' as they are of those which are 'too bad.'

Many theoretical probabilities can be deduced by mathematics, but it must be emphasized that mathematical probability is based on the fact that all the results are equally likely and there is no bias.

This delightful assumption simply does not occur in everyday life. For instance, no manufacturer can manufacture dice *completely* free from bias. Quite often in practical cases an empirical value of probability is obtained by the use, over a very large number of trials, of the ratio

$$\frac{\text{number of 'successful' events}}{\text{number of trials}}$$

Provided the bias is eliminated as far as possible in practical trials, as the number of trials increases, the nearer does the empirical value tend to approach the theoretical value. An empirical value of probability is likely to be more accurate as the number of trials increases.

2.4.6 SAMPLING

Let us assume that there is a large batch of components, of which the proportion of defectives is P, and let us further assume that the extraction of a few samples does not unduly affect the value of P. For instance, imagine 10 000 components of which 1 000 are defectives. The probability of picking out a defective is $0·1$. If a second sample were taken, and the first sample was a defective, the probability of this second sample also being a defective would be $\frac{999}{9\,999}$. If the first sample was not a defective, the probability of the second sample being a defective would be $\frac{1\,000}{9\,999}$.

Neither of these ratios differ substantially from $0·1$.

Let us take two samples in sequence and consider the combinations. The probability of picking a defective is P, and the probability of it not being a defective (i.e. being acceptable) is Q, where $P+Q=1$.

First could be a defective, second could also be a defective.
The probability of this occurring is $P \times P = P^2$

First could be a defective, the second acceptable.
Probability $= P \times Q$ $= PQ$

First could be acceptable, the second a defective.
Probability $= Q \times P$ $= PQ$

Both could be acceptable.
Probability $= Q \times Q$ $= Q^2$

If we summate these probabilities, since every possible combination has been considered, they should total 1.

We note $\quad Q^2 + 2PQ + P^2 = (Q+P)^2 = 1$
(0 def.) (1 def.) (2 def.)

The same analysis could be made with three selections giving
$$Q^3 + 3Q^2P + 3QP^2 + P^3 = (Q+P)^3 = 1$$
(0 def.) (1 def.) (2 def.) (3 def.)

The general rule can, therefore, be deduced.

If a sample of n items is drawn from a batch containing a proportion of defectives of P, and the extraction of a few items does not severely affect the value of P, the probabilities of obtaining 0, 1, 2, 3, 4, etc., defectives is given by the successive terms of $(Q+P)^n$, where $Q=1-P$.

The probability of the sample containing no defectives at all is Q^n, while the probability of the sample containing *exactly* x defectives is:

$$\frac{(n)(n-1)(n-2) \ldots \text{to } x \text{ terms}}{x!} (Q^{n-x}P^x)$$

The expansion of $(Q+P)^n$ is an example of the binomial expansion, and when probabilities are evaluated using the binomial expansion they are said to follow a binomial distribution.

For rapidity of reference, some expansions of $(Q+P)^n$ are tabulated below:

$(Q+P)^2 = Q^2 + 2QP + P^2$

$(Q+P)^3 = Q^3 + 3Q^2P + 3QP^2 + P^3$

$(Q+P)^4 = Q^4 + 4Q^3P + 6Q^2P^2 + 4QP^3 + P^4$

$(Q+P)^5 = Q^5 + 5Q^4P + 10Q^3P^2 + 10Q^2P^3 + 5QP^4 + P^5$

$(Q+P)^6 = Q^6 + 6Q^5P + 15Q^4P^2 + 20Q^3P^3 + 15Q^2P^4 + 6QP^5 + P^6$

Example

If a sample of five items is drawn from a batch containing 10% of defectives, find the probability of the sample containing *exactly* two defectives.

$(Q+P)^5 = \quad Q^5 + 5Q^4P + 10Q^3P^2$ etc.
(0 def.) (1 def.) (2 def.)

Probability of two defectives is $10Q^3P^2$

$$P=0{\cdot}1, \quad Q=1-0{\cdot}1=0{\cdot}9$$

Probability $= 10(0{\cdot}9^3)(0{\cdot}1)^2 = 10 \times 0{\cdot}729 \times 0{\cdot}01 = 0{\cdot}072\ 9$

Answer: Probability of two defectives $= 0{\cdot}073$

Example

If a sample of four items is drawn from a batch containing 20% of defectives, what is the probability of:

(*a*) The sample containing not more than two defectives?

(*b*) A first sample containing one defective being followed by a second sample containing two defectives?

$$(Q+P)^4 = \underset{\text{(0 def.)}}{Q^4} + \underset{\text{(1 def.)}}{4Q^3P} + \underset{\text{(2 def.)}}{6Q^2P^2} + \underset{\text{(3 def.)}}{4QP^3} + \underset{\text{(4 def.)}}{P^4}$$

$$P = 0.2, \quad Q = 1 - 0.2 = 0.8$$

(*a*) If the sample must not contain more than two defectives, it could contain either no defectives, or one defective, or two defectives. Hence the overall probability is the sum of these separate probabilities.

$$p_0 = Q^4 \qquad = (0.8)^4 \qquad\qquad = 0.409\ 6$$
$$p_1 = 4Q^3P = 4(0.8)^3(0.2) \qquad = 0.409\ 6$$
$$p_2 = 6Q^2P^2 = 6(0.8)^2(0.2)^2 = 0.153\ 6$$

$$\text{Probability} = 0.972\ 8$$

(*b*) In this case we have sequential sampling, the two events follow each other

$$p_1 = 0.409\ 6, \quad p_2 = 0.153\ 6$$
$$\text{Probability} = p_1 p_2 = (0.409\ 6)(0.153\ 6) = 0.062\ 9$$

Answers: Probability of not more than two defectives = 0.973
Probability of one defective followed by two defectives in two successive samples = 0.063

In certain applications of statistics to inspection by sampling it is often needed to find the probability of there being '*d* or more defectives' in the sample. Such a probability is best computed using the addition law rather than by adding together a large number of terms.

Example

A large consignment of goods contains 5% of defectives. A random sample of 20 items is taken. What is the probability of the sample containing 2 or more defectives?

$$P = 5\% = 0.05 \quad Q = 1 - P = 1 - 0.05 = 0.95$$
$$n = 20$$
$$(Q+P)^n = (Q+P)^{20}$$
$$= \underset{\text{(0 def.)}}{Q^{20}} + \underset{\text{(1 def.)}}{20Q^{19}P} + \underset{\text{(2 or more def.)}}{\text{a further 19 terms}}$$

There is no need to evaluate and total the 19 terms. The sum of all the terms is unity, hence

$$p_0 = 0.95^{20} \qquad\qquad = 0.358\ 1$$
$$p_1 = 20(0.95^{19})(0.05) = 0.95^{19} = 0.377\ 0$$
$$\therefore\ p_2 \text{ or more} = 1 - (p_0 + p_1)$$
$$= 1 - (0.358\ 1 + 0.377\ 0)$$
$$= 1 - 0.735\ 1 = 0.264\ 9$$

Answer: Probability of 2 or more defectives $= 0.377$

2.4.7 THE POISSON DISTRIBUTION

If a batch has a proportion defective of P, and we take a random sample of n items, the 'expectation' or expected number of defects m in the sample is nP, i.e.

$$m = nP$$

In most of our sampling schemes, p is a very small proportion. Determinations of probabilities using the binomial expansion do not lend themselves to chart form, or to rapidity of calculations, and consequently when a close degree of accuracy is not required and rapidity of results is essential, particularly when only the expectation is known, engineers often use an approximation to the binomial expansion. The first proviso of any such approximation connected with probabilities is that the sum of the terms must be unity. A series which is well known to mathematicians is the series for e^x where $e = 2.718$.

$$e^x = 1 + x + \frac{x^2}{2!} + \frac{x^3}{3!} + \frac{x^4}{4!} \cdots$$

Now
$$1 = \frac{e^m}{e^m} = \frac{1}{e^m}\left(1 + m + \frac{m^2}{2!} + \frac{m^3}{3!} \cdots\right)$$
$$= \frac{1}{e^m} + \frac{m}{e^m} + \frac{m^2}{e^m 2!} + \frac{m^3}{e^m 3!} \cdots$$

It is found that this series is a very close approximation to the binomial expansion of $(Q+P)^n$ when Q is much greater than P (i.e. when P is small) and $m = nP$. The series is considered to be sufficiently accurate when the value of $m\ (=nP)$ is not greater than 5. The series is known as the Poisson expansion, and the probabilities found from this series are said to follow a Poisson distribution.

Provided that the proportion of defectives in a batch is small, the probability that a sample of n items will contain exactly x defectives is given approximately by:

$$\frac{m^x}{e^m x!} \quad \text{where } m = nP$$

P being the proportion of defectives in the batch.

If a single, or few, values of a Poisson series are to be determined, it is advisable to calculate them. If the sum of several terms is required, e.g. the probability of two or more occurring when the expectation is four, reference could be made to a chart which indicates summations.

We will now demonstrate the accuracy of the approximation of a Poisson series with a numerical example.

Example

Random samples of four items are drawn from batches of three different consignments, of defectiveness 50%, 10%, and 1% respectively. Calculate the probability of a sample containing exactly two defectives:

(*a*) Using the binomial expansion.
(*b*) Using the Poisson approximation.

Determine the magnitude of the error of the Poisson approximation in each case to four decimal places.

(*a*) The probability is given by the third term of $(Q+P)^4$, i.e.

$6Q^2P^2$

(i) $P=Q=0.5$. $6Q^2P^2=6(0.5)^2(0.5)^2 \quad =0.375$
(ii) $P=0.1, \ Q=0.9$ $6Q^2P^2=6(0.9)^2(0.1)^2 \quad =0.048\ 6$
(iii) $P=0.01, \ Q=0.99$. $6Q^2P^2=6(0.99)^2(0.01)^2=0.000\ 6$

(*b*) General term for two defectives is $\dfrac{m^2}{e^m 2!}=\dfrac{m^2}{2e^m}$, $(m=nP)$

(i) $m=(4)(0.5)=2$. $\dfrac{m^2}{2e^m}=\dfrac{4}{2\times7.39}=0.270\ 7$

(ii) $m=(4)(0.1)=0.4$. $\dfrac{m^2}{2e^m}=\dfrac{0.16}{2\times1.492}=0.053\ 6$

(iii) $m=(4)(0.01)=0.04$. $\dfrac{m^2}{2e^m}=\dfrac{0.001\ 6}{2\times1.041}=0.000\ 8$

Answers: Probability values and errors are given in the following table:

Defectiveness	Binomial	Poisson	Error
50%	0.375 0	0.270 7	0.104 3
10%	0.048 6	0.053 6	0.005 0
1%	0.000 6	0.000 8	0.000 2

The reader should note that the Poisson series is an approximation, and accuracy is ensured with the binomial expansion if both n and P are known. In some cases, however, only the expectation m is known. In which case, the adoption of the Poisson approximation is inferred, since there is insufficient information to adopt the binomial expansion. This will now be demonstrated in a very practical example.

Example

A small manufacturing unit normally consists of eight employees and when fully operative the production rate is fifty articles per shift. The unit produces at full rate if two or less employees are absent. If three or four employees are absent, the unit produces at half rate, while if five or more employees are absent the unit does not produce, the employees in attendance transfer to maintenance. Over a long period of time 960 man-shifts of absence were recorded over 800 days. If 800 shifts are now worked:

(*a*) How many shifts can be expected to be devoted to maintenance?

(*b*) What total number of articles can be expected from the 800 shifts?

$$\text{Expected absence per shift} = m = \frac{960}{800} = 1.2 \text{ employees}$$

$$\frac{1}{e^{1.2}} = e^{-1.2} = 0.301\ 2 \text{ (from tables)}$$

$$\frac{1}{e^{m}}(e^{m}) = \frac{1}{e^{m}}\left(1 + m + \frac{m^2}{2!} + \frac{m^3}{3!} + \frac{m^4}{4}, \text{ etc.} \ldots\right)$$

$$= 0.301\ 2\left(1 + 1.2 + \frac{1.2^2}{2} + \frac{1.2^3}{6} + \frac{1.2^4}{24} \ldots\right)$$

$$= 0.301\ 2(1 + 1.2 + 0.72 + 0.288 + 0.086\ 4 \ldots)$$

$$= 0.301\ 20 + 0.361\ 44 + 0.216\ 86 + 0.086\ 74 + 0.026\ 06 \ldots$$

These fractions are the probabilities of 0, 1, 2, 3, and 4 employees being absent, and they total 0.992 30.

Probability of 5 or more employees being absent

$$= 1 - 0.992\ 3 = 0.007\ 7$$

= probability of a shift being devoted to maintenance.

∴ In 800 shifts, $0.007\ 7 \times 800 = 6.16$ can be expected to be devoted to maintenance.

Proability of full production = probability of 0, 1, or 2 employees being absent

$$= 0.301\ 20 + 0.361\ 44 + 0.216\ 86 = 0.879\ 50$$

In 800 shifts, 0·879 50×800=703·6 will be fully productive.
Probability of half production=probability of 3 or 4 employees being absent

$$=0{\cdot}086\ 74+0{\cdot}026\ 06=0{\cdot}112\ 80$$

In 800 shifts, 0·112 80×800=90·24 will be operating at half production.

Rounding off values,

704 shifts will operate at full rate producing 50×704=35 200
90 shifts will operate at half rate producing 25×90 = 2 250
6 shifts will be non-productive = 0

Total production=37 450

Answers: (a) 6 shifts can be expected to be devoted to maintenance

(b) Expected production from 800 shifts =37 450 articles

2.4.8 THE 'GAUSSIAN' OR 'NORMAL' DISTRIBUTION

Let us consider the special case of $P=Q$; that is to say, the case when the probability of an event occurring is the same as that of the probability of the event not occurring. Whether the event occurs or not is due to pure chance.

We will first evaluate $(Q+P)^n$ making $P=Q=0{\cdot}5$ and $n=10$. This will be a sampling scheme when a sample of ten items is extracted from a consignment of which 50% are defective. In a single selection it is just as likely that a defective item will be picked as an acceptable item.

$$(Q+P)^{10}=Q^{10}+10Q^9P+45Q^8P^2+120Q^7P^3+210Q^6P^4$$
$$+252Q^5P^5+210Q^4P^6+120Q^3P^7+45Q^2P^8$$
$$+10QP^9+P^{10}$$

Now Q^{10}, Q^9P, Q^8P^2, etc., are all equal to $\dfrac{1}{2^{10}}=\dfrac{1}{1\ 024}$.

Hence the probabilities of obtaining 0, 1, 2, 3, 4, etc., defectives are $\dfrac{1}{1\ 024}$, $\dfrac{10}{1\ 024}$, $\dfrac{45}{1\ 024}$, etc. If we now make 1 024 samples each of 10, the frequencies of the numbers of defectives we should expect (i.e. $m = nP$) is given in the following table:

Defectives	0	1	2	3	4	5	6	7	8	9	10
Frequency	1	10	45	120	210	252	210	120	45	10	1

Figure 2.12 is a histogram (i.e. a diagram of frequencies) showing these results.

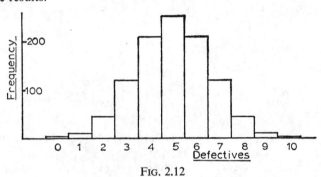

FIG. 2.12

The same general pattern ensues for any expansion of
$$(0{\cdot}5 + 0{\cdot}5)^n.$$

If n is very large, the steps become less noticeable, and the resulting histogram, with appropriate scales, becomes nearer and nearer to the bell-shaped curve shown in Figure 2.13.

If we require an approximation to this curve so that it can be used in connection with probabilities, the following conditions must be satisfied:

    (*a*) The curve must be symmetrical about a vertical centre-line.

    (*b*) The general shape of the curve must closely conform to a histogram based on $(0{\cdot}5 + 0{\cdot}5)^n$ when n is very large.

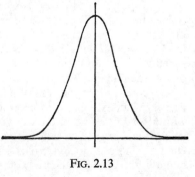

FIG. 2.13

117

A curve which satisfies these conditions is attributed to the mathematician Gauss, and is given by the formula:

$$y = \frac{1}{\sqrt{(2\pi)}} e^{-\left(\frac{x^2}{2}\right)}$$

The use of this somewhat fearsome expression is not as formidable as it appears, since tables are available giving values of y for various values of x.

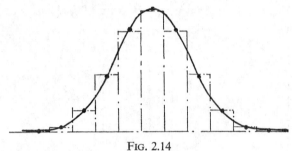

FIG. 2.14

Figure 2.14 shows a Gaussian curve fitted to the histogram of the defectives of the sampling scheme introduced previously in this article. The closeness of fit is extremely good, and the comparison of numerical values follows on the next page:

Defectives	0	1	2	3	4	5	6	7	8	9	10
Binomial	1	10	45	120	210	252	210	120	45	10	1
Gaussian	2	10	43	116	212	258	212	116	43	10	2

The area of a histogram of defectives, to some suitable scale, represents the total number of defectives. One unique characteristic of the Gaussian curve is that the *area* under the curve approaches unity as values of x range from plus infinity to minus infinity. With values of x greater than $+3$ or less than -3, the curve lies extremely close to the x-axis. Since the sum of all probabilities must total unity, we find the Gaussian curve to be an extremely useful aid when dealing with probabilities when the values of P and Q are nearly equal; that is, on the occasions when an event occurs or not is due to pure chance. There is no bias; it is what is normally expected. Consequently, the Gaussian curve is often referred to as the *Normal Curve* and distributions of frequencies based on the Gaussian curve are often referred to as *Gaussian Distributions* or *Normal Distributions*.

In the previous article it was stated that the Poisson approximation was considered sufficiently accurate when $m=nP$ was not greater than 5. Similarly the Gaussian approximation to the binomial distribution is considered to be sufficiently accurate when *both nP and nQ are greater than 5.*

The Gaussian curve fits the histogram of $(0\cdot5+0\cdot5)^n$ very closely when the x-values are units of standard deviation away from the mean. The fit of the curve shown in Figure 2.14 was obtained by finding the standard deviation for the number of defectives expected from the 1 024 samples. (The reader may care to check that it is $\sqrt{2\cdot5}=1\cdot581$ defectives.) The y-values were multiplied by a constant to give a total of 1 024. Hence, if P and Q are nearly equal, the probability of a certain event occurring can be found approximately by *determining the area under the Gaussian curve between appropriate x-ordinates.*

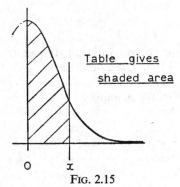

Fɪɢ. 2.15

Referring to Figure 2.15, the following table gives the area under 'one tail' of the curve of normal distribution for values of x at intervals of $0\cdot1$.

x	Area	x	Area	x	Area
0·0	0·000	1·0	0·341	2·0	0·477
0·1	0·040	1·1	0·364	2·1	0·482
0·2	0·079	1·2	0·385	2·2	0·486
0·3	0·118	1·3	0·403	2·3	0·489
0·4	0·155	1·4	0·419	2·4	0·492
0·5	0·191	1·5	0·433	2·5	0·494
0·6	0·226	1·6	0·445	2·6	0·495 5
0·7	0·258	1·7	0·455	2·7	0·497
0·8	0·288	1·8	0·464	2·8	0·497 5
0·9	0·316	1·9	0·471	2·9	0·498
				3·0	0·498 5
				3·1	0·499

The table illustrates a point made previously in this text. With a reasonably symmetrical distribution, virtually all the items fall within the range indicated by the arithmetical mean plus and minus three standard deviations.

Areas under the curve of normal distribution are given in greater detail in many reference books on statistics. Under normal examination circumstances, typical tables, such as the Cambridge Statistical Tables, cannot be provided, and candidates are usually provided with certain values and expected to use proportion. This is illustrated with the second of the worked examples which follow.

Example

A series of 100 readings are normally distributed about a mean of 56 with a standard deviation of 4. How many readings can be expected to lie between
  (a) 52 and 60?
  (b) 54 and 62?

  (a) 52 and 60 are symmetrical with respect to the mean, being 56±4, i.e. 56±1 standard deviation.
From the table of areas under the Gaussian curve, from zero to 1 standard deviation (corresponding to 56 to 60) the area is 0·341.
Similarly, from the mean to minus one standard deviation the area is 0·341.

Total probability=0·341+0·341=0·682
Expectation $m=nP=100\times0·682=68·2$
  (b) 62 is 56+1·5(4), i.e. mean+1·5 standard deviations
p_1=area up to 1·5 standard deviations=0·433
54 is 56−0·5(4), i.e. mean−0·5 standard deviation
p_2=area down to 0·5 standard deviation=0·191
Total probability=0·433+0·191=0·624
$m=nP=100\times0·624=62·4$

Answers: 68 readings can be expected between 52 and 60
        62 readings can be expected between 54 and 62

Example

The products from a particular machine were measured on a specific dimension and were found to be normally distributed with a standard deviation of 0·003. If on this particular dimension the designer had placed limits of ±0·005, what percentage of defectives would be expected? What would be the effect on the proportion of defectives of widening the limits to ±0·010?

$$\pm 0{\cdot}005 = \pm \frac{0{\cdot}005}{0{\cdot}003} \text{ standard deviations}$$

$$= \pm 1\tfrac{2}{3} \text{ standard deviations}$$

From the table on page 119, area up to $1{\cdot}7 = 0{\cdot}455$
area up to $1{\cdot}6 = 0{\cdot}445$

difference $= 0{\cdot}010$

Area up to $1\tfrac{2}{3}$ standard deviations $= 0{\cdot}445 + \tfrac{2}{3}(0{\cdot}010)$
$= 0{\cdot}452$

Area between $\pm 1\tfrac{2}{3}$ standard deviations $= 2(0{\cdot}452) = 0{\cdot}904$

Hence $0{\cdot}904$ of the articles would be within limits and be acceptable, while $1 - 0{\cdot}904 = 0{\cdot}096$ or $9{\cdot}6\%$ would fall outside the limits and be defectives.

If limits were widened to $\pm 0{\cdot}010$, i.e. $\pm 3\tfrac{1}{3}$ standard deviations, the probability of acceptable articles is greater than $2(0{\cdot}499) = 0{\cdot}998$, i.e. there would be virtually no defectives.

Answers: With $\pm 0{\cdot}005$, about 10% defectives
With $\pm 0{\cdot}010$, virtually no defectives

(It is usual to assume that all the items in a normal distribution fall within plus or minus three standard deviations of the mean.)

Problems 2.4

1. Calculate the probabilities of drawing the following cards in a fair cut of a full pack of 52 playing cards:
   (*a*) The queen of spades.
   (*b*) Any diamond.
   (*c*) A red card (i.e. a diamond or heart).
   (*d*) A picture (i.e. a jack, a queen or a king).
   (*e*) A card lower than a 6.

2. A fair coin is tossed four times in succession. What is the probability that:
   (*a*) Two heads and two tails will result?
   (*b*) The result will be head, tail, tail, head in that specific order?

3. What is the probability that in a throw of two fair six-sided dice:
   (*a*) A total of 7 will be obtained?
   (*b*) A total of 11 will be obtained?

(c) A total of 7 *or* 11 will be obtained?
(d) A total of 7 *or* 11 will *not* be obtained?
(e) A total of 5 will *not* be obtained?

4. A sample of three items is drawn from a consignment. What is the probability that the sample will contain no defectives if the consignment contains:
(a) 20% of defectives?
(b) 10% of defectives?
(c) 5% of defectives?

5. A consignment contains 10% of defectives. What is the probability that two successive samples of five items will each contain not more than one defective?

6. Over a long period of time a train has averaged a late arrival of 3 minutes. What is the probability that this train will be 4 or more minutes late on a particular occasion? (Give the answer to two decimal places.)

7. Over a long period of time a football team has averaged a score of 2 goals per match. What is the probability that in any one match the team will score:
(a) 0 goals?
(b) 4 or more goals?
(Give answers to two decimal places.)

8. Samples each of five items are drawn at random from a large consignment which is known to contain 10% of defectives. What is the probability that a particular sample will contain:
(a) No defectives?
(b) Less than two defectives?
(c) Two or more defectives?

9. From a very large stock of bolts in a store 50 different samples were taken, the total number of defectives from all the samples was 65. What is the probability that any particular sample will contain:
(a) No defectives?
(b) Less than two defectives?
(c) Two or more defectives?

10. An inspection scheme states
    'From the batch take a sample of 10. If there is not more than one defective in the sample, accept the whole batch.'
    What is the probability that a batch containing 10% of defectives will be accepted on inspection?
    (C.G.L.I).

11. The inspection scheme for a particular batch of goods states:
    (a) Take a first sample of ten items, if there is not more than one defective, accept the batch.
    (b) If there are two defectives, take a second sample of ten items. If this second sample contains no defectives, accept the batch.
    What is the probability that a batch of goods containing 5% of defectives will be accepted?

12. A sample of components consists of 20 items, of which it is expected that 10% will be defective.
    Calculate the probabilities that the sample will contain not more than two defectives:
    (a) Using the Binomial distribution.
    (b) Using the Poisson distribution.
    (Take $0.9^{20}=0.121$, $0.9^{19}=\dfrac{1}{e^2}=0.135$ and $0.9^{18}=0.150$)
    (C.G.L.I.)

13. The expected number of defectives in a sample is 2. Taking $e^{-2}=0.135$, calculate the possibilities that in a random sample there will be:
    (a) No defectives.
    (b) Two or less defectives.
    (c) Four or more defectives.
    (C.G.L.I.)

14. Over a long period of time the average absence from a shift has been 2 employees. Assuming that this rate can be expected to continue determine the probabilities that:
    (a) No person will be absent from a shift.
    (b) More than two people will be absent from a shift.
    (c) Everyone will be present on two successive shifts.
    (d) Exactly one person will be absent on each of two successive shifts.
    (Take $\dfrac{1}{e^2}=0.135$.)
    (C.G.L.I.)

15. A small manufacturing unit when operating at full strength produces 80 articles per shift. If 2 or fewer employees are absent, full production is maintained. If 3, 4, or 5 are absent, half production is maintained. If 6 or more employees are absent, the line ceases and the employees transfer to maintenance.

    (*a*) If over a long period of time the absentee rate is 2 employees per shift, and this rate is expected to continue, how many articles can be expected from the next 100 shifts?

    (*b*) On how many of these 100 shifts can maintenance work be expected?

    (Take $e^{-2}=0\cdot135$.)

    (C.G.L.I.)

16. Determine the areas under the curve of normal distribution between:

    (*a*) $t=0$ and $t=1$
    (*b*) $t=0$ and $t=2$
    (*c*) $t=-\infty$ and $t=0$
    (*d*) $t=-\infty$ and $t=+\infty$
    (*e*) $t=-\infty$ and $t=2\cdot58$
    (*f*) $t=2\cdot58$ and $t=\infty$
    (*g*) $t=-1\cdot96$ and $t=+1\cdot96$

    (Use the table on page 119 of this book, with proportion where necessary, and give the answers to three decimal places.)

17. A random sample of 50 items was extracted from a production line, measured on a dimension nominally 5·5 to 6·5 units, and put into categories as follows:

Variate (x)	5·6	5·8	6·0	6·2	6·4
Frequency (f)	2	8	19	15	9

    (*a*) Calculate the arithmetical mean and standard deviation of x.

    (*b*) If this sample is representative of large scale production, explain why the production of defective articles outside the limits is unavoidable.

18. An automatic lathe produces shafts of mean diameter 20 mm with a standard deviation of 0·01 mm. Determine the proportion of the shafts (as a percentage to the nearest whole number) that can be expected to lie between 19·990 mm and 20·017 mm in diameter.

(Proportion can be used with the following areas under one tail of the curve of normal distribution.)

Zero up to	0·5	1	1·5	2	2·5
Area	0·191	0·341	0·433	0·477	0·494

(C.G.L.I.)

19. A company manufacturing medicinal tablets nominally of mass 100 milligrammes took a random sample of 100 tablets from a machine engaged on a long run. After sorting, the tablets were allocated to categories, and the distribution was found to be perfectly symmetrical as follows:

Mass (milligrammes)	99·8	99·9	100	100·1	100·2
Frequency	7	22	42	22	7

(a) State the mean and calculate the standard deviation of the mass.

(b) Using a sketch, and without making any calculations, explain how an estimate can be obtained of the percentage of the entire run of tablets that can be expected to have a mass of between 99·85 and 100·05 milligrammes.

(C.G.L.I.)

20. A random sample of 50 castings obtained from a diecasting machine were sorted and allocated to categories. The resulting distribution was symmetrical, as follows:

Mass (kg)	5·0	5·1	5·2	5·3	5·4
Frequency	6	12	14	12	6

(a) State the mean and establish the standard deviation of the mass.

(b) If this sample can be considered to be representative of large scale production, determine:

(i) The approximate maximum and minimum masses of the castings produced in quantities, each to two decimal places.

(ii) The percentage of castings that can be expected to have a mass of over 5·39 kg, to two significant figures.

(Use the following approximate areas under the curve of normal distribution.)

Units of standard deviation	±0·5	±1	±1·5	±2	±2·5	±3·1
Percentage	38%	68%	87%	95%	99%	100%

Answers to problems 2.4

1. (a) $\frac{1}{52}$ (b) $\frac{1}{4}$ (c) $\frac{1}{2}$ (d) $\frac{3}{13}$ (e) $\frac{4}{13}$

2. (a) $\frac{3}{8}$ (b) $\frac{1}{16}$

3. (a) $\frac{1}{6}$ (b) $\frac{1}{18}$ (c) $\frac{2}{9}$ (d) $\frac{7}{9}$ (e) $\frac{8}{9}$

4. (a) 0·512   (b) 0·729   (c) 0·857
5. 0·844
6. 0·35
7. (a) 0·140   (b) 0·140
8. (a) 0·590   (b) 0·919   (c) 0·081
9. (a) 0·272   (b) 0·627   (c) 0·373
10. 0·735
11. 0·913 4+0·044 6=0·958
12. (a) 0·676   (b) 0·675
13. (a) 0·135   (b) 0·675   (c) 0·145
14. (a) 0·135   (b) 0·325   (c) 0·018   (d) 0·073
15. (a) 6 620   (b) 2
16. (a) 0·341   (b) 0·477   (c) 0·500   (d) 1·000
    (e) 0·995   (f) 0·005   (g) 0·949
17. (a) Mean=6·06, standard deviation 0·201 kg
    (b) Because $\bar{x}\pm3s$ lies outside component limits
18. 79·2%
19. (a) Mean=100mg, standard deviation=0·1 mg
    (b) A sketch would be required of the curve of normal distribution showing an area between $t=-1·5$ and $t=0·5$.
20. Mean=5·20 kg, standard deviation=0·12 kg
    (b) Minimum 4·84 kg, maximum 5·56 kg
    (c) 12%

Chapter Three

Graphs

3.1 Determination of Laws

3.1.1 TRANSFORMATION OF EQUATIONS

The graph of the equation $y=ax+b$ is a straight line whose slope has a magnitude of a, the straight line cutting the y-axis at the value of b. Many equations which would produce curves when values of y are plotted against values of x can be transformed so that with different axes a straight line results.

For instance, consider the equation

$$y=px+qx^2$$

If values of x and y were plotted directly, the resulting graph would be a curve known as a parabola.

Dividing through by x produces the transformation

$$\frac{y}{x}=p+qx$$

and if we compare this with

$$y=b+ax$$

we observe that if $\frac{y}{x}$ is plotted vertically and x horizontally, a straight line of slope q will result, the straight line crossing the $\frac{y}{x}$ axis at the value of p.

Some typical transformations and/or plottings to produce straight lines are given in the table which follows on the next page. The general rule is that the equation has to be transformed, if necessary, to bring a constant on the right-hand side. Occasionally that constant is zero.

Equation	Transformation	Plot Vertically	Plot Horizontally
$y=a+bx^2$	None	y	x^2
$y=a+\dfrac{b}{x}$	None	y	$\dfrac{1}{x}$
$y=ax+bx^2$	$\dfrac{y}{x}=a+bx$	$\dfrac{y}{x}$	x
$xy=k$	$y=\dfrac{k}{x}$	y	$\dfrac{1}{x}$
$y=ax^n$	$\log y=\log a+n\log x$	$\log y$	$\log x$
$y=ae^{bx}$	$\log_e y=\log_e a+bx$	$\log_e y$	x
$y=\dfrac{b}{1+ax}$	$\dfrac{b}{y}=1+ax$	$\dfrac{1}{y}$	x

If an equation is suggested for a set of data which would result in a curve by direct plotting, the values of the constants in that equation can often be found by the following sequence of operations:

(a) Transform the suggested equation so that the new equation produces a straight line law.

(b) Re-calculate the variables to suit the new axes.

(c) Plot the new values against the new axes and draw the 'best straight line' through the points.

(d) Choose two points on the line as far apart as possible, but arranging the horizontal difference to be a convenient divisor.

(e) Substitute these values in the transformed equation, and solve the simultaneous equations which result.

Example

It is thought that the following values satisfy the equation
$$p=a+bq^2$$

q	1	2	3	4	5
p	4·4	5·0	6·0	7·4	9·2

By drawing a suitable straight line graph, prove that the suggestion is true, and use the straight line graph to find the values of a and b.

$$p=a+bq^2$$
Comparing with $\qquad y=b+ax$

If p is plotted vertically and q^2 horizontally, a straight line should result.

q^2	1	4	9	16	25
p	4·4	5·0	6·0	7·4	9·2

The graph of p against q^2 is shown in Figure 3.1. The graph is a straight line, proving that $p=a+bq^2$.

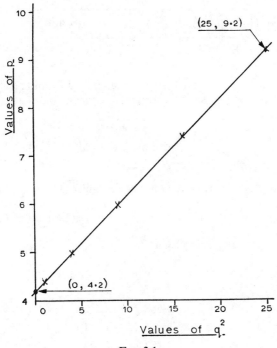

Fig. 3.1

Two suitable points on the line are $(0, 4·2)$ and $(25, 9·2)$

$$p=a+bq^2$$

Using $(0, 4·2)$ $4·2=a+b(0)^2=a$, $\therefore$ $a=4·2$

Using $(25, 9·2)$ $9·2=a+25b$,

since $a=4·2$ $9·2=4·2+25b$

$$9·2-4·2=25b$$

$$5=25b, \quad b=\frac{5}{25}=\frac{1}{5}$$

$$\textbf{Answer: } a=4\cdot2 \text{ and } b=\frac{1}{5},$$

$$\text{the law is } p=4\cdot2+\frac{q^2}{5}$$

Example

The following values were obtained in an experiment:

x	1	2	3	4	5
y	2·425	1·472	0·892	0·541	0·328

It is thought that y and x are connected by a formula of the type $y=Ae^{bx}$. By plotting a suitable straight line graph, find suitable values for A and b.

$$y=Ae^{bx}$$
$$\therefore \ \log_e y = \log_e A + bx$$

Comparing with $\qquad\qquad y=a+bx,$

if $\log_e y$ is plotted vertically and x horizontally, a straight line should result.

Naperian logs of 2·425 and 1·472 can be read directly from tables.

$$\log_e 0\cdot892 = \log_e \frac{8\cdot92}{10} = \log_e 8\cdot92 - \log_e 10$$

$$= 2\cdot188\,3 \quad -2\cdot302\,6 \quad = -0\cdot114\,3$$
$$\log_e 0\cdot541 = \log_e 5\cdot41 - \log_e 10$$
$$= 1\cdot688\,2 \quad -2\cdot302\,6 \quad = -0\cdot614\,4$$
$$\log_e 0\cdot328 = \log_e 3\cdot28 - \log_e 10$$
$$= 1\cdot187\,8 \quad -2\cdot302\,6 \quad = -1\cdot114\,8$$

Values of $\log_e y$ need only be retabulated to three places of decimals, in view of the small scales. It is impossible to plot to a greater accuracy.

Retabulation

x	1	2	3	4	5
$\log_e y$	0·886	0·387	−0·114	−0·614	−1·115

The straight line graph is shown in Figure 3.2, proving the relationship $y = Ae^{bx}$, two suitable points on the line being (0, 1·385) and (5, −1·115).

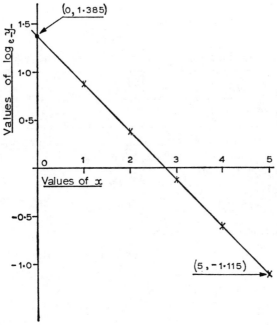

Fig. 3.2

$$\log_e y = \log_e A + bx$$

Using (0, 1·385) $1·385 = \log_e A + 0$

$$\log_e A = 1·385$$

Using Naperian antilogs, $A = 4$ (to an appropriate degree of accuracy).

Using (5, −1·115) $-1·115 = \log_e A + 5b$

$$-1·115 = 1·385 + 5b$$

$$-5b = 1·385 + 1·115 = 2·500$$

$$b = \frac{2·500}{-5} = -0·500$$

Answer: $A = 4$, $b = -0·5$,

the law being $y = 4e^{\frac{-x}{2}}$

131

Example

In an experiment on the resistance of a moving body, it was thought that the total resistance was the sum of two separate resistances, one proportional to velocity and the other proportional to the square of the velocity, so that

$$R=aV+bV^2$$

The results obtained are given in the following table:

V (m/s)	30	40	50	60	70	80
R (N)	13	21	31	40·5	58	74

By drawing a suitable straight line graph, find appropriate values for a and b. One of the readings is obviously in error. Determine a more reasonable result.

$$R=aV+bV^2$$
$$\therefore \frac{R}{V}=a+bV$$

Comparing with
$$y=b+ax$$

If $\frac{R}{V}$ is plotted vertically and V horizontally, a straight line should result.

Retabulation

V	30	40	50	60	70	80
$\dfrac{R}{V}$	0·433	0·525	0·620	0·675	0·829	0·925

The graph is shown in Figure 3.3, with the value of $\frac{R}{V}$ for $V=60$ weel away from the line through other values. The straight line proves the relationship $R=aV+bV^2$.

Two suitable points are (30, 0·43) and (80, 0·92)

$$\frac{R}{V}=a+bV$$

Using (30, 0·43) $0·43=a+30b$ ... (1)
Using (80, 0·92) $0·92=a+80b$

$$\overline{-0·49= -50b}$$

$$b=\frac{-0·49}{-50}=0·0098$$

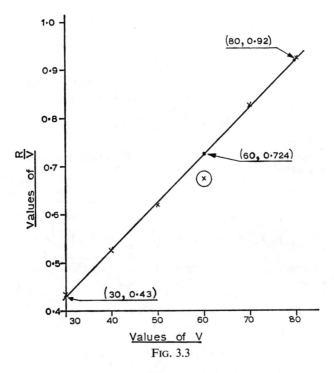

FIG. 3.3

Substituting in equation (1)

$$0.92 = a + 80b = a + 80(0.009\ 8)$$
$$0.92 = a + 0.784$$
$$a = 0.92 - 0.784$$
$$= 0.136$$

If $V=60$,
$$R = aV + bV^2$$
$$= 0.136(60) + 0.009\ 87(3\ 600)$$
$$= 8.16 + 35.28$$
$$= 43.44$$
$$\left(\frac{R}{V} = 0.724 \text{ falls on the line}\right)$$

Answers: $a = 0.136$, $b = 0.01$, to a reasonable degree of accuracy.
More reasonable value of R when $V = 60$ is 43.5 N

Example

In an experiment to determine the relationship between two quantities, T and d, the results shown on the next page were obtained:

133

T	9·05	11·08	12·8	14·31	15·68
d	2	3	4	5	6

Show with the aid of a suitable straight line graph that these values are connected by the law $T=Kd^n$, and determine the values of K and n.

$$T=Kd^n$$
$$\log T=\log K+n\log d$$

Comparing with $\qquad\qquad y=b+ax$

If $\log T$ is plotted vertically and $\log d$ horizontally, a straight line should result.

Retabulation

$\log T$	0·957	1·045	1·107	1·156	1·195
$\log d$	0·301	0·477	0·602	0·699	0·778

The graph is shown in Figure 3.4, the straight line proving the law $T=Kd^n$.

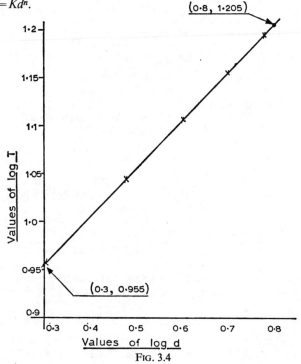

Fig. 3.4

134

Two suitable points on the line are (0·3, 0·955) and (0·8, 1·205)

$$\log T = \log K + n \log d$$

Using (0·3, 0·955)	$0·955 = \log K + 0·3n$	... (1)
Using (0·8, 1·205)	$1·205 = \log K + 0·8n$	
By subtraction	$-0·25 = -0·5n$	

$$n = \frac{-0·25}{-0·5} = 0·5$$

Substituting the value in equation (1)

$$0·955 = \log K + (0·3)(0·5)$$

$$0·955 - 0·15 = \log K$$

$$\log K = 0·805$$

Using antilogs $\qquad K = 6·383$

Rounding off to reasonable values $K = 6·4$, $n = 0·5$.

Answer: $K = 6·4$, $n = 0·5$, the law being
$T = 6·4d^{0·5}$, i.e. $T = 6·4\sqrt{d}$

Problems 3.1

1. A straight line graph passes through the origin and the point (2, 16). Determine:
   (a) The law of the graph.
   (b) The value of y when $x = -2$.

2. A straight line graph passes through the points (3, 16) and (−2, 6). Determine:
   (a) The law of the graph in the form $y = ax + b$.
   (b) The point at which the graph crosses the y axis (i.e. when $x = 0$).
   (c) The point at which the graph crosses the x axis (i.e. when $y = 0$).

3. Find the point of intersection of the straight lines represented by
$$y = 2x + 1$$
and $\qquad 2y = 5x - 2$

4. Measurements of certain gears having a metric form of tooth produced the following data:

No. of teeth T	20	25	30	35	40
Outside diameter D (mm)	88	108	128	148	168

By drawing a suitable straight line graph show that D and T are connected by a law of the type

$$D=aT+b$$

and determine:

(a) The values of the constants a and b.
(b) The value of D when $T=36$.
(c) The value of T when $D=140$ mm.

5. During an experiment conducted on the effort E newtons to lift a load W newtons when using a simple lifting machine, the following values were recorded:

E (N)	20	24·8	30	35	40·2	45
W (N)	100	200	300	400	500	600

Plot these values, and draw the best straight line through the points. If E and W are connected by a law of the type $E=aW+b$, determine:

(a) The values of the constants a and b.
(b) The value of E when $W=250$ N.
(c) The value of W when $E=36$ N.

6. Transform the following equations so that with suitable axes plotted on ordinary linear ruled paper the result is straight line graphs. In each case, state which values have to be plotted vertically, which values have to be plotted horizontally, and which constant is indicated by the slope of the graph.
(a) $T=Kd^n$, K and n being constants.
(b) $R=AV+BV^2$, A and B being constants.
(c) $y=Ae^{bx}$, A and b being constants.
(d) $y=\dfrac{a+bx}{x}$, a and b being constants.
(e) $y(a+bx)=1$, a and b being constants.

7. If W is the nominal size of a certain hand tool and P is its selling price, the values of W and P are as follows:

W (mm)	10	20	30	40	50	60
P	$22\frac{1}{2}$p	30p	$42\frac{1}{2}$p	60p	$82\frac{1}{2}$p	£1·10

It is thought that W and P are connected by a law of the type $P=A+BW^2$. By drawing a suitable straight line graph, find suitable values of A and B, and hence deduce the value of P when W is 80 mm.

8. An experiment was conducted to investigate the coefficient of friction between steel wheels and steel rails at varying velocities, producing the following results:

μ	0·14	0·065	0·05	0·04	0·02	0·015
Velocity V (m/s)	10	20	25	30	50	60

Show, by drawing a suitable straight line graph, that over this particular range a law of the type

$$\mu=\frac{A}{V}-B$$

is approximately true, and determine suitable values for A and B.

9. At a particular place, the intensity of illumination I, due to single light source, was composed of two items. The first was a constant value A due to reflected light. The second, due to direct illumination, was inversely proportional to the square of the distance from the light source to the workplace, so that

$$I=A+\frac{B}{D^2}$$

when A and B are constants.
As D was varied, the following results were obtained:

I	65	40	25	21·8	21·25
D	2	3	6	10	12

By drawing a suitable graph, determine approximate values for the constants A and B.

(C.G.L.I.)

10. The following values give the cost per hour C in pounds sterling when a continuous process operates with a throughput of N articles per hour:

C	21	28	47	84	145
N	10	20	30	40	50

It is suggested that these values follow a law of the type
$$C = a + bN^3$$
By drawing a suitable straight line graph, determine the values of the constants a and b, and hence the hourly cost when $N=60$ articles per hour.

11. A works accountant obtained the cost per item C in pounds sterling of producing batches of size x articles. It was thought that the cost C consisted of a fixed charge per item a plus an additional cost b shared by the articles in that batch, so that

$$C = a + \frac{b}{x}$$

The data obtained was:

C	164	92	56	38	32
x	5	10	20	40	60

By drawing an appropriate straight line graph show that the suggestion is reasonable, and determine suitable values for the constants a and b.

12. Following an experiment concerned with the frictional resistance of a body moving through a fluid, it was thought that the total resistance R newtons was the sum of two resistances. The first was proportional to the velocity V metres per second, the second being proportional to the square of the velocity, so that
$$R = aV + bV^2$$

The experimental results were:

R	1·5	3·9	7·5	12·0	17·4	24·0
V	10	20	30	40	50	60

Rearrange the equation $R=aV+bV^2$ so that, with appropriate axes, it will produce a straight line graph. Hence determine approximate values for the constants a and b.

(C.G.L.I.)

13. When a vehicle is brought to an emergency stop, it is considered that the distance travelled consists of two parts:
    (a) A decision-making distance, during which the car travels at constant speed.
    (b) A braking distance, which is proportional to the square of the velocity of the car.
    Thus if s is the total distance in metres and v is the velocity of the car in metres per second, then
    $$s=av+bv^2$$
    The following values are suggested:

v	5	10	13	20	25	30
s	5	15	50	50	75	105

With the aid of a suitable straight line graph, determine the values of a and b and hence deduce the time it is suggested occurs between the emergency and applying the brakes.

(C.G.L.I.)

14. It is suggested that the safe torque T newton metres that can be safely transmitted by circular shafts of a certain material having diameters of d millimetres is as follows:

d	20	30	40	50	60
T	80	270	640	1 250	2 160

By drawing a suitable straight line graph show that these values conform to the law $T=Kd^n$ and decide values for the constants K and n.

15. Readings were taken of the intensity of illumination I units at a distance of d metres from a light source, producing the following results:

d	2	4	6	8	10
I	360	90	40	22·5	14·4

By plotting a suitable straight line graph show that these values conform to the law $I = Kd^n$ and find the values of the constants K and n.

16. The following information has been extracted from an engineers' reference book and quotes the mass M (per metre run) for hexagonal bars of a particular alloy, the distance across flats being F mm:

F	20	30	40	50	60
M	1·00	2·25	4·00	6·25	9·00

(a) By plotting a suitable straight line graph show that M and F are related by a law of the type $M = KF^n$ and determine the values of the constants K and n.

(b) Using the law, find values of:
   (i) M when $F = 32$ mm
   (ii) F when $M = 16$ kg

17. Persons are invited to deposit a certain amount of money with a banking concern, and they are informed that for every £500 they invest the value £V after n years will conform to the following table:

n	1	2	3	4	5	6
V	542	587	636	689	746	808

By drawing a suitable straight line graph show that the values of V and n are approximately related by a law of the type $V = Ae^{kt}$ and deduce values for the constants A and k.

18. During an experiment on vibrations the amount of swing S units after a time t seconds was noted, producing the following results:

t	1	2	3	4	5	6
S	81·9	67·0	54·9	40·7	3€·8	30·1

By drawing a suitable straight line graph show that S and t are connected by a law of the type $S = Ae^{kt}$ and hence deduce suitable values for the constants A and k.

19. When testing a certain electrical capacitor the current i units was noted t units of time after discharging was commenced, producing the following values:

t	10	20	40	60	80
i	12·1	7·36	2·71	0·996	0·366

By drawing a suitable straight line graph, show that i and t are connected by a law of the type $i = Ae^{kt}$ and obtain values for the constants A and k.

Answers to problems 3.1

1. (a) $y = 8x$ (b) -16
2. (a) $y = 2x + 10$ (b) $(0, 10)$ (c) $(-5, 0)$
3. $(4, 9)$
4. (a) $D = 4T + 8$, $a = 4$ and $b = 8$ (b) 152   (c) 33
5. (a) $a = \dfrac{1}{20}$, $b = 15$ N   (b) 27·5 N   (c) 420 N
6.

	Transformation	Horizontal	Vertical	Constant
(a)	$\log T = \log K + n \log d$	$\log d$	$\log T$	n
(b)	$\dfrac{R}{V} = a + BV$	V	$\dfrac{R}{V}$	B
(c)	$\log_e y = \log_e A + bx$	x	$\log_e y$	b
(d)	$xy = a + bx$	x	xy	b
(e)	$\dfrac{1}{y} = a + bx$	x	$\dfrac{1}{y}$	b

7. $A=20$ p, $B=0.025$; £1.80
8. $A=1.5$, $B=0.01$
9. $A=20$, $B=180$
10. $a=20$, $b=0.001$; £236
11. $a=£20$, $b=£720$
12. $a=0.1$, $b=0.005$
13. $a=0.5$, $b=0.1$; time$=0.5$ second
14. $K=0.01$, $n=3$
15. $K=1\,440$, $n=-2$
16. (a) $K=0.002\,5$, $n=2$; law is $M=\dfrac{F^2}{400}$
    (b) (i) $M=2.56$ kg (ii) $F=80$ mm
17. $A=£500$, $k=0.08$
18. $A=100$, $k=-0.2$
19. $A=20$, $k=-0.05$

3.2 Logarithmic Graphical Rulings

3.2.1 USE OF LOG-LOG GRAPHICAL FIELDS

In the previous article a method of determining the constants A and n for a law of the type $y=Ax^n$ was demonstrated. The equation was transformed to log $y=$ log $A+n$ log x, and log y was plotted against log x. The rulings of the graph paper were such that the ruled distances were directly proportional to the magnitudes of values on the axes, these being known as linear rulings. The retabulated values of log x and log y do not make for ease of plotting, since they are invariably difficult numbers to plot.

Graph paper can be ruled with rulings other than linear sub-divisions of the metre (or the inch). One particular type of ruling has logarithmic scales on both axes. If values of y and x are plotted on this *log-log* paper, distances will be proportional to the logarithms of numbers and not proportional to the numbers themselves. Hence on log-log ruled paper, if $y=Ax^n$, *direct plotting of y and x will produce a straight line.*

3.2.2 CYCLES ON LOG-LOG PAPERS

The common log of 1 is zero, while the common logs of 10 and 100 are 1 and 2 respectively. The actual distance on a log-ruled graphical field is the same for the range 1 to 10 as it is for the range 10 to 100, each one of these distances being known as one cycle. On log-log rulings, the distance for one cycle of logs on the *y*-axis is invariably identical with the distance for one cycle of logs on the *x*-axis. In plotting laws of the type $y=Ax^n$, a suitable paper is chosen depending upon the number of cycles needed by the data. For example, a 'log 3 cycles×2 cycles' paper has 3 cycles on the *y*-axis and 2 cycles on the *x*-axis.

If the law $y=4x^2$ had to be plotted on log-log paper, with values of *x* ranging from 2 to 60, the values of *y* would range from 16 to 14 400 and the most suitable ruling would be obtained as follows:

Vertical cycles (y-axis)

> log maximum value=log 14 400=4·158 4
>> nearest whole number characteristic above   =5
>
> log minimum value=log 16=1·204 1
>> nearest whole number characteristic below   =1
>
> By subtraction, number of log-cycles on *y*-axis =4

Horizontal cycles (x-axis)

> log maximum value=log 60=1·778 2
>> nearest whole number characteristic above   =2
>
> log minimum value=log 2=0·301 0
>> nearest whole number characteristic below   =0
>
> By subtraction, number of log-cycles on λ-axis =2

Figure 3.5 shows the law $y=4x^2$ plotted on a 'log 4 cycles×2 cycles' graphical field.

3.2.3   DETERMINATION OF LAWS ON LOG-LOG RULED FIELDS

When an equation has the form $y=Ax^n$, if *x*=unity, then x^n is also unity, irrespective of the value of *n*, and $y=A$ when *x*=1.

Consequently, the value of *A* can be read directly from a log-log graph if the value of *x*=1 is included in the horizontal plotting. Once *A* has been obtained, the value of *n* can be obtained by selecting another point on the line as far away from *A* as possible and substituting in the general equation $y=Ax^n$. However, it is sometimes more convenient to determine *n* graphically rather than analytically.

In order to determine *n* graphically, let us consider the original equation $y=Ax^n$ transformed to $\log y=\log A+ n \log x$.

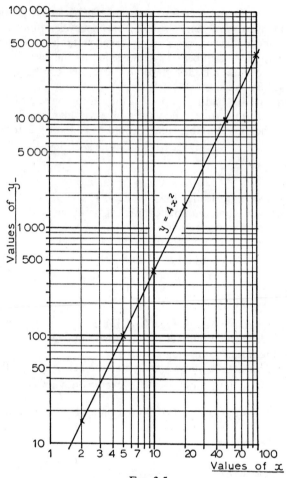

FIG. 3.5

If two sets of values which satisfy $y=Ax^n$ are (x_1, y_1) and (x_2, y_2)

then
$$\log y_2 = \log A + n \log x_2$$
$$\log y_1 = \log A + n \log x_1$$

whence, by subtraction,
$$\overline{\log y_2 - \log y_1 = n(\log x_2 - \log x_1)}$$

and
$$n = \frac{\log y_2 - \log y_1}{\log x_2 - \log x_1}$$

If the more common type of log-log ruling is used, that is, when the length of one cycle of logs on the y-axis is identical with the length of one cycle of logs on the x-axis, n can be determined by direct measurement of linear distances on the graph.

A right-angled triangle is constructed on the graphical field, using the straight line of the graph as the hypotenuse. The larger the triangle, the more accurate is the determination of n. The base of the triangle is of a length that will allow simple division, such as 100 mm. The base and vertical height of the triangle are then measured, and

$$n = \frac{\text{vertical height}}{\text{base length}}$$

Reviewing the information in the foregoing articles, the determination of the constants A and n if the suggested formula is of the type $y = Ax^n$ can be accomplished by the following sequence of operations.

1. Select a suitable set of log-cycles for each axis, including in the x-axis the value of $x = 1$ if it does not occur in the range of x-values stated.

2. Plot the values directly on log-log paper, and draw the 'best straight line' through the points.

3. Read off the value of A, being the value of y when $x = 1$.

4. If one cycle of logs on the y-axis is the same length as one cycle of logs on the x-axis, determine the value of n by evaluating

$$\frac{\text{increase in vertical direction}}{\text{increase in horizontal direction}}$$

from direct measurement.

If not, choose a point on the line as far as possible from $x = 1$, and substitute in the equation

$$n \log x = \log \left(\frac{y}{A}\right)$$

Let us illustrate the determination of a law of the type $y = Ax^n$, by solving the question on page 134 by the use of log-log paper. The original data were as follows, and the law $T = Kd^n$ was suggested.

T	9·05	11·08	12·8	14·31	15·68
d	2	3	4	5	6

T will be plotted vertically, with d plotted horizontally.

Vertical cycles

    log maximum value of T=log 15·68=1·195 3
      nearest whole number above   =2
    log minimum value of T=log 9·05=0·956 6
      nearest whole number below   =0
    By subtraction, number of vertical cycles   =2

Horizontal cycles

    log maximum value of d=log 6=0·778 2
      nearest whole number above   =1
    The minimum value of d will be 1, since we
      require this value to determine K, log 1   =0
    By subtraction, number of horizontal cycles =1

Figure 3.6 shows the data plotted directly on 'log 2 cycle × 1 cycle' log-log paper, with the value K=6·4 being read off directly and the value n=0·5 being obtained by direct measurement, producing the formula $T=6·4\sqrt{d}$ obtained previously.

3.2.4 SEMI-LOG RULED GRAPHICAL FIELDS

If the suggested equation is $y=Ae^{bx}$, the transformation that will result in a straight line graph on the usual field with linear rulings is

$$\log_e y=\log_e A+bx,$$

$\log_e y$ being plotted against x.

This will involve the determination of Naperian logarithms, and the subsequent plotting of rather awkward values. It has been shown earlier in this book that $\log_e N=2·303 \log N$, log N being the common logarithm of N to the base 10. Plotting is therefore simplified by using a logarithmic ruling on the y-axis with a linear ruling on the x-axis. This type of graphical field is colloquially termed *semi-log* ruling. Other names in common use are *log-linear* and *logarithmic one-way* rulings.

If the value x=0 is included in the horizontal range, the value of A can be read directly, since if x=0, $e^{bx}=e^0=1$, and $y=A$ when x=0. It is only on certain very rare combinations of scales that the value of b can be obtained by direct measurement, and hence the value of b should be obtained by selecting a point on the line as far away from x=0 as possible. The co-ordinates of this point are determined, and substituted in the equation

$$\log_e y=\log_e A+bx$$

Since A, $\log_e y$, and x are all known, b can be determined.

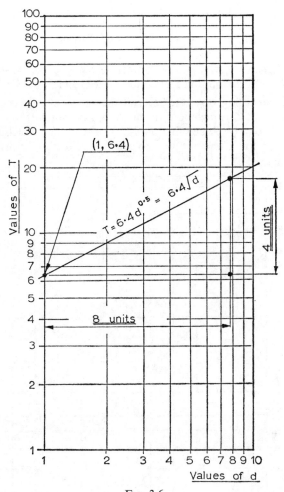

Fig. 3.6

We will illustrate the determination of a law using semi-log paper in solving the question on page 130, where the following data suggested a law of the type $y = Ae^{bx}$:

x	1	2	3	4	5
y	2·425	1·472	0·892	0·541	0·328

log maximum value of $y = \log 2 \cdot 425 = 0 \cdot 384\ 7$
  nearest whole number above $\qquad = 1$
log minimum value of $y = \log 0 \cdot 328 = \bar{1} \cdot 5159$
  $\bar{1} \cdot 5159 = -0 \cdot 484\ 1$
Nearest negative whole number below $\qquad = -1$
By subtraction, number of log-cycles $\quad = 1 - (-1) = 2$

The linear ruling is selected to suit the values of x, ensuring that the value of $x = 0$ is included. In this case, the values of x will range from $x = 0$ to $x = 5$. A suitable semi-log paper is one which has two log-cycles, with a linear ruling to allow a minimum of five equal

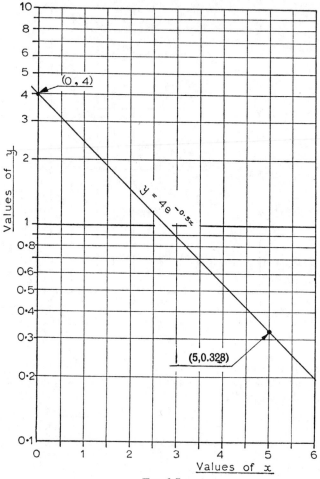

FIG. 3.7

divisions. A standard printed sheet is available which will suit; it actually allows for six equal divisions on the x-axis. Figure 3.7 shows the data plotted on the standard printed sheet.

When $x=0$, $y=4$, $\therefore$ $A=4$

To find the value of b, the point (5, 0·328) is used.

$$\log_e y = \log_e A + bx$$

Using $A=4$, with (5, 0·328)

$$\log_e 0·328 = \log_e 4 + 5b$$

$$\begin{aligned}5b &= \log_e 0·328 - \log_e 4 \\ &= (\log_e 3·28 - \log_e 10) - \log_e 4 \\ &= 1·187\ 8 - 2·302\ 6 - 1·386\ 3 \\ &= 1·187\ 8 - 3·688\ 9 \\ &= -2·501\ 1\end{aligned}$$

$$b = \frac{-2·501\ 1}{5} = -0·500\ 2 = -0·5 \text{ to an appropriate}$$
degree of accuracy.

Whence $y=4e^{-0·5x}$, as previously obtained.

Another way to obtain b, once skill has been acquired in the use of Naperian logarithms, is to use the table on page 50 of Castle's *Four-figure Tables*.

$$y=4e^{bx}, \text{ since } A=4$$

using (5, 0·328) $\quad 0·328=4e^{5x}$

$$e^{5x}=\frac{0·328}{4}=0·082$$

From the table $e^{-2·5}=0·082$

$\therefore$ $e^{5x}=e^{-2·5}$, and by equating indices,

$$5x=-2·5, \quad x=-0·5$$

Problems 3.2

1. Select suitable log-log graphical fields, by stating the number of cycles for each axis, to be used when plotting the following graphs on log-log paper:
   (a) $PV^{1·4}=2\ 000$, V ranging from 2 to 15.
   (b) $T=400\sqrt{\theta}$, θ ranging from 0 to 2π.

2. What is the minimum number of log-cycles that would be needed on semi-log paper if the law $y=30e^{2x}$ is plotted, the values of x ranging from zero to 2?

3. A graph indicates a straight line on log-log paper, passing through the points (1, 8) and (16, 32), y being plotted vertically and x horizontally. What is the simplest law connecting y and x?

4. A graph indicates a straight line on semi-log paper, y being plotted vertically on logarithmic ruling and x horizontally on linear ruling. The line passes through the points (0, 2) and (2, 14·78). Find the simplest law connecting y and x.

5. A set of data was plotted on semi-log (or log linear) ruled paper, the logarithmic rulings being used for values of y, and the linear rulings used for x. The graph was a straight line passing through the points (0, 5) and (1, 36·95). Determine the simplest law connecting y and x, and calculate the value of y when $x=1·5$.

(C.G.L.I.)

6. The following table gives suggested rivet diameters d mm for plates of thickness t mm:

Thickness t	4	10	16	25	40	63
Diameter d	12	20	24	30	40	50

By plotting the values directly on to a 2 cycle × 2 cycle log-log graphical field show that an approximate relationship $d=Kt^n$ exists, and hence deduce appropriate values for K (to the nearest whole number) and n (to the nearest 0·1).
Reminder—remember to include $t=1$ in the horizontal scale.

7. During an experiment concerning the flow of water over a vee-notch, the discharge Q was obtained for various heights H of water above the point of the vee. It was thought that Q and H were connected by a formula of the type $Q=KH^n$. The results that were obtained were as follows:

H (m)	0·4	0·5	0·6	0·7	0·8
Q (m³/s)	0·26	0·45	0·71	1·05	1·47

By plotting these values directly on to a 2 cycle × 1 cycle log-log graphical field determine appropriate values for the constants K and n.

8. The following table gives the nominal pitch p mm, together with the major diameter D mm, of British Association screw threads:

p	1	0·81	0·66	0·53	0·43	0·35
D	6	4·7	3·6	2·8	2·2	1·7

By plotting these values directly on to a 1 cycle × 1 cycle log-log graphical field, show that D and p are connected approximately by a law of the type $D=Ap^n$.

(a) Determine appropriate values for the constants A and n.

(b) Suggest, with the aid of the graph, a suitable outside diameter for a thread of pitch 0·28 mm.

9. As a liquid was cooling, its temperature T degrees Celsius was noted t minutes after a datum time. The following results were obtained:

Temperature T	30	20	15	12	10
Time t	4	9	16	25	36

(a) Using log-log plottings on a 1 cycle × 2 cycle graphical field show that over this particular range a formula of the type $T=Kt^n$ is applicable, and hence determine suitable values of K and n.

(b) From your graph, read off values of:
   (i) T when $t=6·25$ min
   (ii) t when $T=40°$ C

10. It was thought that the following values of absolute pressure P were connected with volume V by a law of the type $P=CV^n$:

V	2	4	6	8	10
P	37·9	14·4	8·14	5·44	3·98

(a) By plotting the values on a 2 cycle × 1 cycle graphical field deduce suitable values for the constants C and n.

(b) Read off from the graph the values of:
   (i) V when $P=20$
   (ii) P when $V=5$

11. For reference purposes it is required to produce a graph which will give the safe torque T newton metres that can be transmitted by shafts of a particular material having diameters d ranging from 10 mm to 100 mm. The data provided is as follows:

T	10	80	640	2 160	5 120	10 000
d	10	20	40	60	80	100

(a) Make a plot of these values, making full use of a 3 cycle $\times$ 2 cycle log-log graphical field.

(b) Noting that a value for $d=1$ is *not* included, deduce the equation connecting T and d.

12. Construct on a suitable log-log graphical field, a straight line graph that will give the mass (kg) per m run of aluminium alloy bars whose diameters range from 10 mm to 100 mm. Assume that the aluminium alloy has a relative density of 2·8 and take π as $\frac{22}{7}$.

Use the graph to determine:

(a) The mass per metre run of bars of diameter 40 mm.

(b) The mass of a 4-metre length of alloy pipe of outside diameter 80 mm and inside diameter 60 mm.

13. If a sum of money P is invested at a certain rate of compound interest, the value V pounds sterling after t years follows the law
$$V=Pe^{kt}$$
In a certain instance the following values connected t and V:

t	2	4	6	8	10	14	20
V	332	366	405	448	495	604	815

Find by plotting on a one-cycle semi-log graphical field suitable values of the constants P and k.

14. The following values were obtained for the tension T in a belt drive for angles of lap θ radians:

T	33	54	100	148	244
θ	2	4	6	8	10

If T and θ are connected by a law of the type

$$T = Ae^{b\theta}$$

plot these values on a 2-cycle log-linear graphical field and determine suitable values for the constants T and K.

15. During an experiment on vibrations the following results were obtained for the amount of swing S divisions after a time of t seconds:

t	2	4	6	8	10
S	335	225	151	101	68

It was thought that the variables were connected by a law of the type $S = Ae^{kt}$. By direct plotting on a 2-cycle log-linear graphical field find suitable values of A and k.

16. The temperature of a hot solid was originally 50° C and it was allowed to cool freely. Readings of temperature $T°$ C and time t minutes were taken, producing the following results:

T	50	37	27·5	20·3	15
t	0	5	10	15	20

By plotting the values on a one-cycle semi-log graphical field show that the variables follow a law of the type $T = Ae^{kt}$ and find, graphically, suitable values of A and k.
Read off from the graph the values of
(a) T when $t = 12·5$
(b) t when $T = 30$

17. When a certain electrical capacitor was being tested the discharge current i amperes after a time t units from the commencement of discharge was noted, producing the following data:

i	81·9	67·0	54·9	44·9	36·8
t	2	4	6	8	10

By plotting on one-cycle semi-log paper show that i and t are connected by a law of the type

$$i = Ae^{bt}$$

and find suitable values of A and b. Hence deduce the time it takes for i to fall to 50 % of the value when $t = 0$.

18. During experiments on probability, the frequency of occurrence f of a particular event was compared with a characteristic of size x, resulting in the following data:

f	500	490	462	418	363	303
x	0	0·2	0·4	0·6	0·8	1·0

Using one-cycle semi-log paper, plotting f on the log scale with x^2 (note—not x) on the linear scale show that a relationship

$$f = Ne^{kx^2}$$

exists. Hence determine suitable values of N and k. Use your graph to find the frequency when $x = 0·5$.

Answers to problems 3.2

1. Quoting the y-axis first
   (a) 2 cycles × 2 cycles   (b) 3 cycles × 1 cycle
2. 3 cycles
3. $y = 8\sqrt{x}$
4. $y = 2e^x$
5. $y = 5e^{2x}$, 100·425
6. $K = 6$, $n = 0·5$
7. $K = 2·56$, $n = 2·5$
8. (a) $A = 6$, $n = 1·2$ (b) 1·3 mm
9. (a) $K = 60$, $n = -0·5$ (b) (i) 24° C (ii) 2·25 min
10. (a) $C = 100$, $n = -1·4$ (b) (i) 3·16 (ii) 10·5
11. (b) $T = 0·01d^3$
12. Plot values of $m = 0·002\,2d^2$ on a 3 cycle × 1 cycle log-log graphical field (0·22 kg when $d = 10$ to 22 kg when $d = 100$)
    (a) 3·52 kg   (b) 24·6 kg
13. $P = £300$, $k = 0·05$
14. $A = 20$, $k = 0·25$
15. $A = 500$, $b = -0·2$
16. (a) $A = 50$, $k = -0·06$ (b) (i) 23·5° (ii) 8·5 min
17. $A = 100$, $b = -0·1$; 6·9 seconds
18. $N = 500$, $k = -0·5$; $f = 441$

3.3 The Slope of a Curve

3.3.1 FUNCTIONAL NOTATION

If two variables are connected by a formula, say y and x, so that the value of y depends upon the value we give to x, we say that *y is a function of x*. There are various mathematical conventions for indicating the expression 'function of x' such as f(x), F(x), and $\phi(x)$, the first being the more common. Instead of $y=x^2+3x-4$ we could say f$(x)=x^2+3x-4$.

If we want to indicate the value of y when a specific value is given to x, such as the value of a particular function when $x=4$, we indicate this as f(4).

Example

If f$(x)=x^2+3x-4$, find the values of

$$\text{f}(2), \quad \text{f}(-1), \quad \text{f}(0), \quad \text{f}(a), \quad \text{and} \quad \text{f}(x+h).$$
$$\text{f}(x)=x^2+3x-4$$
$$\text{f}(2) \quad =2^2+3(2)-4=4+6-4=6$$
$$\text{f}(-1) \quad =(-1)^2+3(-1)-4=1-3-4=-6$$
$$\text{f}(0) \quad =0+0-4=-4$$
$$\text{f}(a) \quad =a^2+3a-4$$
$$\text{f}(x+h)=(x+h)^2+3(x+h)-4$$
$$=x^2+2xh+h^2+3x+3h-4$$

Answers: 6, -6, -4, a^2+3a-4,
$x^2+2xh+h^2+3x+3h-4$

Example

If f$(x)=x^2-5x+2$, find the value of $\dfrac{\text{f}(x+h)-\text{f}(x)}{h}$, as h approaches zero.

$$\text{f}(x+h)=(x+h)^2-5(x+h)+2$$
$$=x^2+2xh+h^2-5x-5h+2$$
$$\text{f}(x)=x^2 \qquad\qquad -5x \qquad +2$$

By subtraction, $\quad \text{f}(x+h)-\text{f}(x)= \quad 2xh+h^2 \quad -5h$

$$\frac{\text{f}(x+h)-\text{f}(x)}{h}=\frac{2xh+h^2-5h}{h}=2x+h-5$$
$$=2x-5, \text{ as } h \text{ approaches zero}$$

Answer: $2x-5$

Example

If $f(x)=\dfrac{1}{x^2}$, find the value of $\dfrac{f(x+h)-f(x)}{h}$, as h approaches zero.

$$f(x+h)=\frac{1}{(x+h)^2}=(x+h)^{-2}=x^{-2}\left(1+\frac{h}{x}\right)^{-2}$$

$$=\frac{1}{x^2}\left(1-\frac{2h}{x}+\text{other terms involving } h^2 \text{ and higher powers of } h\right)$$

$$=\frac{1}{x^2}-\frac{2h}{x^3}+\text{other terms involving } h^2 \text{ and higher powers of } h$$

$$f(x+h)-f(x)=\frac{-2h}{x^3}+\text{other terms involving } h^2 \text{ and higher powers of } h$$

$$\frac{f(x+h)-f(x)}{h}=\frac{-2}{x^3}+\text{ other terms involving } h \text{ and higher powers of } h$$

$$=\frac{-2}{x^3} \text{ as } h \text{ approaches zero}$$

Answer: $\dfrac{-2}{x^3}$

3.3.2 THE SLOPE OF A CURVE

When a straight line graph is obtained from the plotting of data, the slope of the line is constant. The magnitude of the slope can be found by substituting pairs of co-ordinates from two points on the line in the general equation $y=ax+b$, and solving the simultaneous equations which result for a. If the plotted data result in a curve, the *slope of the curve* at a particular point on the curve is defined as the slope of the tangent to the curve at that particular point.

In Figure 3.8 let the equation $y=f(x)$ result in a curve. Let us consider two points on the curve, P_1 and P_2. The difference in the x-values of P_1 and P_2 is h, so that the y-value of P_1 is $f(x)$ and the y-value of P_2 is $f(x+h)$.

If P_1 and P_2 are joined by a straight line, the slope between P_1 and P_2 is given by

$$\frac{(y\text{-value at } P_2)-(y\text{-value at } P_1)}{(x+h)-(x)}$$

that is, by

$$\frac{f(x+h)-f(x)}{h}$$

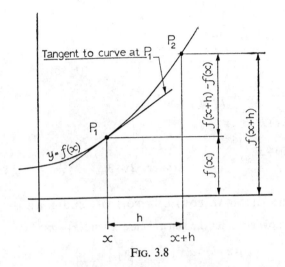

Tangent to curve at P_1

P_2

$f(x+h) - f(x)$

$f(x+h)$

$f(x)$

$y = f(x)$

P_1

h

x $x+h$

FIG. 3.8

Now if P_1 remains where it is, and P_2 be brought down the curve towards P_1, then as the value of h approaches zero, the nearer does the line P_1P_2 approach to the actual tangent to the curve at P_1. The nearer h becomes to zero, the nearer does the value of $\dfrac{f(x+h)-f(x)}{h}$ become to the slope of the tangent.

Hence, the slope of the tangent on the curve $y=f(x)$ is given by

$$\frac{f(x+h)-f(x)}{h} \quad (h \to 0)$$

This formula is so important in mathematics that it is given a specific title, being known as 'the differential coefficient of y with respect to x'.

The abbreviation for this expression is $\dfrac{\mathrm{d}y}{\mathrm{d}x}$, read as 'dee y by dee x'.

It should be noted that the fraction is considered as a complete whole and not as a formula; *the 'dees' cannot be cancelled.*

Example

If $y = x^2 + 3x + 2$, find $\dfrac{\mathrm{d}y}{\mathrm{d}x}$.

$$f(x+h) = (x+h)^2 + 3(x+h) + 2$$
$$= x^2 + 2xh + h^2 + 3x + 3h + 2$$

157

$$\frac{dy}{dx}=\frac{f(x+h)-f(x)}{h} \quad (h\to 0)$$

$$=\frac{(x^2+2xh+h^2+3x+3h+2)-(x^2+3x+2)}{h} \quad (h\to 0)$$

$$=\frac{2xh+h^2+3h}{h} \quad (h\to 0)$$

$$=2x+h+3 \quad (h\to 0)$$

$$=2x+3$$

Answer: $2x+3$

3.3.3 THE GENERAL FORMULA FOR THE SLOPE OF A CURVE

Let us now consider the general case when $f(x)=ax^n$

$$f(x+h)=a(x+h)^n=a\left\{x\left(1+\frac{h}{x}\right)\right\}^n$$

$$=ax^n\left(1+\frac{h}{x}\right)^n$$

Now if h is very small, $\left(1+\frac{h}{x}\right)^n$ is approximately equal to $1+\frac{nh}{x}$, and the smaller that h becomes, the more accurate becomes the approximation.

$$ax^n\left(1+\frac{h}{x}\right)^n=ax^n\left(1+\frac{nh}{x}\right) \text{ approx}$$

$$ax^n\left(1+\frac{nh}{x}\right)=ax^n+\frac{nahx^n}{x}$$

$$=ax^n+nahx^{n-1}$$

$$\therefore \frac{dy}{dx}=\frac{f(x+h)-f(x)}{h} \quad (h\to 0)$$

$$=\frac{ax^n+nahx^{n-1}-ax^n}{h}$$

$$=\frac{nahx^{n-1}}{h}=nax^{n-1}$$

i.e. $\dfrac{dy}{dx}=nax^{n-1}$

This should be remembered as 'the power becomes a multiplier, any existing coefficient remains, whilst the power of x is decreased by one'.

This general form is correct for any term of the type $y=ax^n$, provided n is not zero. It should be observed that if n is zero, y will be a constant, e.g. $y=5x^0=5$. The resulting graph is a horizontal straight line whose slope is zero. Thus if $y=$ a constant, $\dfrac{\mathrm{d}y}{\mathrm{d}x}=0$.

Suppose a value of y is a sum of terms involving x, a typical example being

$$y=2x^3-5x^2+3x$$

This can be written as $\quad y=\mathrm{f}(x)+\mathrm{F}(x)+\phi(x)$
where $\qquad \mathrm{f}(x)=2x^3, \quad \mathrm{F}(x)=-5x^2 \quad$ and $\quad \phi(x)=3x$

$\dfrac{\mathrm{d}y}{\mathrm{d}x}=\dfrac{\text{increase in value of } y}{\text{increase in value of } x}$

(as the increase in the value of x approaches zero)

$=\dfrac{\text{increase in f}(x)+\text{increase in F}(x)+\text{increase in }\phi(x)}{\text{increase in value of } x}$

(as the increase in the value of x approaches zero)

$=\dfrac{\mathrm{f}(x+h)-\mathrm{f}(x)}{h}\underset{(h\rightarrow 0)}{}+\dfrac{\mathrm{F}(x+h)-\mathrm{F}(x)}{h}\underset{(h\rightarrow 0)}{}+\dfrac{\phi(x+h)-\phi(x)}{h}\underset{(h\rightarrow 0)}{}$

Hence if y is the sum of algebraic terms, then $\dfrac{\mathrm{d}y}{\mathrm{d}x}$ is given by the sum

of the differential coefficients of the separate terms.

Example

If $s=8+5t-16{\cdot}1t^2$, find $\dfrac{\mathrm{d}s}{\mathrm{d}t}$.

$$s=8+5t-16{\cdot}1t^2$$

$$\frac{\mathrm{d}s}{\mathrm{d}t}=0+(1)(5)(t^{1-1})-(2)(16{\cdot}1)(t^{2-1})$$

$$=5t^0-32{\cdot}2t^1$$

$$=5-32{\cdot}2t$$

Answer: $\dfrac{\mathrm{d}s}{\mathrm{d}t}=5-32{\cdot}2t$

3.3.4 PRACTICAL APPLICATIONS OF THE SLOPE OF A CURVE

Figure 3.9 shows a graphical representation of the distance travelled by a moving body.

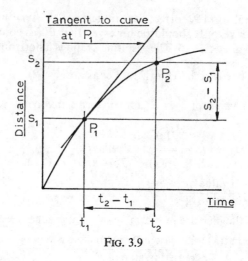

FIG. 3.9

Since the body does not cover equal distances in equal intervals of time, the velocity of the body is varying. Let us consider in particular the actual instant P_1 when the body has travelled a distance of s_1 m after t_1 seconds, together with a later instant P_2, when the body has travelled a distance of s_2 m, after t_2 seconds.

Average velocity from

$$P_1 \text{ to } P_2 = \frac{\text{distance covered}}{\text{time taken}}$$

$$= \frac{s_2 - s_1}{t_2 - t_1}$$

Now let us imagine that $t_2 - t_1$ becomes smaller and smaller so that the sloping line $P_1 P_2$ becomes closer and closer to the tangent to the curve at P_1. The numerical value of the slope of the line still represents the average velocity of the body, but the time interval after t_1 is becoming smaller and smaller.

As $t_2 - t_1$ approaches zero, the value of $\frac{s_2 - s_1}{t_2 - t_1}$ becomes nearer to the value of the actual velocity of the moving body at the instant represented by P_1. Hence the value of the slope of a distance-time graph at a particular point represents the velocity at that point.

If we use the notation of the previous article, if the distance s is plotted vertically while the time t is plotted horizontally, then $\frac{ds}{dt}$

represents velocity. In a similar manner, if a graph has velocity v plotted vertically, and time t horizontally, then $\dfrac{\mathrm{d}v}{\mathrm{d}t}$ represents 'the rate of increase of velocity with respect to time', which is termed 'acceleration', the usual symbol being a.

Example

A body moves so that the distance s m that the body is away from a particular datum is given by the formula

$$s = 64t - 16t^2, \quad t \text{ being the time in seconds.}$$

(a) What is the velocity after 1 second, and how far is the body from datum?

(b) Show that the body has a constant acceleration, and determine this acceleration.

(c) How far is the body from datum when it is instantaneously at rest?

(a) $\qquad\qquad\qquad s = 64t - 16t^2$

Velocity $\qquad v = \dfrac{\mathrm{d}s}{\mathrm{d}t} = 1(64)t^{1-1} - 2(16)t^{2-1}$

$\qquad\qquad\qquad\quad = 64 - 32t$

When $t = 1$, $v = 64 - 32 = 32$, and since metre and second units only have been used, the unit of velocity is m/s.

$$v = 32 \text{ m/s}$$

When $t = 1$, $s = 64t - 16t^2 = 64 - 16 = 48$, the unit being m.

(b) $\qquad\qquad\qquad v = 64 - 32t$

Acceleration $\qquad a = \dfrac{\mathrm{d}v}{\mathrm{d}t} = 0 - 1(32)t^{1-1}$

$\qquad\qquad\qquad\quad = -32$

The unit of acceleration will be $\dfrac{\text{m/s}}{\text{s}}$ or m/s²

$$a = -32 \text{ m/s}^2$$

which does not depend on t or s, and is constant.

(c) When the body is instantaneously at rest, it has no velocity, hence $v = 0$.

$$\text{Now } v = 64 - 32t$$
$$\therefore \ 0 = 64 - 32t$$
$$32t = 64, \quad t = 2$$
$$s = 64t - 16t^2$$
$$= 128 - 64 = 64$$

Answers: (a) Velocity = 32 m/s, distance = 48 m

(b) Constant acceleration = -32 m/s²

(c) Body is motionless when it is 64 m from datum

3.3.5 MAXIMUM AND MINIMUM

In pure mathematics, the words 'maximum' and 'minimum' have slightly different meanings from those used in everyday life. In pure mathematics, a *maximum* point on a curve such as $y=f(x)$ is a point which has a greater y-value than those either side of it, while a *minimum* has a y-value which is less than those either side of it. Let us illustrate these definitions by considering the graph of $y=x^3-3x^2+6$, which is shown in Figure 3.10.

The point P_1 represents a maximum value of y, since points on the curve on either side of P_1 both have a value of y which is less than the y-value of P_1. Although the point represented by P_2 has a greater numerical y-value than that of P_1, as far as pure mathematics is concerned P_2 is *not* a maximum. Similarly P_3 is a minimum although P_4 has a lower numerical value.

If tangents to the curve are drawn so as to touch the curve at P_1 and P_3, they will be horizontal lines. Thus at both a maximum and a minimum on the curve $y=f(x)$, the value of $\dfrac{dy}{dx}$ is zero. To distin-

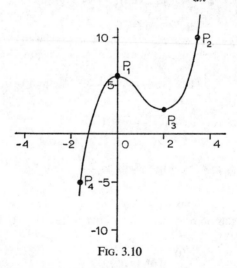

FIG. 3.10

guish between a maximum or minimum, for the time being the curve will have to be drawn and the appropriate decision made. Alternatively, values of y can be determined using values of x which are a little smaller and a little larger than the values obtained from the solution of the equation $\dfrac{dy}{dx}=0.$

Example

The plate shown in Figure 3.11 is bent along the dotted lines so as to form a rectangular box. Determine, the value of x so that the volume of the box shall be a maximum and calculate this maximum volume.

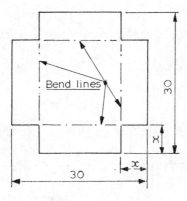

Fig. 3.11

x	0	2	4	6	8	10
Length	30	26	22	18	14	10
Breadth	30	26	22	18	14	10
Height	0	2	4	6	8	10
$C=LBH$	0	1 352	1 936	1 944	1 568	1 000

Figure 3.12 is a plot of these values, showing that C is a maximum when $x=5$, the maximum value of C being 2 000 mm². (In view of the sharp nose of the curve a further value was obtained at $x=5$, when $C=20\times20\times5=2\,000$.)

Now let us proceed to solving the question mathematically.

If tangents are drawn to a curve at minimum and maximum values they are horizontal lines. The slope of a horizontal line is zero, and hence at a maximum value, and also at a minimum value

$$\frac{\mathrm{d}y}{\mathrm{d}x}=0$$

Applying this method to the previous problem, we note that it is the value of C which has to be a maximum. We therefore have to

163

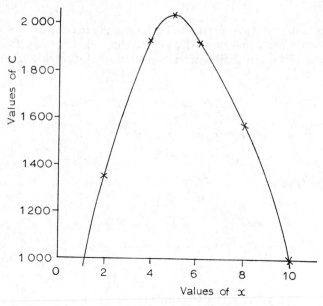

FIG. 3.12

find an expression for C in terms of x, so that C can be differentiated with respect to x, and the value of $\dfrac{dC}{dx}$ equated to zero.

Now the length of the base of the tray $= 30 - 2x$,
then the area of the tray $\qquad = (30 - 2x)(30 - 2x)$
and the capacity of the tray $\qquad = (30 - 2x)(30 - 2x)x$

$$\therefore \ C = (30 - 2x)(30 - 2x)(x)$$
$$C = (900 - 120x + 4x^2)(x)$$
$$C = 900x - 120x^2 + 4x^3$$

For a maximum or a minimum,

$$\frac{dC}{dx} = 0$$

$$\therefore \ 900x^{1-1} - 2(120)x^{2-1} + 3(4)x^{3-1} = 0$$
$$900x^0 - 240x^1 + 12x^2 \qquad = 0$$
$$900 - 240x + 12x^2 \qquad = 0$$

Dividing by 12, and putting in standard quadratic form,

$$x^2 - 20x + 75 = 0$$
$$(x - 15)(x - 5) = 0$$

Either $x-15=0$, $x=15$
or $x-5 =0$, $x=5$

Thus far then, $x=15$ or $x=5$ could provide a maximum, but we have to decide which. We can discount $x=15$ because it is an illogical value and it is impossible to cut out corners of this size. One could say it provides a minimum value because $C=0$ when $x=15$. We are left with $x=5$, but because $x=15$ gives a minimum, we cannot presume that $x=5$ automatically gives a maximum.

Now
$$C=900x-120x^2+4x^3$$
$$=4\,500-3\,000+500 \text{ when } x=5$$
$$=2\,000 \text{ mm}^2$$

If this value of C is a maximum, then values of C when x is a little less than 5 or a little greater than 5 must be less than 2000.

When $x=4$ $C=3\,600-1\,920+256$
$$=1\,936$$

and when $x=6$, $C=5\,400-4\,320+864$
$$=1\,944$$

Hence C is proved to be a maximum when $x=5$.

Answer: Maximum capacity of 2000 mm^2 occurs when $x=5$

Problems 3.3

1. If $f(x)=x^2-3x+7$, find $f(0)$, $f(1)$, $f(-2)$, $f(a)$, and $f(x+h)-f(x)$.

2. If $f(x)=x^2+2$, find the value of $\dfrac{f(x+h)-f(x)}{h}$ as h approaches zero.

3. If $f(x)=\dfrac{1}{x^3}$, find the value of $\dfrac{f(x+h)-f(x)}{h}$ as h approaches zero.

4. Find the values of $\dfrac{f(x+h)-f(x)}{h}$ as the value of h approaches zero, when

   (a) $f(x)=x^2-2x+3$
   (b) $f(x)=\dfrac{-3}{x^4}$

5. A body is accelerating down an inclined plane, and it is observed that the total distance travelled s metres t seconds after release is given by the formula
$$s=4t^2$$

(*a*) Find the values of *s* corresponding to values of *t* of 1·2, 1·1
1·05, 1·01, and 1 second.

(*b*) What is the average velocity in the intervals 0·2, 0·1, 0·05, and
0·01 seconds after the first second?

(*c*) Estimate the velocity when *t*=1 second.

6. A vehicle starts from rest, and after a time of *t* seconds the
distance *s* m that the vehicle has travelled from its starting point
is given by the following data:

Time *t*	0	10	20	30	40	50	60
Distance *s*	0	80	320	720	1280	2000	2880

Plot the graph of *s* against *t* and, by a graphical method, find the
velocity of the vehicle when *t*=40 seconds.

7. A body moves with oscillatory motion so that its distance *s* m
from a datum point after a time of *t* seconds is given by the
equation

$$s=5 \sin \omega t$$

ω being constant at 2 radians per second. Plot the graph of *s*
against *t* when *t* varies from zero to 1 second and, by a graphical
method, find the velocity of the body when *t*=0·5 second.

8. When a particular body is rotating and has constant angular
retardation, the angle turned in radians is given by the formula

$$\theta=32t-16t^2$$

Find an expression for angular velocity $\left(\text{i.e. } \dfrac{d\theta}{dt}\right)$ and determine:

(*a*) The angular velocity when *t*=0·25 second.

(*b*) The time *t* when the body ceases rotating

$\left(\text{i.e. when the value of } \dfrac{d\theta}{dt} \text{ is zero}\right).$

9. A vehicle passes a certain datum point while it is moving and is
subjected to a retardation. The distance *s* m that the vehicle is
away from datum after a time of *t* seconds is given by the formula

$$s=40t-2t^2$$

(a) What is its velocity
 (i) when passing datum, i.e. when $t=0$, and
 (ii) when $t=5$ seconds?
(b) How long does it take the vehicle to come to rest (i.e. at what value of t is the velocity zero), and what is the corresponding value of s?

10. If $A=10+20x+\dfrac{500}{x}$ for what values of x is $\dfrac{dA}{dx}$ equal to zero?

11. A rectangular prism has a square cross-section of side x mm. The combined girth and length (i.e. $4x$ plus the length) is 60 mm. Determine a formula for the volume V as a function of x. Plot suitable values of volume V against x when x varies from 6 mm to 16 mm, and find the value of x, and the resulting volume, when the volume is a maximum.

12. A square plate of sheet metal has a side of length 150 mm. Square corners having a length of side x mm are notched at each corner of the square, and the plate is then folded to form an open tray with a square base and having a depth of x. Determine a formula for the volume of the tray in terms of x. Find the volumes when x varies from 10 mm to 50 mm at intervals of 10 mm. Plot these values and determine:
(a) The value of x and the resulting volume when the volume is a maximum.
(b) The two values of x which give a volume of 180 000 mm³, to nearest whole numbers.
(It will be advisable to calculate and plot extra values in the vicinity of desired values.)

13. When a certain article is produced at the rate of N articles per hour, the hourly cost of production in pounds sterling H is given by the formula
$$H=80+\frac{N^3}{200}$$
Determine a formula for the total cost C of producing 400 articles as a function of N. Plot suitable values of total cost C when N varies from 10 to 30. Hence find the rate of production and the total cost when the total cost is a minimum.

14. A tank with an open top and square in cross-section is to have a capacity of 62·5 m³.

(*a*) Representing the length of the side of the square by x, express the height of the tank as a function of x.

(*b*) Deduce a formula for the surface area A of the tank (i.e. four rectangular sides and a square base) in terms of x.

(*c*) Plot suitable values of A as x varies from 3 m to 7 m, and hence determine the value of x when the tank has a minimum surface area.

15. When a thin circular shell of diameter D mm and height H mm is formed from a circular blank of diameter 10 mm, then approximately

$$H = \frac{25}{D} - \frac{D}{4}$$

Calculate values of H when D varies from 3 mm to 7 mm at intervals of 1 mm. Use these values to find the volume of the shell. Plot the values of the volume against values of D, and hence determine the value of D when the volume is a maximum.

16. On the machined block shown in Figure 3.13 the angle θ varies with the distance x.

For the angles given

$$\cot \theta = \frac{\sqrt{(100 + x^2)}}{4 + \dfrac{x}{4}} \quad \text{approximately.}$$

Plot a graph of $\cot \theta$ against x, as x varies from zero 0m to 2m at intervals of 4 mm.

Draw a smooth curve through the points and hence find:

(*a*) The distance x when $\cot \theta$ is a minimum (to the nearest whole number).

(*b*) The corresponding angle θ (to the nearest degree).

17. A strip of metal 20 mm wide has two right angle bends formed x mm from each edge so as to form a rectangular channel of depth x mm (see Figure 3.14).

(*a*) Obtain an expression for the cross-sectional area of flow A (shown by section lining) in terms of x.

(*b*) Differentiate A with respect to x and obtain a value for $\dfrac{\mathrm{d}A}{\mathrm{d}x}$.

(*c*) Put this value of $\dfrac{\mathrm{d}A}{\mathrm{d}x}$ equal to zero, and find the value of x which satisfies the equation.

(*d*) Find the value of A which is a maximum.

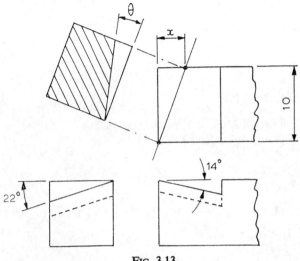

FIG. 3.13

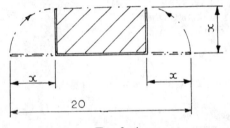

FIG. 3.14

18. An open topped tank, to be constructed of sheet metal, has to have a horizontal square base and vertical sides and to have a maximum capacity of 108 m³. Taking the side of the square base as x, show that the total surface area A of the tank can be obtained from the formula

$$A = x^2 + \frac{432}{x}$$

By a mathematical method find the maximum value of A, and the corresponding value of x.

169

Answers to problems 3.3

1. $7, \ 5, \ 17, \ a^2-3a+7, \ 2hx+h^2-3h$
2. $2x$
3. $\dfrac{-3}{x^4}$
4. (a) $2x-2$ (b) $\dfrac{-12}{x^5}$
5. (a) $5\cdot76$ m, $4\cdot84$ m, $4\cdot41$ m, $4\cdot080\ 4$ m, 4 m
   (b) $8\cdot8$ m/s, $8\cdot4$ m/s, $8\cdot2$ m/s, $8\cdot04$ m/s
   (c) 8 m/s
6. 64 m/s
7. $5\cdot4$ m/s
8. $\dfrac{d\theta}{dt}=32-32t$ (a) 24 rad/s   (b) 1 second
9. (a) (i) 40 m/s   (ii) 20 m/s   (b) $t=10$ s, $s=200$ m
10. $x=\pm5$
11. $V=60x^2-4x^3$; $2\ 000$ mm³ when $x=10$
12. $V=4x^3-600x^2+22\ 500x$
    Volumes are $169\ 000$ $242\ 000$ $243\ 000$
                          $196\ 000$ $125\ 000$
    (a) V max$=250\ 000$ when $x=25$
    (b) $x=11$ mm or 43 mm
13. $C=\dfrac{32\ 000}{N}+2N^2$

    Minimum is £2400 at the rate of 20 per hour
14. (a) $H=\dfrac{62\cdot5}{x^2}$ (b) $A=x^2+\dfrac{250}{x}$
    (c) A min$=75$ m² when $x=5$ m
15. Minimum when $D=5\cdot8$ mm
16. (a) $x=7$ mm   (b) $\theta=25°$
17. (a) $A=20x-2x^2$ (b) $\dfrac{dA}{dx}=20-4x$
    (c) $x=5$ (d) $A=50$ mm²
18. A max$=108$ m² when $x=6$ m

Chapter Four

Geometry and Trigonometry

4.1 Measurement of Large Bores and Large Radii

4.1.1 MEASUREMENT OF LARGE BORES

There is no further fundamental work on trigonometry required for the Part II Syllabus in Mathematics for Mechanical Engineering Technicians beyond that contained in Part I. All the basic mathematical formulae have been established, and Part II work confines itself to an extension of Part I work to problems which require more careful thought and which, in general, lead to more complex calculations. (The reader has already been introduced to the degree of accuracy of mathematical tables. All the problems in this chapter have been solved with the aid of four-figure tables in order to concentrate on the principles involved. In many practical cases, the resulting accuracy would be insufficient, and the use of seven-figure tables would be essential.)

Let us take as an example the Theorem of Pythagoras, which we must note only applies to a right-angled triangle. Figure 4.1(*a*) shows a method of determining the diameter of a large bore. A calibrated gauge of length L is kept in contact with one side of the bore, the other end having a total travel or 'rock' of w. Referring to Figure 4.1(*b*), ABC is a right-angled triangle, C being the angle in a semi-circle. If we now let δ be the difference between the diameter of the bore and the length of the gauge, then

$$AB = L + \delta, \quad AC = L, \quad BC = \frac{w}{2} \sec \theta$$

Applying the Theorem of Pythagoras to the right-angled triangle ABC,

$$(AB)^2 = (BC)^2 + (AC)^2$$

$$(L + \delta)^2 = (L)^2 + \left(\frac{w}{2} \sec \theta\right)^2$$

$$L^2 + 2L\delta + \delta^2 = L^2 + \frac{w^2}{4} \sec^2 \theta$$

$$2L\delta + \delta^2 = \frac{w^2}{4} \sec^2 \theta$$

171

Mathematics for Mechanical Technicians 2

Now δ is very small, rarely exceeding 0·1 mm, and hence δ^2 rarely exceeds 0·01 mm² which, in comparison with the value of $2L\delta$, is insignificant. Furthermore, the total angle of rock 2θ rarely exceeds 10°, for which $\sec^2 \theta$ is about 1·008.

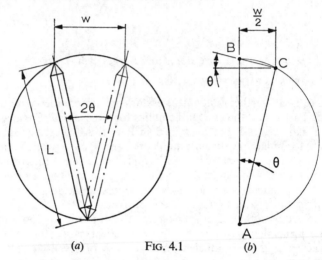

(a)   Fig. 4.1   (b)

Consequently, if δ^2 is small when compared with the value of $2L\delta$, and θ is a small angle, then approximately

$$2L\delta = \frac{w^2}{4}$$

and

$$\delta = \frac{w^2}{8L} \text{ approximately.}$$

It should be noted that the formula $\delta = \dfrac{w^2}{8L}$ becomes more accurate as the amount of rock w becomes smaller.

Example

The limits on a large bore are 120 mm $^{+0·12 \text{ mm}}_{+0·04 \text{ mm}}$. The bore is to be checked by the use of a calibrated pin gauge of length 120 mm. If one end of the pin gauge is kept in contact with a point in the bore, what limits are allowable on the lateral movement of the other end of the pin gauge? What is the actual diameter, to the nearest 0·005 mm, if the lateral movement is 8 mm?

$$\delta = \frac{w^2}{8L}, \quad w^2 = 8L\delta, \quad \therefore \quad w = \sqrt{8L\delta}$$

(a) Lower limit, $\delta = 0.04$ mm

$w = \sqrt{(8L\delta)} = \sqrt{(8 \times 120 \times 0.04)} = \sqrt{38.4} = 6.197$ mm

Upper limit, $\delta = 0.12$ mm

$w = \sqrt{(8L\delta)} = \sqrt{(8 \times 120 \times 0.12)} = \sqrt{115.2} = 10.73$ mm

∴ The limits of movement are 6·20 mm to 10·7 mm.

(b) If $w = 8$,

$$\delta = \frac{w^2}{8L} = \frac{8 \times 8}{8 \times 120} = \frac{1}{15} = 0.066\ 7 \text{ mm}$$

Diameter $= L + \delta = 120 + 0.066\ 7$ mm

$= 120.066\ 7$ mm

$= 120.065$ mm to the nearest 0·005 mm

Answers: (a) Limits of lateral movement = 6·20 mm to 10·7 mm

(b) Actual diameter $= 120.065$ mm

It would be convenient at this juncture to discuss the methods of measuring large radii. In article 4.4 of Book 1 it was then shown that if a large radius was measured as shown in Figure 4.2, we can apply the Theorem of Pythagoras to triangle *OPQ* to obtain the radius.

Applying the Theorem of Pythagoras to triangle *OPQ*,

$$(OP)^2 = (PQ)^2 + (QO)^2$$

$$\left(R + \frac{d}{2}\right)^2 = \left(\frac{C}{2}\right)^2 + \left(R + h - \frac{d}{2}\right)^2$$

$$\left(R + \frac{d}{2}\right)^2 - \left(R + h - \frac{d}{2}\right)^2 = \frac{C^2}{4}$$

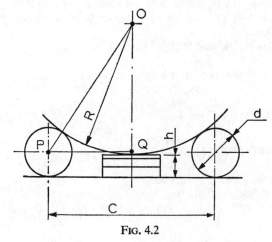

Fɪɢ. 4.2

By using the factors of the difference of two squares,

$$\left(R+\frac{d}{2}+R+h-\frac{d}{2}\right)\left(R+\frac{d}{2}-R-h+\frac{d}{2}\right)=\frac{C^2}{4}$$

$$(2R+h)(d-h)=\frac{C^2}{4}$$

$$2R+h=\frac{C^2}{4(d-h)}$$

$$2R=\frac{C^2}{4(d-h)}-h$$

$$R=\frac{C^2}{8(d-h)}-\frac{h}{2}$$

It was shown in Book 1 that if R is required, the calculations are relatively simple. It is not so easy when the values of R and C are known and the value of h is required. In this case, the final formula should not be used, but rather the equation

$$(2R+h)(d-h)=\frac{C^2}{4}$$

which occurred during the development of the formula.

Example

Large quantities of work having a radius of 120 mm$^{+4}_{+0}$ mm are to be checked as shown in Figure 4.2. A fixture is to be used with rollers of diameter 50 mm at a centre distance of 200 mm. A simple slip gauge of the 'go' and 'not-go' type is to be used instead of the slip gauge pile.

Calculate the 'go' and 'not-go' sizes of this gauge.

The 'go' size occurs with the smallest radius.

$$R=120 \quad d=50 \quad C=200$$

$$(2R+h)(d-h)=\frac{C^2}{4}$$

$$(240+h)(50-h)=\frac{200\times200}{4}$$

$$12\,000-190h-h^2=10\,000$$
$$h^2+190h-2000=0$$

$$h=\frac{-190\pm\sqrt{\{(190^2)-(4\times1\times-2\,000)\}}}{2}$$

$$=\frac{-190\pm\sqrt{(36\ 100+8\ 000)}}{2}$$

$$=\frac{-190\pm\sqrt{44\ 100}}{2}$$

$$=\frac{-190+210}{2} \quad \text{(negative root inadmissible)}$$

$$=\frac{20}{2}=10 \text{ mm}$$

The 'not go' size occurs with the larger radius

$$R=124 \quad d=50 \quad C=200$$

$$(2R+h)(d-h)=\frac{C^2}{4}$$

$$(248+h)(50-h)=\frac{200\times200}{4}$$

$$12\ 400-198h-h^2=10\ 000$$

$$h^2+198h-2\ 400=0$$

$$h=\frac{-198\pm\sqrt{\{(198)^2-(4\times1\times-2\ 400)\}}}{2}$$

$$=\frac{-198\pm\sqrt{(39\ 294+9\ 600)}}{2}$$

$$=-198\pm\sqrt{48\ 804}$$

$$=\frac{-198+220\cdot9}{2} \quad \text{(negative root inadmissible)}$$

$$=\frac{22\cdot9}{2}=11\cdot45 \text{ mm}$$

Answers: Go size $=10\cdot00$ mm
Not-go size$=11\cdot45$ mm

A less accurate, but very rapid, manner of determining a large radius is shown in Figure 4.3.

An angle gauge of included angle θ is used and the distance x from the apex of the angle to the curve is measured.

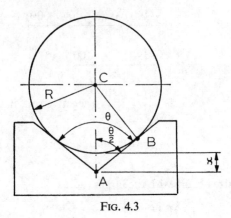

FIG. 4.3

In the right-angled triangle ABC,

$$BC=R, \quad AC=R+x$$

$$\frac{R+x}{R}=\operatorname{cosec}\frac{\theta}{2}$$

$$\therefore \ R\operatorname{cosec}\frac{\theta}{2}=R+x$$

$$R\operatorname{cosec}\frac{\theta}{2}-R=x$$

$$R\left(\operatorname{cosec}\frac{\theta}{2}-1\right)=x$$

$$R=\frac{x}{\operatorname{cosec}\dfrac{\theta}{2}-1}$$

or
$$R=Kx \text{ where } K=\frac{1}{\operatorname{cosec}\dfrac{\theta}{2}-1}$$

For a given value of θ, $\dfrac{1}{\operatorname{cosec}\dfrac{\theta}{2}-1}$ is constant and this can be engraved

on the gauge. For example, if θ is 120°,

$$K=\frac{1}{\operatorname{cosec}60°-1}=\frac{1}{1\cdot154\,7-1}=\frac{1}{0\cdot154\,7}=6\cdot465.$$

This value of K demonstrates the inbuilt inaccuracy of the method. It is not only difficult to measure x accurately, it is also difficult to manufacture the gauge with a sharp corner. If θ is 120°, any error in

x is magnified over six times when determining R. The first of these objections can be overcome with the use of the modified gauge shown in Figure 4.4, where a measurement x is taken to a flat surface, instead of to a point.

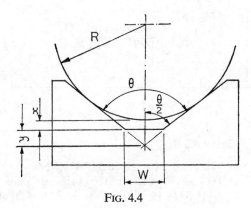

FIG. 4.4

In this case the value of y is constant and equal to $\dfrac{W}{2} \cot \dfrac{\theta}{2}$, and hence

$$R = K(x+y) = K\left(x + \frac{W}{2} \cot \frac{\theta}{2}\right)$$

$$= Kx + K_1$$

where

$$K = \frac{1}{\operatorname{cosec} \dfrac{\theta}{2} - 1}$$

and

$$K_1 = \frac{KW}{2} \cot \frac{\theta}{2}$$

Example

Figure 4.5 shows a template which can be used to determine the magnitude of a large radius.
Calculate:

(a) The radius R when $x = 19\cdot35$ mm.

(b) The minimum value of R that can be measured with this particular template.

(C.G.L.I.)

177

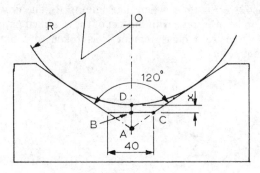

FIG. 4.5

Referring to Figure 4.5

$$AB = BC \tan 30° = 20 \times 0.577\ 4 = 11.548$$
$$AD = AB + BD = AB + x \text{ from original figure}$$
$$= 11.548 + 19.35 = 30.898 = 30.90 \text{ to 4 figures}$$

$$\frac{R}{OA} = \cos 30°, \quad \frac{R}{R+30.9} = 0.866\ 0,$$

$$R = 0.866\ 0(R+30.9)$$
$$R = 0.866R + 26.759\ 4$$

$$R - 0.866R = 26.759\ 4$$
$$0.134R = 26.759\ 4$$

$$R = \frac{26.759\ 4}{0.134} = 199.7 \text{ mm}$$

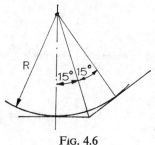

FIG. 4.6

The minimum value of R occurs when the radius is tangential to both of the flats, as shown in Figure 4.6.

That is, when $\quad R \tan 15° = 20$ mm

$$R = \frac{20}{\tan 15°} = 20 \cot 15° = 20 \times 3.732\,1$$
$$= 74.642 \text{ mm}$$

Answers: (a) Radius when $x = 19.35$ mm is 200 mm
(b) Minimum radius = 74.6 mm

Problems 4.1

1. A bore was checked by rocking a calibrated pin gauge of length 200 mm. When one end of the pin gauge was kept in contact with the bore the other end had a total travel of 16 mm. Calculate the diameter of the bore to the nearest 0.05 mm.

2. The limits on a bore are 300 mm$^{+0.3 \text{ mm}}_{+0.1 \text{ mm}}$. The bore is to be checked by rocking a calibrated pin gauge of length 300 mm. Calculate the minimum and maximum lateral movements of one end of the pin gauge.

3. A bore has limits of 250 mm$^{+0.20 \text{ mm}}_{+0.04 \text{ mm}}$, and is to be checked by rocking a pin gauge of length 250 mm in the bore.
   (a) Calculate the minimum and maximum amounts of travel at the free end.
   (b) In an actual determination, two measurements of rock taken at right angles were 16 mm and 12 mm. If these represent the maximum and minimum amounts of rock, calculate the value of the difference between maximum and minimum diameters, i.e. the amount of ovality.

4. When an angle gauge having a vee of 120° was placed on a large radius the distance from the circumference to the point of the vee was 15.6 mm. Determine the magnitude of the radius.

5. Calculate the angle θ for the measuring instrument shown in Figure 4.7, so that the variation in the dial indicator reading is five times the variation in the bar diameter.

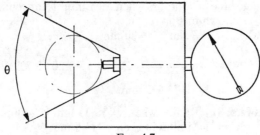

FIG. 4.7

6. (a) The gauge shown in Figure 4.8 is used for checking large radii. Show that if x is the distance between the flat of the width 43·3 mm and the radius R which has to be determined, then $R=K_1+K_2 x$, where K_1 and K_2 are constants, and determine the values of K_1 and K_2.

(b) Find the value of R when $x=6$ mm.

(c) What are the maximum and minimum values of R for which this gauge can be used?

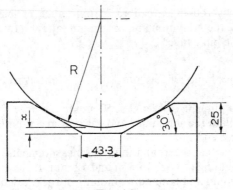

FIG. 4.8

Answers to problems 4.1

1. 200·15 mm
2. 15·5 mm to 26·8 mm
3. (a) 8·94 mm to 20·0 mm   (b) 0·056 mm
4. 100 mm
5. 10° 26′
6. (a) $K_1=80·8$ mm, $K_2=6·46$ (b) 120 mm
   (c) 80·8 mm to 130 mm

180

4.2 Measurement using Balls and/or Rollers

4.2.1 THE GENERAL CASE

We will now proceed to extend the Part I work on measurement, using balls and rollers. The common basic geometrical items in these problems are that

(*a*) when a circle rests in a vee then a radius to a point of tangency on the face of a vee lies at right angles to that face of the vee, and that

(*b*) a line drawn from the centre of the circle to the apex of the vee bisects the included angle of the vee.

Let us illustrate this with examples.

Example

Figure 4.9 shows the essential parts of a measuring instrument. With a 25 mm test bar in the vee the dial gauge is set to read zero. Assuming that a larger bar results in an increased indicator reading, what does the indicator read for a bar of diameter 25·8 mm?

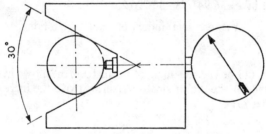

FIG. 4.9

Referring to Figure 4.10, A is a fixed point on the instrument. The triangle ABC is right-angled. CA bisects the vee-angle.

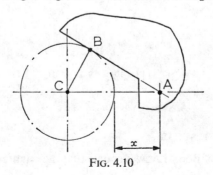

FIG. 4.10

181

Let the diameter of the bar be d.

Then $$AC=\frac{d}{2}\,\text{cosec }15°$$

$$x=AC-\frac{d}{2}$$

$$=\frac{d}{2}\,\text{cosec }15°-\frac{d}{2}$$

$$=\frac{d}{2}(\text{cosec }15°-1)$$

or $$x=Kd \text{ where } K=\frac{\text{cosec }15°-1}{2}$$

$$K=\frac{3\cdot863\,7-1}{2}=\frac{2\cdot863\,7}{2}=1\cdot431\,85$$

When bar diameter is 25 mm, $x=K(25)=1\cdot431\,85\times25=35\cdot796\,25$
When bar diameter is 25·8 mm, $x=K(25\cdot8)=1\cdot431\,85\times25\cdot8=$
$$36\cdot941\,73$$

Increase in $x=36\cdot941\,73-35\cdot796\,25=1\cdot145\,48$

Answer: Dial indicator reads$+1\cdot15$ mm

Example

What should be the vee-angle of the instrument shown in the previous example for the dial indicator to show twice the increase of the bar diameter?

If θ is the vee-angle, $$K=\frac{\text{cosec}\frac{\theta}{2}-1}{2}$$

Hence $$\frac{\text{cosec }\frac{\theta}{2}-1}{2}=2$$

$$\text{cosec }\frac{\theta}{2}-1=4,\quad \text{cosec }\frac{\theta}{2}=5$$

$$\therefore \frac{\theta}{2}=11°\,32',\quad \theta=23°\,4'$$

Answer: Vee-angle is 23° 4'

4.2.2 DOVETAIL SLOTS

In article 4.9 of Book 1, it was shown that the relationship between

W, X, d, and θ of the symmetrical dovetail slot shown in Figure 4.11 is given by the equation

$$X = W - d\left(1 + \cot\frac{\theta}{2}\right)$$

The calculations assumed that the angle θ was correct.

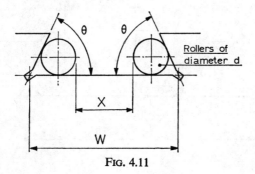

FIG. 4.11

If it is known that both angles are equal, their actual magnitude can be determined by first measuring X_1 with rollers of diameter d_1, and then measuring X_2 with rollers of diameter d_2. In which case,

$$X_1 = W - d_1\left(1 + \cot\frac{\theta}{2}\right)$$

$$X_2 = W - d_2\left(1 + \cot\frac{\theta}{2}\right)$$

By subtraction, $\quad X_1 - X_2 = (d_2 - d_1)\left(1 + \cot\frac{\theta}{2}\right)$

$$1 + \cot\frac{\theta}{2} = \frac{X_1 - X_2}{d_2 - d_1}$$

and $\qquad\qquad \cot\frac{\theta}{2} = \left(\frac{X_1 - X_2}{d_2 - d_1}\right) - 1$

θ can now be found and substituted in one of the original equations to find W.

It should not be assumed that the angles are equal unless this has been stated, implied, or proved. If the angles are not equal, their actual magnitude can be deduced with the method used in the following example.

183

Example

In the checking of the asymmetrical dovetail slot shown in Figure 4.12, a 20 mm slip gauge was secured in the slot

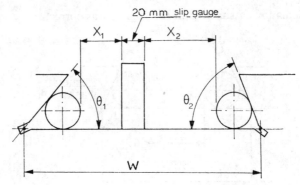

FIG. 4.12

When the rollers were of diameter 10 mm, the dimensions X_1 and X_2 were 26·34 mm and 42·83 mm respectively. With rollers of diameter 20 mm, X_1 and X_2 were 12·68 mm and 25·86 mm respectively. Calculate the values of θ_1, θ_2, and W.

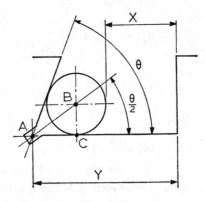

FIG. 4.13

Referring to Figure 4.13, ABC is a right-angled triangle

$$AC = BC \cot \frac{\theta}{2} = \frac{d}{2} \cot \frac{\theta}{2}$$

$$Y = AC + \frac{d}{2} + X$$

$$= \frac{d}{2}\cot\frac{\theta}{2} + \frac{d}{2} + X$$

$$Y = X + \frac{d}{2}\left(1 + \cot\frac{\theta}{2}\right)$$

Considering the left-hand side of the dovetail slot,

$$Y_1 = X_1 + \frac{d}{2}\left(1 + \cot\frac{\theta_1}{2}\right)$$

Using $\quad X_1 = 26\cdot34, \quad d=10, \quad Y_1 = 26\cdot34 + 5\left(1 + \cot\frac{\theta_1}{2}\right)$

Using $\quad X_1 = 12\cdot68, \quad d=20, \quad Y_1 = 12\cdot68 + 10\left(1 + \cot\frac{\theta_1}{2}\right)$

By subtraction $\qquad 0 = 13\cdot66 - 5\left(1 + \cot\frac{\theta_1}{2}\right)$

$$5\left(1 + \cot\frac{\theta_1}{2}\right) = 13\cdot66$$

$$1 + \cot\frac{\theta_1}{2} = \frac{13\cdot66}{5} = 2\cdot732, \quad \cot\frac{\theta_1}{2} = 1\cdot732$$

$$\frac{\theta_1}{2} = \text{arccot } 1\cdot732 = 30°, \quad \theta_1 = 60°$$

By substitution, $\quad Y_1 = 26\cdot34 + 5\left(1 + \cot\frac{\theta_1}{2}\right) = 26\cdot34 + 5(2\cdot732)$

$$= 26\cdot34 + 13\cdot66 = 40\cdot00$$

Considering the right-hand side

Using $\quad X_2 = 42\cdot93, \quad d=5, \quad Y_2 = 42\cdot93 + 5\left(1 + \cot\frac{\theta_2}{2}\right)$

Using $\quad X_2 = 25\cdot86, \quad d=10, \quad Y_2 = 25\cdot86 + 10\left(1 + \cot\frac{\theta_2}{2}\right)$

By subtraction $\qquad 0 = 17\cdot07 - 5\left(1 + \cot\frac{\theta_2}{2}\right)$

$$5\left(1 + \cot\frac{\theta_2}{2}\right) = 17\cdot07$$

$$1 + \cot\frac{\theta_2}{2} = \frac{17\cdot07}{5} = 3\cdot414$$

$$\cot\frac{\theta_2}{2}=3\cdot414-1=2\cdot414$$

$$\frac{\theta_2}{2}=\text{arccot}\quad 2\cdot414=22°\ 30',\quad \theta_2=45°$$

By substitution $$Y_2=42\cdot93+5\left(1+\cot\frac{\theta_1}{2}\right)$$

$$=42\cdot93+5(3\cdot414)$$
$$=42\cdot93+17\cdot07$$
$$=60\cdot00$$

$$W=Y_1+20+Y_2=40\cdot00+20\cdot00+60\cdot00$$
$$=120\cdot00\ \text{mm}$$

Answers: $\theta_1=60°$, $\theta_2=45°$, $W=120$ mm

4.2.3 ROLLER IN AN ASYMMETRICAL VEE

The slight modification caused by a vee being asymmetrical with respect to a datum surface can best be demonstrated with an example, the guiding principle of this type of problem being to establish the position of the apex of the vee.

Calculate the dimension Y of the checking arrangement shown in Figure 4.14.

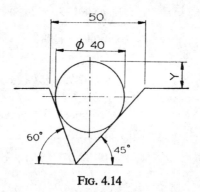

FIG. 4.14

We will commence by positioning the apex of the vee. Referring to Figure 4.15

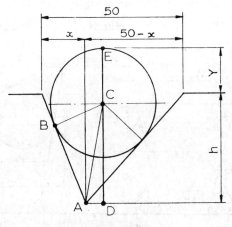

FIG. 4.15

$$h = x \cot 30° = (50 - x) \cot 45°$$

$$\therefore \ 1.732 \ 1x = 50 - x, \text{ since } \cot 45° = 1$$
$$2.732 \ 1x = 50$$

$$x = \frac{50}{2.732 \ 1} = 18.31$$

$$h = 50 - x = 50 - 18.31 = 31.69$$

This establishes the position of the apex of the vee.
We now have to establish the position of the centre of the roller.

$$\text{Vee-angle} = 75°$$

$$AC = BC \ \text{cosec} \ \frac{75°}{2} = 20 \ \text{cosec} \ 37° \ 30'$$

$$= 20 \times 1.641 \ 7 = 32.854$$

In quadrilateral $ABCD$, angle $A = 120°$
while in triangle ABC, angle $A = 37° \ 30'$
$\therefore$ In triangle ACD, angle $A = 120° - 37° \ 30' = 82° \ 30'$
$$DC = AC \sin 82° \ 30' = 32.854 \times 0.9914 = 32.57$$
$$DE = DC + CE = 32.57 + 20 = 52.57$$
$$Y = DE - h = 52.57 - 31.69 = 20.88$$

Answer: $Y = 20.9$ mm

G

187

Mathematics for Mechanical Technicians 2

4.2.4 CHECKING OF EXTERNAL AND INTERNAL TAPERS

Article 4.9 of Book 1 showed methods of determining the included angle of tapers.

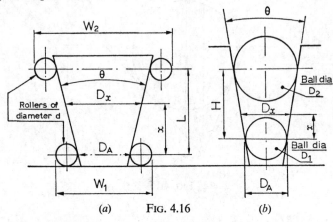

(*a*)   FIG. 4.16   (*b*)

In Figure 4.16(*a*)

$$\tan\frac{\theta}{2}=\frac{W_2-W_1}{2L}$$

In Figure 4.16(*b*)

$$\sin\frac{\theta}{2}=\frac{D_2-D_1}{2H}$$

The diameter of the taper at a particular plane, such as D_x, can be established by determining the taper diameter in line with the centre of a roller or ball and then adjusting by an amount due to x. It is important to note that a line drawn through the centres of the rollers or balls at right angles to the axis of the taper does NOT pass through the point of tangency. Let D_A be a diameter in line with the centre of the lower rollers (Figure 4.16(*a*)), or lower ball (Figure 4.16(*b*))

In Figure 4.16(*a*)

$$D_A=W_1-d\left(1+\sec\frac{\theta}{2}\right)$$

and $D_x=D_A+2x\tan\dfrac{\theta}{2}$

In Figure 4.16(*b*)

$$D_A=D_1\sec\frac{\theta}{2},$$

$$D_x=D_A+2x\tan\frac{\theta}{2}$$

With internal tapers it is often difficult to obtain balls of diameters D_2 and D_1 which will make measurement convenient. It is possible to obtain a greater selection of sizes of rollers than of balls, and quite often a combination of rollers and balls leads to ease of measurement, as shown in Figure 4.17.

188

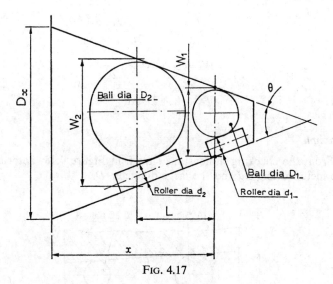

FIG. 4.17

Referring to Figure 4.17

$$W_1 = \frac{D_1}{2} \sec \frac{\theta}{2} + \left(\frac{D_1}{2} + d_1\right) \sec \frac{\theta}{2}$$

$$= (D_1 + d_1) \sec \frac{\theta}{2}$$

Similarly,

$$W_2 = (D_2 + d_2) \sec \frac{\theta}{2}$$

Now

$$\tan \frac{\theta}{2} = \frac{W_2 - W_1}{2L}$$

$$= \frac{(D_2 + d_2) \sec \frac{\theta}{2} - (D_1 + d_1) \sec \frac{\theta}{2}}{2L}$$

$$\therefore \quad \frac{\tan \frac{\theta}{2}}{\sec \frac{\theta}{2}} = \frac{(D_2 + d_2) - (D_1 + d_1)}{2L}$$

$$\text{As} \quad \frac{\tan \frac{\theta}{2}}{\sec \frac{\theta}{2}} = \sin \frac{\theta}{2}$$

189

$$\sin\frac{\theta}{2}=\frac{(D_2+d_2)-(D_1+d_1)}{2L}$$

$$W_1=(D_1+d_1)\sec\frac{\theta}{2}$$

hence $\qquad\qquad D_x=W_1+2x\tan\frac{\theta}{2}$

Example

From the checking dimensions shown in Figure 4.18, determine the included angle θ and the large diameter D.

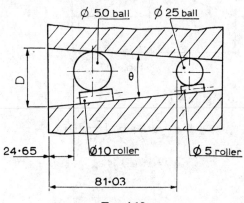

FIG. 4.18

Separation of ball centres $L=(81{\cdot}03+12{\cdot}5)-(24{\cdot}65+25{\cdot}00)$

$$=93{\cdot}53-49{\cdot}65$$
$$=43{\cdot}88$$

Using the formula deduced previously,

$$\sin\frac{\theta}{2}=\frac{(D_2+d_2)-(D_1+d_1)}{2L}$$

$$=\frac{(50+10)-(25+5)}{2(43{\cdot}88)}$$

$$=\frac{60-30}{87{\cdot}76}=\frac{30}{87{\cdot}76}$$

$$\operatorname{cosec}\frac{\theta}{2}=\frac{87{\cdot}76}{30}=2{\cdot}925,\ \frac{\theta}{2}=20^{\circ},\ \theta=40^{\circ}$$

Diameter at level of 50 mm ball $=(50+10)\sec 20°$
$$=60\,(1{\cdot}064\,2)$$
$$=63{\cdot}852$$

Centre of 50 mm ball is 49·65 mm below end surface

Increase in diameter $\qquad =2(49{\cdot}65\tan 20°)$
$$=99{\cdot}3(0{\cdot}364\,0)$$
$$=36{\cdot}145\,2$$

Large diameter $\qquad\qquad =63{\cdot}852+36{\cdot}145\,2$
$$=99{\cdot}995\,2\text{ mm}$$

Answers: Included angle$=40°$
Large diameter$=100$ mm

Problems 4.2

1. The symmetrical dovetail slot shown in Figure 4.19 is to be checked with rollers of diameter 15 mm. Calculate the maximum and minimum distance W between rollers.

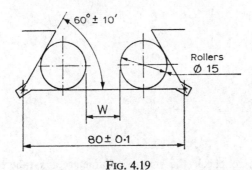

FIG. 4.19

2. Figure 4.20 shows a groove turned in a bore for seating an oil seal. Calculate the checking diameter D.

3. Find the diameter of the circle of greatest diameter that will lie within a right-angled triangle having sides of length 60 mm, 80 mm, and 100 mm.

191

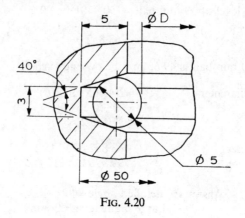

FIG. 4.20

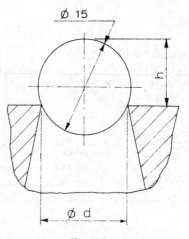

FIG. 4.21

4. In order to check the smallest diameter of a tapered bore, a sphere of diameter 15 mm was positioned as shown in Figure 4.21. The dimension h was found to be 12·6 mm. Determine the diameter d.

5. The British Association thread form has a flank angle of $47\frac{1}{2}°$, and the fundamental triangle is truncated symmetrically to give a thread depth of 0·6 of the pitch. Determine, in millimetres, the crest radius of a 4 BA thread which has a pitch of 0·66 mm.

6. In checking the half dovetail slot shown in Figure 4.22, when d was 5 mm, W was 17·14 mm. In a second measurement, d was 10 mm and W was 9·28 mm. Calculate the magnitude of the angle θ and the nominal dimension L.

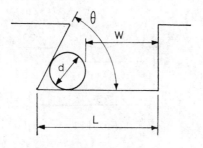

FIG. 4.22

7. An asymmetrical dovetail slot was checked using the setting shown in Figure 4.23. With rollers of diameter 5 mm the dimensions X_1 and X_2 were 17·70 mm and 28·58 mm respectively. With rollers of diameter 10 mm the dimensions X_1 and X were 10·40 mm and 22·15 mm respectively. Calculate the dimension W and the angles θ_1 and θ_2.

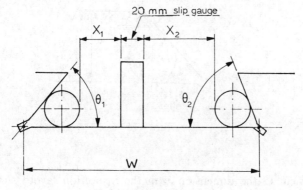

FIG. 4.23

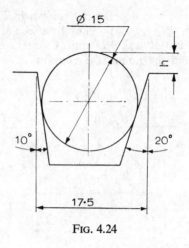

FIG. 4.24

8. Determine the distance h shown in Figure 4.24.

9. Calculate the vee-angle θ of the inspection set-up shown in Figure 4.25.

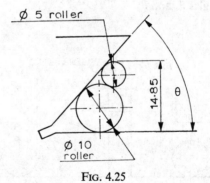

FIG. 4.25

10. Calculate the dimension x in the inspection layout shown in Figure 4.26.

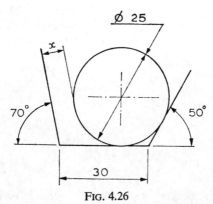

FIG. 4.26

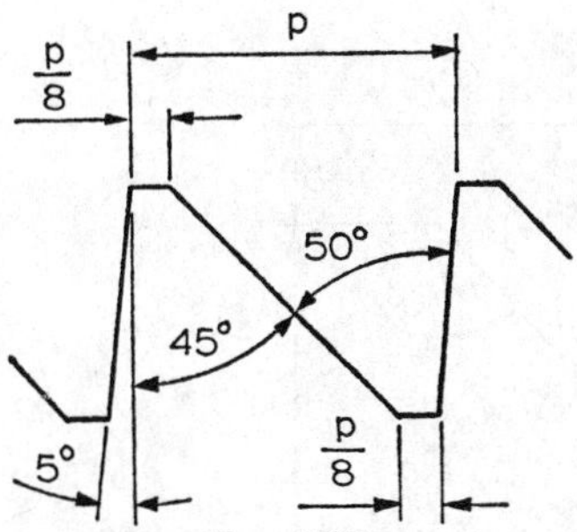

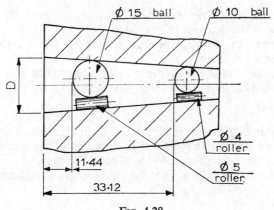

11. Figure 4.27 shows the profile of a general purpose Buttress thread form. Determine, for a pitch of 4 mm, the roller diameter d so that the centre of the roller lies on the effective diameter.

FIG. 4.27

12. Calculate the large diameter D and the included angle θ of the internal taper shown in Figure 4.28.

FIG. 4.28

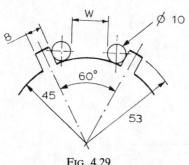

Fɪɢ. 4.29

13. Figure 4.29 shows a six-splined shaft being checked with a slip-gauge pile and rollers. Calculate the checking size *W*.

(C.G.L.I.)

14. Calculate the checking distance *x* of the notch and roller layout shown in Figure 4.30.

(C.G.L.I.)

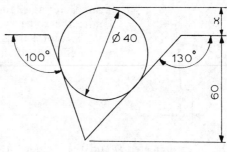

Fɪɢ. 4.30

15. An acme thread has theoretical form and a pitch of 5 mm. Determine the diameter of the roller:
   (*a*) That makes contact with the flanks of the thread form at the effective diameter.
   (*b*) That lies in the thread form in such a manner that its circumference lies level with the outside diameter of the thread.

(C.G.L.I.)

16. In checking the half-dovetail slot shown in Figure 4.31, when the roller had a diameter of 10 mm the dimension *X* was 26·34 mm. With a roller of diameter 20 mm, *X* was 12·68 mm.
   (*a*) Deduce a formula giving *Y* in terms of *X*, *d*, and a trigonometric function of $\dfrac{\theta}{2}$.

(b) Substitute the values given and hence find the values of Y and θ.

(C.G.L.I.)

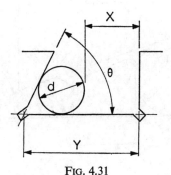

FIG. 4.31

17. Determine the co-ordinates x and y for the centre of the radius shown in Figure 4.32.

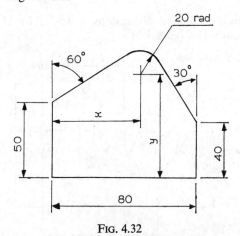

FIG. 4.32

18. In order to find the radius of a concave spherical shape a fixture was used which had three points lying at the corners of an equilateral triangle of side 100 mm. When these three points contacted the spherical radius the lowest point of the radius lay 5·0 mm below the plane containing the points. Find the radius of the spherical shape.

197

19. Figure 4.33 shows an inspection set for checking a taper.

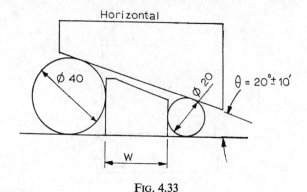

FIG. 4.33

The angle θ is to be checked by using a 'go' and 'not-go' gauge for the distance W. Calculate the nominal sizes for this gauge. Note that the dimension of W is horizontal.

20. Calculate the nominal dimensions X and Y for the inspection set-up shown in Figure 4.34.

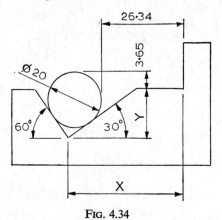

FIG. 4.34

Answers to problems 4.2

1. 39·2 mm and 38·8 mm
2. 38·6 mm
3. 40 mm
4. 11·0 mm

5. 0·118 mm
6. $\theta=50°$, $L=25·0$ mm
7. $W=80$ mm, $\theta_1=55°$, $\theta_2=65°$
8. 3·98 mm
9. 60°
10. 14·5 mm
11. 1·65 mm
12. $D=26·25$ mm, $\theta=18°$
13. 23·6 mm
14. 5·70 mm
15. (a) 2·58 mm   (b) 2·44 mm
16. (a) $Y=X+\dfrac{d}{2}\left(1+\cot\dfrac{\theta}{2}\right)$ (b) $Y=40·0$ mm, $\theta=60°$
17. (48·4, 54·8)
18. 336 mm
19. Go 26·2 mm, not-go 27·2 mm
20. $X=40·0$ mm, $Y=20·0$ mm

4.3 'Three-wire' Measurement of External Screw Threads

4.3.1 PRINCIPLES OF MEASUREMENT

The load-carrying surfaces of a bolt and nut screw assembly are the flanks of the threads. The roots and crests of most common vee-thread forms are rounded merely for convenience during manufacturing and safety in handling. In the case of an external thread, a

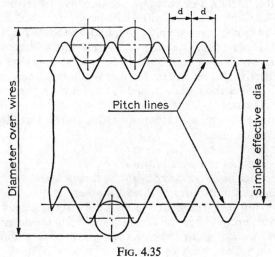

FIG. 4.35

measurement of the major (i.e. the outside) diameter gives no reliable indication of the accuracy of the thread. A more useful measurement would be one taken in relation to the flanks of the thread. If we consider the cross-section of a theoretically accurate external thread, a 'pitch line' could be drawn through the thread form so that the widths of metal and space are equal, as shown in Figure 4.35.

The diameter across opposite pitch lines is known as the 'simple effective diameter', often colloquially called the *effective diameter*. (In the U.S.A. it is known as the *pitch diameter*.) It is virtually impossible to measure an effective diameter directly and use is made of small rollers such as wires. If we take a cross-section of a bolt, the lower thread forms are displaced by half of one pitch from the upper thread forms. Three wires of equal diameter are therefore usually used so that the measurement over wires is taken at right angles to the centre-line of the thread. In some precision measuring devices it may be possible to use two wires only, the measuring being aligned at right angles to the centre-line of the thread by the construction of the instrument.

The so-called '*best size*' of wire is one which makes contact at the effective diameter, the diameter d is then given by $\dfrac{p}{2}$ sec $\dfrac{\theta}{2}$, p being the pitch of the thread and θ being the thread angle. *Any* size of wire which contacts the flanks of the thread can be used, but there is a practical lower limit of d so that the wires will project above the crests of the threads. For common vee-threads, if the wires are of the 'best size' the size over wires will be greater than the major diameter. Manufacturers supply calibrated wires which are accompanied with a certificate quoting a C value. The C value indicates the amount which must be subtracted from a 'reading over wires' to give the effective diameter. The C value is constant for a given set of wires used in a thread of a stated form and pitch, irrespective of the major diameter.

In the three-wire measurement of external screw threads, certain assumptions are made, viz.:

(*a*) The pitch of the thread is correct.
(*b*) The angle of the thread form is correct.
(*c*) The wires lie at right angles to the thread axis.
(*d*) Compression of wires or thread is absent.

Whether or not it is permissible to discount errors caused by these assumptions depends upon the accuracy desired in the measurement. For general workshop use, when measurement made with a micrometer would suffice, such as may occur with a M36–6$_g$ external thread it is reasonable to discount them. The tolerance on the effective diameter of the quoted thread is 0·2 mm.

If, on the other hand, a more precise measurement is required, such as would be the case with a screw plug gauge, then the assumptions create significant errors. In this case correcting amounts must be included, and the effective diameter that would be computed would be known as a 'virtual effective diameter'. This is the effective diameter of a nut that would just assemble with the actual gauge. It is not necessary in the Part II M.E.T. syllabus to proceed further with a study of the virtual effective diameter. It will be assumed that errors caused by the assumptions are insignificant in the actual problems encountered.

The common external vee-thread forms are based upon a fundamental triangle and amounts of truncation, which may be different at the crest and the root. For the purposes of the present studies we are only concerned with truncation at the crest of the thread.

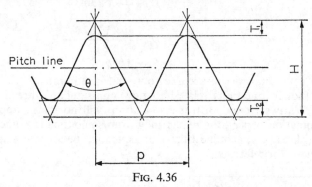

Pitch line

θ

FIG. 4.36

From Figure 4.36 if H is the height of the fundamental triangle and T_1 is the amount of truncation at the crest of an external thread, effective diameter=major diameter+$2T_1 - H$. If θ is the thread angle and p the pitch of the thread,

$$H = \frac{p}{2} \cot \frac{\theta}{2}$$

With the changeover from 'Imperial' to 'Metric' dimensions, the standard thread form to be adopted will be the 'ISO-metric' form. It is a most convenient thread form because its major characteristics are identical with those of the 'Unified' thread form. For those establishments which continue to work in inch units the expression 'Unified' will gradually be replaced by the expression 'ISO-inch'. The ISO thread form is nominally flat-topped and flat-bottomed, but in practice the rounding of crests and roots is permissible, within limits, to facilitate handling, to give greater fatigue resistance and to reduce the wear on screwcutting tools.

If H is the nominal height of the fundamental triangle, as shown in Figure 4.36, the truncation T_1 of the ISO form is $\dfrac{H}{8}$. The thread angle θ is 60°.

$$
\begin{aligned}
\text{Effective diameter } D_e &= \text{major diameter } D_m + 2T_1 - H \\
&= D_m + \frac{H}{4} - H \\
&= D_m - \frac{3H}{4} \\
&= D_m - \frac{3}{4}\left(\frac{p}{2}\cot\frac{60°}{2}\right) \\
&= D_m - \frac{3p}{8}\cot 30° \\
&= D_m - \frac{3p \times 1.732\ 1}{8} \\
&= D_m - 0.65p
\end{aligned}
$$

(to a sufficient order of accuracy our studies require).

Although questions related to now non-standard thread forms (e.g. Whitworth and British Association) will no longer appear in examination papers, the reader may from some time to come meet these thread forms in industry. Consequently, the following table is provided for reference.

Thread	Thread angle	Effective diameter D_e
ISO-metric (Metric)	60°	$D_m - 0.65p$
ISO-inch (Unified)	60°	$D_m - 0.65p$
Whitworth	55°	$D_m - 0.64p$
British Association	47½°	$D_m - 0.60p$

With metric thread designations, a thread other than a coarse thread has the pitch included in the designation. As examples, a thread designated M24 is the standard metric coarse thread of major diameter 24 mm. A reference to BS 3643 will provide the information that the pitch is 3·0 mm. A thread designated M24×2 is a metric thread of major diameter 24 mm and of pitch 2 mm. Unless specified to the contrary, all threads are presumed to be right-hand, single start, medium fit.

Calculate the nominal effective diameter of the following thread forms:

        (*a*) M16 (pitch is 2·0)
        (*b*) M64×4

(*a*) For metric threads $D_e = D_m - 0·65p$
    For M16 thread, pitch is 2·0 mm
$$D_e = 16 - 0·65(2)$$
$$= 16 - 1·3 = 14·7$$

(*b*) For a thread designated M64×4, pitch is 4 mm
$$D_e = D_m - 0·65p$$
$$= 64 - 0·65(4)$$
$$= 64 - 2·6 = 61·4$$

Answers: (*a*) D_e for M16 = 14·7 mm
             (*b*) D_e for M64×4 = 61·4 mm

We will now develop a formula connecting the diameter over wires with the effective diameter, such as occurs in the wire measurement of screw threads.

Figure 4.37 shows a wire positioned in an external vee-thread form.

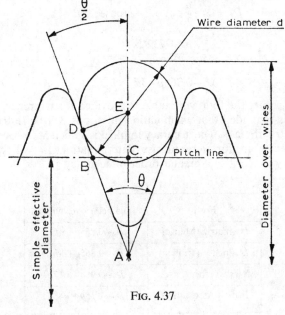

Fig. 4.37

Referring to Figure 4.37,

$$BC=\frac{p}{4}, \quad AC=BC \cot \frac{\theta}{2}=\frac{p}{4} \cot \frac{\theta}{2}$$

$$DE=\frac{d}{2}, \quad AE=DE \operatorname{cosec} \frac{\theta}{2}=\frac{d}{2} \operatorname{cosec} \frac{\theta}{2}$$

Diameter over wires

$$=\text{effective diameter}-2(AC)+2(AE)+2\left(\frac{d}{2}\right)$$

$$=\text{effective diameter}-\frac{p}{2} \cot \frac{\theta}{2}+d \operatorname{cosec} \frac{\theta}{2}+d$$

$\therefore$ Diameter over wires

$$=\text{effective diameter}-\frac{p}{2} \cot \frac{\theta}{2}+d\left(\operatorname{cosec} \frac{\theta}{2}+1\right)$$

For threads of ISO form, whether 'Metric' or 'Unified', $\theta=60°$. Diameter over wires

$$D_w=D_e-\frac{p}{2} \cot \frac{60°}{2}+d\left(\operatorname{cosec} \frac{60°}{2}+1\right)$$

$$D_w=D_e-\frac{p}{2} \cot 30°+d(\operatorname{cosec} 30°+1)$$

$$=D_e-\frac{p \times 1 \cdot 732\ 1}{2}+d\ (2 \cdot 000\ 0+1)$$

$$=D_e-0 \cdot 866p+3d$$

Once more, the following table is provided for reference, and the reader is reminded that examination questions will be restricted to ISO-metric threads. The accuracy implied is sufficient for our studies at present, but for very precise determinations it will often be necessary to work to a greater order of accuracy.

Form	Diameter over wires
Iso-metric (Metric)	$D_e-0 \cdot 865p+3d$
Iso-inch (Unified)	$D_e-0 \cdot 865p+3d$
Whitworth	$D_e-0 \cdot 96p+3 \cdot 17d$
British Association	$D_e-1 \cdot 35p+3 \cdot 48d$

Example

Calculate the

    (*a*) nominal effective diameter, and

    (*b*) the diameter over wires of diameter 2·50 mm for an external screw designated M60×4.

(*a*)
$$D_e = D_m - 0{\cdot}65p$$
$$= 60 - 4(0{\cdot}65)$$
$$= 60 - 2{\cdot}60 = 57{\cdot}40$$

(*b*)
$$D_w = D_e - 0{\cdot}865p + 3d$$
$$= 57{\cdot}40 - 4(0{\cdot}865) + 3(2{\cdot}50)$$
$$= 57{\cdot}40 - 3{\cdot}46 + 7{\cdot}50$$
$$= 53{\cdot}94 + 7{\cdot}50$$
$$= 61{\cdot}44$$

Answers: (*a*) Nominal effective diameter = 57·4 mm
              (*b*) Distance over wires   = 61·4 mm

Problems 4.3

1. Calculate the nominal effective diameters of the following thread forms:

    (*a*) M10 (pitch is 1·5 mm)
    (*b*) M64 (pitch is 6·0 mm)
    (*c*) M30×2
    (*d*) M48×3

2. Calculate the so-called 'best size' of wire for checking external ISO-metric threads of pitch 4 mm. Give the answer to the nearest 0·01 mm.

3. Calculate the checking distance over wires for the following external threads:
    (*a*) M6 with wires of diameter 0·6 mm (pitch is 1·0 mm)
    (*b*) M36 with wires of diameter 2·5 mm (pitch is 4·0 mm)
    (*c*) M30×2 with wires of diameter 1·25 mm.

4. A thread form is designated on a drawing as

$$M48 \times 3 - 8g$$

The symbol 8g indicates the tolerance on the effective diameter, and a reference to BS 3643 shows allowable limits of from 46·004 mm to 45·668 mm.

A sample from the production lines was measured with the aid of wires of diameter 2·0 mm. The diameter over the wires was 49·255 mm. State, with a reason, whether the sample should be accepted.

5. The theoretical acme thread is based on a square thread with the flanks inclined at $14\frac{1}{2}°$ to produce an included angle of 29°.

(a) If the connection between the major diameter D_m and the effective diameter D_e is represented by
$$D_e = D_m - K_1 p \; (p \text{ being the pitch}),$$
determine the value of K_1.

(b) If the wire diameter which makes contact at the effective diameter is given by $K_2 p$, determine the value of K_2, to the nearest 0·01.

(c) If the diameter D_w over wires of diameter d is given by
$$D_w = D_e - K_3 p + K_4 d,$$
determine the values of K_3 and K_4, each to the nearest 0·01.

(d) Calculate the diameter over wires of diameter 2·60 mm for a theoretical acme thread of major diameter 40 mm and pitch 5 mm.

6. Deduce a formula of the type
$$W = E + K_1 d - K_2 p$$
for checking threads of Whitworth form,
where W is the dimension over wires of diameter d
E is the effective diameter
and p is the pitch of the thread.
Include in the formula the numerical values of K_1 and K_2.

7. A special fine thread has a nominal outside diameter of 4 in, the pitch is 0·25 in, and the threads are of Whitworth form. The thread is acceptable if the effective diameter is between nominal size and minus 0·008 in. When checked with wires of diameter 0·15 in, the dimension over wires was 4·070 in. If the flank angle and pitch are correct, calculate the effective diameter and hence state whether or not the thread is acceptable.

8. A thread often found on certain instruments of high precision manufactured in Germany is the Lowenherz thread. The thread is of vee form, the flank angle being 53° 8', and the fundamental triangle is equally truncated to produce a thread depth of 0·75 pitch. Calculate the checking dimension over rollers of diameter 0·50 mm for checking a 5-mm Lowenherz thread, the pitch being 0·80 mm.

Answers to problems 4.3

1. (a) 9·025 mm (b) 60·1 mm
   (c) 28·7 mm (d) 46·05 mm
2. 2·31 mm
3. (a) 6·285 mm (b) 37·44 mm (c) 30·72 mm
4. Acceptable, D_e is 45·85 mm which is within limits.
5. (a) $K_1=0·50$ (b) $K_2=0·52$
   (c) $K_3=1·93$, $K_4=5·00$ (d) 40·85 mm
6. $W=E+3·166d-0·96p$
7. Nominal effective diameter 3·840 in.
   Actual effective diameter 3·835 in.
   Thread is acceptable.
8. 5·22 mm

4.4 Circular Form Tools

4.4.1 BASIC GEOMETRY

An interesting example of the application of the cosine rule occurs with calculations in connection with circular form tools. These form tools are in considerable use when the expense of their manufacture is justified by their long life, the maintenance of their accuracy when reground, the ease of re-setting, and the ease of grinding an accurate form on the tool. The gashing of the tool and its mounting are arranged to produce a clearance angle β as shown in Figure 4.38.

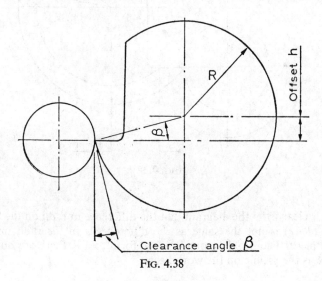

Clearance angle β

FIG. 4.38

The form tool is intentionally mounted with its centre offset from the centre of the workpiece by an amount h, and is set so that its leading edge is level with the centre of the workpiece. If β is the clearance angle, then

$$\beta = \arcsin \frac{h}{R}$$

If the form tool cuts differing diameters on the work, then the clearance angle varies according to the particular value of R, the clearance angle being a minimum when R is greatest.

Figure 4.39 shows a form tool with zero cutting rake machining concentric radii on a workpiece. The amount of offset and the resulting clearance rake have been intentionally exaggerated. The larger radius on the form tool cuts the smaller radius on the workpiece, and vice versa.

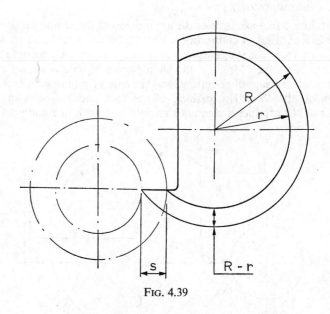

Fig. 4.39

It is clear from the diagram that the difference in radii on the form tool $(R-r)$ is not the same as the difference s in the radii on the workpiece. The profile ground on the form tool is therefore not the same as the profile on the workpiece.

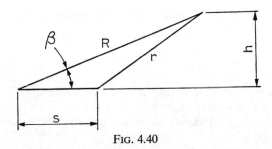

FIG. 4.40

Figure 4.40 shows the basic triangle when two concentric radii are being cut with zero rake, R being the largest radii on the form tool, r being the smallest, s is the *difference* in workpiece radii, and β is the clearance angle, where $\beta = \arcsin\dfrac{h}{R}$. R is usually fixed, and in most cases r has to be determined.

Applying the cosine rule

$$r^2 = R^2 + s^2 - 2Rs \cos \beta$$

Example

A circular form tool with zero cutting rake has a maximum diameter of 120 mm and its centre is offset relative to the workpiece by 12 mm. The form tool cuts concentric workpiece diameters of 60 mm and 80 mm.

Calculate:

(*a*) The minimum clearance angle on the form tool.

(*b*) The smaller cutting diameter of the form tool.

(*c*) The clearance angle when cutting the diameter of 80 mm.

(*a*) The minimum clearance angle occurs at the leading edge of the form tool

$$\beta = \arcsin \frac{h}{R} = \arcsin\frac{12}{60} = \arcsin 0{\cdot}2 = 11° \ 32'$$

(*b*)

$$R=60, \quad s=\frac{80-60}{2}=10, \quad \beta=11° \ 32'$$

$$\begin{aligned}
r^2 &= R^2 + s^2 - 2Rs \cos \beta \\
&= 60^2 + 10^2 - 2(60)(10)(0{\cdot}979\ 8) \\
&= 3\ 600 + 100 - 1\ 175{\cdot}76 \\
&= 2\ 524{\cdot}24 \\
r &= \sqrt{2\ 524{\cdot}24} = 50{\cdot}24
\end{aligned}$$

Smaller cutting diameter $= 2r = 2(50{\cdot}24) = 100{\cdot}48$.

Mathematics for Mechanical Technicians 2

(c) Let β_1=clearance angle at smaller diameter of form tool
$$h=12 \text{ mm} \quad R_1=50\cdot24$$

$$\beta_1=\arcsin\frac{12}{50\cdot24}=\arcsin 0\cdot238\ 9=13°\ 49'$$

Answers: (a) Clearance angle at major diameter=11° 32'
(b) Minor diameter=110·48 mm
(c) Clearance angle at minor diameter=13° 49'

Example

A circular form tool has concentric diameters of 100 mm and 88 mm. It is mounted in a holder so that its centre lies 8 mm above the workpiece diameter. The larger diameter of the form tool is set to cut a workpiece diameter of 40 mm. What is the resulting workpiece diameter cut by the smaller radius of the circular form tool?

$$\beta=\arcsin\frac{h}{R}=\arcsin\frac{8}{50}=\arcsin 0\cdot16=9°\ 12'$$

$$R=100=50, \quad r=\frac{88}{2}=44$$

$$r^2=R^2+s^2-2Rs\cos\beta$$
$$s^2-2Rs\cos\beta+(R^2-r^2)=0$$
$$s^2-(2)(50)(s)(0\cdot987\ 1)+(50^2-44^2)=0$$
$$s^2-98\cdot71s-564=0$$

Comparing with $\qquad ax^2+bx+c=0$

for which $\qquad x=\dfrac{-b\pm\sqrt{(b^2-4ac)}}{2a}$

$$x=s, \ a=1, \ b=-98\cdot71 \text{ and } c=564$$
$$s=\frac{-(-98\cdot71)\pm\sqrt{\{(-98\cdot71)^2-(4\times1\times564)\}}}{2}$$

$$=\frac{98\cdot71\pm\sqrt{(9\ 744-2\ 256)}}{2}$$

$$=\frac{98\cdot71\pm\sqrt{7\ 488}}{2}$$

$$=\frac{98\cdot71\pm86\cdot54}{2}$$

$$=\frac{12\cdot17}{2} \quad \text{(the other root is inadmissable)}$$
$$=6\cdot085$$

Larger diameter on workpiece$=40+2s$
$$=40+12 \cdot 17=52 \cdot 17$$

Answer: Diameter cut by smaller radius of form tool$=52 \cdot 17$ mm

When the solution of a problem in trigonometry finally resolves into the solution of quadratic equation, the resulting calculations usually prove to be time consuming and laborious. Occasionally, a reversion to basic fundamentals produces a method of solution which can be effected more rapidly. The foregoing problem is typical. Let us obtain a solution based on the Theorem of Pythagoras and the trigonometry of right-angled triangles. The basic information is shown in Figure 4.41.

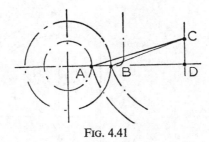

FIG. 4.41

$CD=$offset$=8$ mm
$CA=$major radius of form tool $=50$ mm
$CB=$minor radius of form tool$=44$ mm
$AB=$difference of workpiece radii.

Using the Theorem of Pythagoras
$$(AD)^2=(CA)^2-(CD)^2=(50)^2-(8)^2$$
$$=2\ 500-64=2\ 436$$
$$AD=\sqrt{2\ 436}=49 \cdot 36$$

Similarly
$$(BD)^2=(CB)^2-(CD)^2=(44)^2-(8)^2$$
$$=1\ 936-64=1\ 872$$
$$BD=\sqrt{1\ 872}=43 \cdot 26$$
$$AB=AD-BD=49 \cdot 36-43 \cdot 26=6 \cdot 10$$

Larger workpiece diameter$=40+2(6 \cdot 10)$
$$=40+12 \cdot 20=52 \cdot 20$$

Answer: Diameter cut by smaller radius of form tool$=52 \cdot 20$ mm

(The reader is reminded that we have decided to carry out all calculations in this chapter using four-figure tables, but that in many problems

211

encountered in practice the use of four-figure tables does not provide sufficient accuracy. It is the adoption of four-figure tables which has led to the slight difference between the results.)

Although the calculations in the Part II syllabus are limited to tools with zero cutting rake, the reader may care to note the interesting combination of the use of the sine and cosine rules when it does become necessary to include a cutting rake.

Figure 4.42 shows the form tool cutting concentric diameters of W_1 and W_2, with cutting rake α. If R is the larger radius of the form tool, then the clearance angle β is again $\arcsin\dfrac{h}{R}$. Figure 4.43 shows the basic triangles.

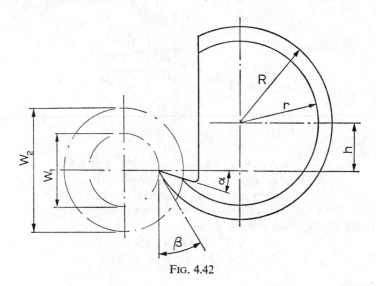

FIG. 4.42

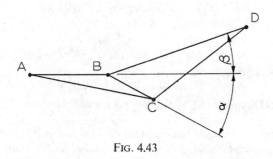

FIG. 4.43

In triangle ABC, $AB = \dfrac{W_1}{2}$ and $AC = \dfrac{W_2}{2}$, while angle B is $180° - a$.

The sine rule can be used to find angle C, and since angle B is known, angle A can be determined. The use of the sine rule once more enables side BC to be found. If we now consider triangle BCD and apply the cosine rule,

$$r^2 = R^2 + x^2 - 2\,Rx \cos(a + \beta)$$
where x = side BC in triangle ABC

Problems 4.4

1. A circular form tool with zero top rake has a major diameter of 100 mm. Its centre is offset relative to the work by 10 mm. Calculate the clearance angle at the leading edge.

2. A circular form tool with zero top rake has cutting diameters of 100 mm, 90 mm, and 70 mm. If the offset of the workpiece and the cutting tool is 5 mm, calculate the clearance angles at each of the cutting diameters.

3. A circular form tool with zero top rake is to cut concentric diameters of 34 mm and 50 mm. The major diameter of the form tool is 100 mm and the offset of form tool and workpiece is 10 mm. Calculate:
   (a) The minor diameter of the form tool.
   (b) The clearance angle when cutting the diameter of 50 mm.

4. Figure 4.44 shows a circular form tool with zero top rake cutting two concentric diameters which differ by 15 mm. The circular form tool has a major diameter of 100 mm and its centre is offset relative to the work by 12 mm. Calculate:
   (a) The clearance angle A when cutting the smaller work diameter.
   (b) The minor diameter of the form tool (shown as d in the figure).
   (c) The clearance angle B when cutting the larger work diameter.

(C.G.L.I.)

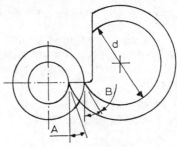

FIG. 4.44

5. Concentric diameters of 60 mm and 80 mm are to be turned on a workpiece. The minimum clearance angle is to be 8°, and the maximum diameter of the form tool of zero cutting rake to be used is to be 120 mm.

Calculate:

(*a*) The offset of the form tool centre relative to the centre of the workpiece.

(*b*) The smaller cutting diameter of the form tool.

(*c*) The clearance angle at the smaller cutting diameter.

6. Two concentric diameters are required on a workpiece of diameters 50 mm and 80 mm. A circular form tool with zero cutting rake is drawn from the stores, having cutting diameters of 100 mm and 130 mm and used in a form tool holder having an offset of 10 mm. If the 50-mm diameter on the workpiece is held, what is the resulting error on the diameter nominally 80mm?

7. A symmetrical vee of 60° included angle is required to be cut on a workpiece so that the depth of the vee is 8 mm. The cutting is to be accomplished with a circular form tool of outside diameter 80 mm, its centre being offset with respect to the centre of the workpiece by 10 mm. Calculate the included vee-angle to be ground on the form tool. (The very slight deviation from straight sides of the vee on the workpiece can be neglected, and the tool has zero cutting rake.)

Answers to problems 4.4

1. 11° 32′
2. 5° 44′, 6° 23′, and 8° 13′
3. (*a*) 84·4 mm   (*b*) 13° 43′
4. (*a*) 13° 53′   (*b*) 71·3 mm   (*c*) 19° 40′

5. (*a*) 8·35 mm   (*b*) 100·2 mm   (*c*) 9° 37′
6. Oversize on diameter by 0·48 mm
7. 62° 2′

4.5 Spur Gear Tooth Profiles

4.5.1 THE METRIC MODULE

When the teeth of a spur gear are being cut in a blank it becomes necessary to check whether or not the resulting teeth are of correct form. There are interesting inspection machines available for the rapid inspection of gears, but these are expensive and need considerable usage to justify their installation. Nevertheless, their installation is essential if a high degree of accuracy is required. In certain circumstances, the desired accuracy may be such that other methods of checking may be acceptable. One method of checking is to use a *gear tooth vernier caliper*. This consists of two vernier calipers permanently assembled at right angles so that the width of a tooth at a specific distance from the outside of the spur gear can be determined.

When gears are designed in metric sizes, the characteristic size is denoted by what is called the *module*, usually given the symbol *m*. The pitch circle diameter is found by multiplying the module by the number of teeth. Hence, if

m=the module
N=the number of teeth on the spur gear,

then the p.c.d.$=mN$

The addendum of a spur gear is equal to the module. Hence the outside diameter of a spur gear having *N* teeth of metric module is obtained from

$$o.d. = p.c.d. + 2 \text{ (addendum)}$$
$$= mN + 2m$$
$$= m(N+2)$$

If the gear has *N* teeth of module *m*, we have already stated that the pitch circle diameter is given by *mN*. The pitch circle circumference is therefore πmN and the *equivalent circular pitch p* is given by

$$\frac{\text{pitch circle circumference}}{\text{number of teeth,}}$$

i.e. $$p = \frac{\pi mN}{N}$$

or $$p = \pi m$$

For instance, taking π as 3·142, the equivalent circular pitch of gears of 5 mm module is 15·71 mm.

4.5.2 CHORD AT THE PITCH CIRCLE

One easily established pair of co-ordinates are those which apply to the chordal distance at the pitch circle, shown as x and y in Figure 4.45. Let us consider a spur gear of N teeth having a module of m.

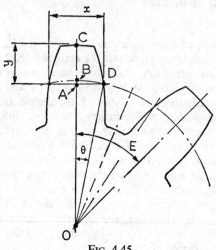

FIG. 4.45

In the right-angled triangle OAD,

$$AD=\frac{x}{2}, \quad OD=\text{pitch circle radius}=\frac{mN}{2}$$

If there are N teeth, angle $E=\dfrac{360°}{N}$

The angle θ is

$$\frac{E}{4}=\left(\frac{360°}{N}\div4\right)=\frac{90°}{N}$$

$$AD=OD \sin \theta$$

$$\frac{x}{2}=\frac{mN}{2} \sin \frac{90°}{N}$$

whence

$$x=mN \sin \frac{90°}{N}$$

$$y=CA=CB+BA$$

$$CB=\text{addendum}=m$$

$$BA=OB-OA$$

$$=\text{pitch circle radius}$$

$$-\text{pitch circle radius}\left(\cos \frac{90°}{N}\right)$$

$$= \frac{mN}{2} \left(1 - \cos \frac{90°}{N} \right)$$

$$\therefore \quad y = m + \frac{mN}{2} \left(1 - \cos \frac{90°}{N} \right)$$

If the circular pitch system is used, then $P\pi$ can be substituted for m.

It should be noted that the x and y co-ordinates thus obtained apply to a tooth of theoretically perfect form. Meshing spur gears must be provided with backlash so that an oil film can form and for the gears to expand due to heat generated in running, without applying bending loads to the shafts of the gears. It is usual to sink in the cutter a little further than the theoretical distance to provide the backlash. In which case the vernier can be set to theoretical dimensions and a feeler gauge used to determine the amount of backlash. (If the excess cut is applied to both of the meshing gears and the pressure angle is 20°, the extra depth of sinking the cutter is given by the amount of backlash multiplied by 0·73.)

4.5.3 THE CONSTANT CHORD

A minor difficulty caused by using co-ordinates applying to the chordal thickness at the pitch line is that every combination of N and m requires individual calculations. It is possible to establish a set of co-ordinates which, for a given pressure angle, depend upon m only, being constant for any value of N. These are often referred to as *constant chord* co-ordinates.

All involute spur gears of a given diametral pitch mesh with the appropriate basic involute rack. A tooth in a rack is shown in Figure 4.46.

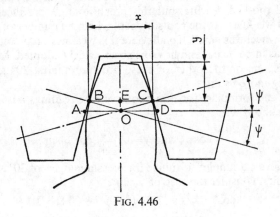

FIG. 4.46

Irrespective of the number of teeth on the gear, if the gear and rack are of theoretically correct form, contact occurs at points B and C, the angle ψ being the pressure angle of the gear system. Consequently, co-ordinates x and y apply to a gear of any number of teeth for a given metric module of given pressure angle. In particular the co-ordinate x is known as the *constant chord*.

In triangle AOB, $$OA = \frac{\text{circular pitch}}{4} = \frac{\pi m}{4}$$

$$OB = OA \cos \psi = \frac{\pi m}{4} \cos \psi$$

In the triangle OBE,

$$\frac{x}{2} = BE = OB \cos \psi = \frac{\pi m}{4} \cos^2 \psi$$

hence $$x = \frac{\pi m}{2} \cos^2 \psi \text{ (when } m \text{ is the module)}$$

or $$x = \frac{p}{2} \cos^2 \psi \text{ (when } p \text{ is the circular pitch)}$$

$$EO = OB \sin \psi$$

$$= \frac{\pi m}{4} \cos \psi \sin \psi$$

$$y = \text{addendum} - EO = m - \frac{\pi m}{4} \cos \psi \sin \psi \text{ (when } m \text{ is the module)}$$

or $$y = \frac{p}{\pi} - \frac{p}{4} \cos \psi \sin \psi \text{ (when } p \text{ is the circular pitch)}$$

At one time, a pressure angle of $14\frac{1}{2}°$ was invariably applied to standard toothed gearing, but this pressure angle produced a pronounced weakness at the roots of teeth when the number of teeth on the gear wheel was small. To alleviate this weakness, a pressure angle of $20°$ was introduced, and has since been widely adopted. Most spur gears use one or the other of these pressure angles, $20°$ gradually becoming more usual.

Using the formulae for gear tooth vernier readings based on the constant chord, viz.

$$x = \frac{\pi m}{2} \cos^2 \psi \text{ and } y = m - \frac{\pi m}{4} \cos \psi \sin \psi,$$

we will develop simpler formulae for pressure angles of $20°$ and $14\frac{1}{2}°$. We will first consider the case of $\psi = 20°$.

$$\cos^2 \psi = \cos^2 20° = (0.939\ 7)^2 = 0.883\ 0$$

$$x=\frac{\pi m}{2}\cos^2 \psi=1\cdot570\ 8m\times0\cdot883\ 0=1\cdot387\ 1m$$

$$y=m-\frac{\pi m}{4}\cos \psi \sin \psi$$

$$=m\left(1-\frac{\pi}{4}\cos 20°\sin 20°\right)=0\cdot747\ 6m$$

For circular pitch

$$x=\frac{p}{2}\cos^2 \psi=\frac{p}{2}\times0\cdot883\ 0=0\cdot441\ 5p$$

$$y=p\left(\frac{1}{\pi}-\frac{1}{4}\cos \psi \sin \psi\right)$$

$$=p\{0\cdot318\ 3-(0\cdot25)(0\cdot939\ 7)(0\cdot342\ 0)\}$$
$$=p\{0\cdot318\ 3-0\cdot080\ 3\}=0\cdot238\ 0p$$

Similar calculations could be made for a $14\frac{1}{2}°$ pressure angle, finally producing the following results:

	20° pressure angle		$14\frac{1}{2}°$ pressure angle	
	x	y	x	y
Module m	$1\cdot387\ 1m$	$0\cdot747\ 6m$	$1\cdot472\ 3m$	$0\cdot809\ 6m$
Circular pitch p	$0\cdot441\ 5p$	$0\cdot238\ 0p$	$0\cdot468\ 6p$	$0\cdot257\ 7p$

Example

A spur gear has 20 teeth of 5 mm module, the pressure angle being 20°. Determine co-ordinates for use of a gear tooth vernier caliper:
(a) Based on the chordal thickness at the pitch circle.
(b) Based on the constant chord.

(a)
$$x=mN \sin \frac{90°}{N}=20\times5\times\sin \frac{90°}{20}$$

$$=100 \sin 4°\ 30'=100\times0\cdot0785=7\cdot85\text{ mm}$$

$$y=m+\frac{mN}{2}\left(1-\cos \frac{90°}{N}\right)=5+\frac{5\times20}{2}(1-\cos 4°\ 30')$$

$$=5+50(1-0\cdot996\ 9)=5+50(0\cdot003\ 1)$$
$$=5+0\cdot155=5\cdot155\text{ mm}$$

(b)
$$x = \frac{\pi m}{2} \cos^2 \psi = \frac{\pi \times 5}{2}(\cos 20°)^2$$
$$= 3\cdot141\ 6 \times 2\cdot5 \times (0\cdot939\ 7)^2$$
$$= 7\cdot854 \times 0\cdot883\ 0 = 6\cdot935 \text{ mm}$$

$$y = m - \frac{\pi m}{4} \cos \psi \sin \psi$$
$$= 5 - \frac{3\cdot1416 \times 5}{4}(\cos 20°)(\sin 20°)$$
$$= 5 - 3\cdot927(0\cdot939\ 7)(0\cdot342\ 0)$$
$$= 5 - 1\cdot262 = 3\cdot738 \text{ mm}$$

Answers: (a) $x = 7\cdot85$ mm, $y = 5\cdot16$ mm
(b) $x = 6\cdot94$ mm, $y = 3\cdot74$ mm

Referring to Figure 4.46, if a roller has a radius of OB it will lie in the rack with its centre on the pitch point O. Such a roller will also lie with its centre at the pitch point if it lay in a tooth space of a theoretical gear. This provides a convenient method of checking pitch errors over tooth spaces.

If d = diameter of roller, $d = 2(OB) = \frac{\pi m}{2} \cos \psi$. If the number of tooth spaces is T, the angle subtended at the centre of the gear by the centre-lines of the tooth spaces is $\frac{T}{N}(360°)$ when the gear has N teeth.

The centre distance of rollers is given by

$$2 \text{ (pitch circle radius) } \sin \left\{ \frac{\frac{T}{N}(360°)}{2} \right\},$$

hence the centre distance $= mN \sin \frac{T}{N}(180°)$.

Example

Calculate the nominal diameter of plugs for checking a spur gear of 20 teeth of 5 mm module, pressure angle 20°. Calculate also the centre distance of these plugs over 8 tooth spaces.

Diameter of plugs
$$= \frac{\pi m}{2} \cos \psi$$
$$= \frac{3\cdot141\ 6 \times 5}{2}(\cos 20°)$$
$$= 7\cdot854 \times 0\cdot939\ 7$$
$$= 7\cdot380 \text{ mm}$$

Centre distance $= mN \sin \dfrac{T}{N} (180°)$

$$= 5 \times 20 \sin \left(\frac{8 \times 180°}{20} \right)$$

$$= 100 \sin 72° = 100 \times 0·951 1$$

$$= 95·11 \text{ mm}$$

Answers: Plug diameter $= 7·38$ mm
Centre distance $= 95·1$ mm

Problems 4.5

1. Calculate a pair of gear tooth vernier readings for the chord at the pitch circle for a spur gear having 36 teeth of 2·5 mm module.

2. Calculate a pair of gear tooth vernier readings for the chord at the pitch circle for a spur gear of 20 teeth meshing with a rack of circular pitch 5 mm.

3. Calculate the 'constant chord' of the following gear forms:
   (a) 20° pressure angle, 2 mm module.
   (b) 15 mm circular pitch, $14\frac{1}{2}$° pressure angle.
   (c) $14\frac{1}{2}$° pressure angle, 5 mm module.

4. Calculate the diameter of a roller that will lie in a gear tooth form of 10 mm module, 20° pressure angle, so that its centre will lie on the pitch circle diameter.

5. Calculate the centre distance between two rollers which lie on the pitch circle of a spur gear having 30 teeth of 10 mm circular pitch, the rollers being 7 tooth spaces apart.

6. A spur gear having 40 teeth is to mesh with a rack of pitch 5 mm, the pressure angle being 20°.
   Calculate:
   (a) The pitch circle diameter of the gear.
   (b) The outside diameter of the gear.
   (c) The settings for a gear tooth vernier caliper,
      (i) based on chordal contact at the pitch circle diameter,
      (ii) based on the 'constant chord'.

7. It is common continental practice to describe a spur gear tooth size by quoting the 'metric module', this being the addendum in

millimetres. The metric module is therefore the pitch circle diameter in millimetres divided by the number of teeth. A spur gear has 50 teeth of 5 mm metric module, the pressure angle being 20°. Determine, in millimetres:

(*a*) The pitch circle diameter.

(*b*) The outside diameter.

(*c*) The plug diameter so that the centre of the plug lies on the pitch circle diameter.

(*d*) The checking distance over 10 tooth spaces.

(*e*) The 'constant-chord' settings for a gear tooth vernier caliper.

8. A spur gear has 40 teeth of 1 mm module, the pressure angle being 20°. The pitch circle diameter is known to be correct.

(*a*) Determine the diameter of a plug so that when placed in a tooth space, its centre will lie on the pitch circle diameter.

(*b*) Using plugs of correct diameter, chordal distances were found over differing numbers of tooth spaces, producing the following data:

No. of tooth spaces	2	4	6	8	10	12	14
Chord (mm)	6·316	12·46	18·22	23·51	28·22	32·26	35·58

By determining the errors in chordal distances, show that the angular dividing is in error.

Answers to problems 4.5

1. $x=3·92$ mm, $y=2·55$ mm
2. $x=2·50$ mm, $y=1·64$ mm
3. (*a*) 2·77 mm   (*b*) 7·03 mm   (*c*) 7·36 mm
4. 14·8 mm
5. 63·9 mm
6. (*a*) 63·7 mm   (*b*) 66·8 mm
   (*c*) (i) $x=2·50$ mm, $y=1·62$ mm
        (ii) $x=2·21$ mm, $y=1·19$ mm
7. (*a*) 250 mm   (*b*) 260 mm   (*c*) 7·38 mm
   (*d*) 147 mm   (*e*) $x=6·94$ mm, $y=3·74$ mm
8. (*a*) 1·48 mm
   (*b*) Errors, in units of 0·01 mm, are
        +6, +10, +6, 0, −6, −10, −6

4.6 Solid Geometry

4.6.1 STANDARD CONVENTION FOR INDICATING A POINT IN SPACE

In Chapter 3 of Book 1, it was shown how a point on a plane could be represented by cartesian co-ordinates, that is, by reference to two axes at right angles which intersect at the origin. The position of a point in space can be represented in a similar manner by the introduction of a third reference axis.

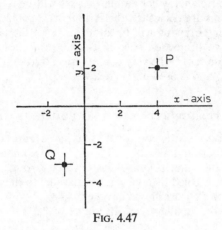

FIG. 4.47

In Figure 4.47, P represents the point $(4, 2)$, and Q represents the point $(-1, -3)$. Now let us introduce a third reference axis which passes through the origin at right angles to both the x-axis and the y-axis. This axis, quite logically, can be termed the z-axis. If the xy plane is horizontal, this axis will pass through the origin vertically. If we agree to let distances above the xy plane be positive and distances below the xy plane be negative, then $(4, 2, 5)$ will be a point 5 units above P. Similarly $(-1, -3, -2)$ will be a point 2 units below Q.

The use of this convention will considerably assist in the solving of problems involving solid geometry. There are many problems associated with points, lines, and planes in space to which rapid solutions can be effected by means of specific formulae pertinent only to those particular problems. *The reader is warned against collecting a set of such formulae. It is far better to adopt fundamental principles which can be applied generally than a set of trick solutions applicable only to special cases.*

A major difficulty facing the student in solving problems on solid geometry is the construction of diagrams to illustrate points, lines and planes in space. *No attempt should ever be made to do this by perspective or isometric sketches since this leads to interesting but most disconcerting optical illusions.* Some problems in solid geometry eventually lead to the positioning of two points in space. We will adopt two conventions, viz. :

(a) That if P is a point in space having the co-ordinates (x, y, z), then P_o is a point vertically in line with P on some arbitrary horizontal plane, which in many cases will be the xy plane.

(b) If diagrams are necessary, the formal orthogonal projection of engineering drawing will be adopted. Since the advantages of third-angle projection over first-angle projection are obvious to all those except the very conservative, third-angle projection is advised and is used in this text.

4.6.2 THE DISTANCE BETWEEN TWO POINTS IN SPACE

Let P be a point having co-ordinates (x_1, y_1, z_1) and Q be another point having co-ordinates (x_2, y_2, z_2). Let Q_0 be a point immediately underneath Q on a horizontal plane passing through P. The true length of PQ is revealed by a view taken parallel to the xy plane and at right angles to PQ_0, as shown in Figure 4.48.

Referring to the auxiliary view in Figure 4.48,

$$QQ_0=(z_2-z_1)$$

Since Q_0 is directly underneath Q

$$(PQ_0)^2=(x_2-x_1)^2+(y_2-y_1)^2$$

Using the Theorem of Pythagoras,

$$(PQ)^2=(PQ_0)^2+(QQ_0)^2$$
$$=(x_2-x_1)^2+(y_2-y_1)^2+(z_2-z_1)^2$$

whence $\quad PQ=\sqrt{\{(x_2-x_1)^2+(y_2-y_1)^2+(z_2-z_1)^2\}}$

4.6.3 THE ANGLE THAT A LINE MAKES WITH A HORIZONTAL PLANE

Referring to the auxiliary view in Figure 4.48, the true angle that PQ makes with any horizontal plane is the angle QPQ_0.

$$\angle QPQ_0=\arctan\frac{QQ_0}{PQ_0}$$

$$=\arctan\frac{z_2-z_1}{\sqrt{\{(x_2-x_1)^2+(y_2-y_1)^2\}}}$$

$$=\arctan\sqrt{\left(\frac{(z_2-z_1)^2}{(x_2-x_1)^2+(y_2-y_1)^2}\right)}$$

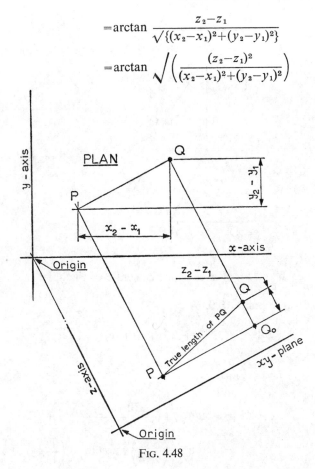

FIG. 4.48

Example

    $ABCDE$ is a right rectangular pyramid with the apex at E. The vertical height is 6 m. $AB=CD=4$ m, $BC=DA=6$ m.
Calculate.

(*a*) The true length of AE.

(*b*) The true angle that an edge such as AE makes with the horizontal.

(*c*) The true angle that a face such as AEB makes with the horizontal.

The pyramid is shown in Figure 4.49.

225

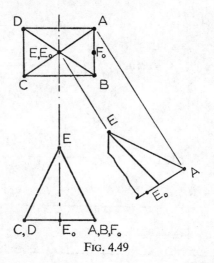

FIG. 4.49

(a) Let the origin of axes lie at the centre of the base.
E_0 is the origin
E is the point $(0, 0, 6)$
A is the point $(3, 2, 0)$
$$EA = \sqrt{\{(3-0)^2+(2-0)^2+(0-6)^2\}}$$
$$= \sqrt{\{(3)^2+(2)^2+(-6)^2\}}$$
$$= \sqrt{(9+4+36)}$$
$$= \sqrt{49}$$
$$= 7 \text{ units}$$

(b)
$$\angle EAE_0 = \arctan \sqrt{\left(\frac{(0-6)^2}{(3-0)^2+(2-0)^2}\right)}$$
$$= \arctan \sqrt{\left(\frac{36}{9+4}\right)} = \arctan \sqrt{\left(\frac{36}{13}\right)}$$
$$= \arctan \sqrt{2 \cdot 770} = \arctan 1 \cdot 664 = 59° \ 0'$$

(c) Let F_0 be a point midway between A and B.
The true angle that face EAB makes with the horizontal is
$\angle EF_0E_0$
E is the point $(0, 0, 6)$
F_0 is the point $(3, 0, 0)$
$$\angle EF_0E_0 = \arctan \sqrt{\left(\frac{(0-6)^2}{(3-0)^2+(0-0)^2}\right)}$$
$$= \arctan \sqrt{\left(\frac{36}{9+0}\right)} = \arctan \sqrt{4}$$
$$= \arctan 2 \cdot 000 = 63° \ 26'$$

The answers can be rough-checked by scaling the diagram.

Answers: (*a*) *AE* is 7 m long
(*b*) *AE* is at 59° 0' to the horizontal
(*c*) Face *AEB* is at 63° 26' to the horizontal

4.6.4 THE ANGLE BETWEEN A PLANE IN SPACE AND A HORIZONTAL PLANE

When a plane in space intersects a horizontal plane, the intersection of the two planes produces a single line lying on the horizontal plane. Any number of lines can be drawn on the plane in space, these lying at varying angles in space depending upon their position on the plane in space. There will, however, be a series of lines on the plane in space which lie at a maximum angle to the horizontal plane, these being termed '*lines of greatest slope*'. The angle that a plane in space makes with a horizontal plane is taken as the true angle that any line of greatest slope makes with any horizontal plane. Hence, in order to determine the angle that a plane in space makes with the horizontal, two points on any line of greatest slope can be determined, and their co-ordinates used to determine the required angle. The plan view of a line of greatest slope lies at right angles to the line of intersection of the planes, hence the true angle that a line of greatest slope makes with the horizontal plane is revealed by an auxiliary view taken horizontally, at right angles to the projection of the line of greatest slope onto the horizontal plane.

If the dimensioning of the original problem is mainly in rectangular co-ordinates, a solution can be obtained by determining the co-ordinates of two points on a line of greatest slope and then determining the angle θ (to the horizontal) using the formula

$$\theta = \arctan \sqrt{\left(\frac{(z_2 - z_1)^2}{(x_2 - x_1)^2 + (y_2 - y_1)^2} \right)}$$

If the dimensioning of the original problem is mainly in angles, an auxiliary view should be drawn to indicate a line of greatest slope, and applications of trigonometrical ratios used to determine the angle. *It is repeated that it is unwise to remember a set of formulae suitable for specific dimensioning.*

Example

Calculate the angle θ that the end of the rectangular bar shown in Figure 4.50 makes with the horizontal.

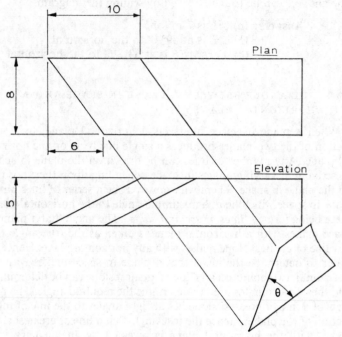

FIG. 4.50

Let the xy horizontal plane be the base of the rectangular bar. In Figure 4.51, the graphical field is the xy plane, O being the origin of rectangular co-ordinates.

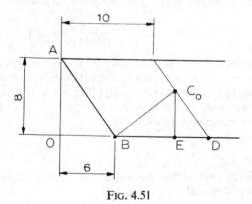

FIG. 4.51

AB is the intersection line of the sloping plane with the horizontal plane. *C* is an imaginary point on the sloping plane immediately above C_0. The angle made by the sloping plane is the angle CBC_0. We will solve the problem by determining the solid co-ordinates of *B* and *C*.

With rectangular co-ordinates, *A* is the point (0, 8)

B is the point (6, 0)

$AB = \sqrt{(8^2 + 6^2)} = 10$, *AOB* being a right-angled triangle with its sides in the proportion of 3, 4, 5.

The triangles *AOB*, BC_0D and BEC_0 are all similar.

If $BD = 10$, $\qquad BC_0 = 8$

$$EC_0 = \frac{3}{5} \times 8 = 4 \cdot 8$$

$$BE = \frac{4}{5} \times 8 = 6 \cdot 4$$

In terms of solid co-ordinates, *O* being the origin of co-ordinates,

B is the point (6, 0, 0)

C is the point (12·4, 4·8, 5)

$$\text{Tan } \angle CBC_0 = \sqrt{\left(\frac{(5-0)^2}{(12\cdot4-6)^2 + (4\cdot8-0)^2} \right)} = \sqrt{\left(\frac{5^2}{6\cdot4^2 + 4\cdot8^2} \right)}$$

$$= \sqrt{\left(\frac{25}{40\cdot96 + 23\cdot04} \right)} = \sqrt{\left(\frac{25}{64} \right)} = \frac{5}{8} = 0\cdot625$$

$$\angle CBC_0 = 32°$$

Answer: Plane makes 32° with the horizontal

Let us now consider the solving of the previous problem using trigonometrical ratios instead of solid co-ordinates. We will first establish the basic formula, which is the only one in connection with auxiliary views of such general usage that the author recommends the reader to memorize.

Figure 4.52 shows a triangular prism, the true angle of the sloping face to the horizontal base is the angle *A*. The angle *A* is the angle seen when the prism is viewed normally. If we look at a triangular face from an angle which lies at *B* to the normal, the angle *A* apparently increases to *C*. Let us establish a connection between

(i) the true angle *A*

(ii) the angle from normal *B*

and (iii) the apparent angle *C*.

229

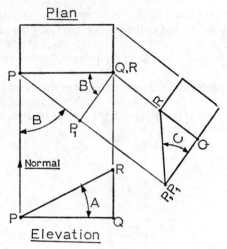

Fig. 4.52

Let the base of the prism have unit length.
Then $PQ=1$ and $RQ=\tan A$.

$$P_1Q = PQ\cos B = \cos B, \text{ since } PQ=1$$

$$\tan C = \frac{RQ}{P_1Q} = \frac{\tan A}{\cos B}$$

$$\therefore \tan A = \cos B \tan C$$

We will now use this relationship to solve the previous problem

$$\tan A \text{ (when viewed normally)} = \frac{5}{10} = 0{\cdot}5$$

Angle of view from normal $=$ angle $B = \arctan \dfrac{6}{8}$

$$= \arctan 0{\cdot}75 = 36° \ 52'$$

$$\cos B = \cos 36° \ 52' = 0{\cdot}8$$
$$\tan A = \cos B \tan C$$
$$0{\cdot}5 = 0{\cdot}8 \tan C$$

$$\tan C = \frac{0{\cdot}5}{0{\cdot}8} = 0{\cdot}625$$

$\theta =$ the angle C, $\quad \therefore \quad \theta = \arctan 0{\cdot}625 = 32°$

Answer: Plane makes 32° with the horizontal, as obtained
previously

Example

The block shown in Figure 4.53 has a square base. Calculate the angle that the sloping face makes with the base of the block.

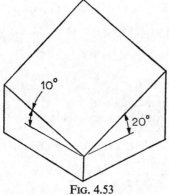

Fig. 4.53

We will take as the origin of solid co-ordinates the lowest point on the sloping face, and let it be O. The other three corners are A, B, and C. A_0, B_0 and C_0 are points on the same level as O, directly below A, B, and C. Figure 4.54 shows the plan view, EO being the line of intersection of the sloping face with a horizontal plane through O, and OD, at right angles to EO, is a line of greatest slope.

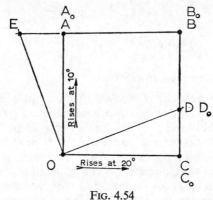

Fig. 4.54

Let the side of the square be of unit length

$$AA_0 = \tan 10° = 0.176\ 3$$
$$EA_0 = AA_0 \cot 20° = 0.176\ 3 \times 2.747\ 5 = 0.484\ 4$$
$$\text{Tan } \angle EOA_0 = \frac{EA_0}{A_0O} = 0.484\ 4 = 25° 51'$$
$$\angle D_0OC_0 = \angle EOA_0 = 25° 51'$$
$$C_0D_0 = EA_0 = 0.484\ 4$$
$$OD_0 = 1 \times \sec 25° 51' = 1.111\ 2$$
$$DD_0 = 1 \times \tan 20° + 0.484\ 4 \tan 10°$$
$$= 0.364\ 0 + 0.484\ 4(0.176\ 3)$$
$$= 0.364\ 0 + 0.085\ 4 = 0.449\ 4$$

231

Angle of plane=angle of line of greatest slope

$$=\arctan \frac{DD_0}{OD_0}=\arctan \frac{0\cdot449\ 4}{1\cdot111\ 2}$$

$$=\arctan 0\cdot404\ 4=22°$$

Answer: Sloping face lies at 22° to the base

The same result could be obtained in a slightly different way, once the angle 25° 51′ has been obtained.

$$\tan A=\cos B \tan C.$$

The normal view of the edge OC shows an angle A of 20°.
The plane is now viewed at 25° 51′ to the normal, the angle B is therefore 25° 51′.
A line of greatest slope makes an angle C with the horizontal.

$$\tan C=\frac{\tan A}{\cos B}=\frac{\tan 20°}{\cos 25° 51′}$$

$$=\frac{0\cdot364\ 0}{0\cdot899\ 9}=0\cdot404\ 5$$

$$\therefore \text{ Angle } C=22°, \text{ as previously}$$

4.6.5 THE COMPOUND SINE TABLE

A hole whose centre-line lies at a compound angle in space can be brought into a desired position by a combination of rotational movements. A typical example of the type of equipment used for such positioning is the compound 'rotate and tilt' table supplied as ancillary equipment with a jig-boring machine of high quality. This is not the only item of equipment that can be used for positioning lines and/or planes in space. A cheaper and more commonly occurring item of workshop equipment is the *compound sine table*. Article 4.9 of Book 1 described the use of the sine bar. It was shown that if the sine bar is tilted to an angle of θ, the centre distance of the rollers being L, then the vertical separation of the roller centres h is given by

$$h=L \sin \theta$$

Figure 4.55 shows diagrammatically how two sine bars are incorporated at right angles in the compound sine table.

One roller of each sine bar acts as a hinge, and by using two different slip gauge piles, the table containing the tee slots can be arranged to lie at a required angle in space. In certain cases, for convenience, a precision rectangular prism may be used on the tee-slotted table to keep the height of the slip gauge piles to reasonable values, since in view of the loss of accuracy shown in article 4.9 of Book 1, a sine bar should not be tilted to an angle approaching 90°.

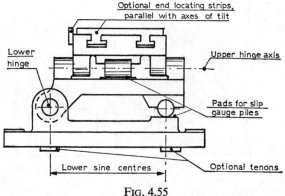

Fig. 4.55

If no slip gauge piles are inserted, the top of the compound sine table, in its closed position, is horizontal.

It will be observed that there are two locating strips at right angles to the tee-slotted table, these lying parallel to the hinge axes. Most problems eventually resolve into finding two angles at right angles to each other so that a particular surface is brought into a horizontal position when suitable slip gauge piles are used. Occasionally, the compound sine table may be used to arrange for the centre-line of a hole to lie vertically. Usually the calculation of the first angle of tilt is quite a simple one, but it must be clearly recognized that once this first tilting has been performed, it could affect the positioning of planes and centre-lines when these are being considered in the determination of the second angle of tilt.

Example

Figure 4.56 shows three views, in third-angle projection, of a bar of rectangular cross-section having a machined face lying at a compound angle in space.

ABCD is the base of the bar. This base is to lie on a compound sine table, located along edges *AB* and *BC*. The machined face is to be brought to a horizontal position, first by tilting about axis *AB* and then a subsequent tilting about an axis at right angles to *AB*. If both sine bar centres are 200 mm, determine the heights of suitable slip gauge piles.

233

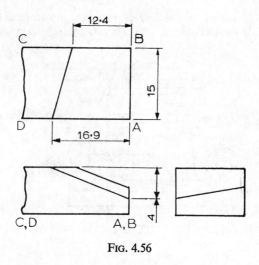

FIG. 4.56

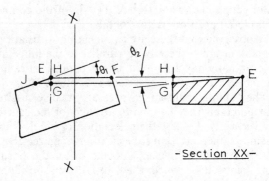

FIG. 4.57

The first tilting will bring line *EF* to a horizontal position, the angle of tilt being θ_1, as shown in Figure 4.57

$$\angle \theta_1 = \operatorname{arccot} \frac{16 \cdot 9}{4} = \operatorname{arccot} 4 \cdot 225$$
$$= 13° \ 19'$$

Height of slip gauge pile $= 200 \sin 13° \ 19' = 200(0 \cdot 2303) = 46 \cdot 06$. The first tilting will bring section *XX* vertical. The second tilting must be through an angle θ_2, so that line *GE* becomes horizontal.

$$JH=JE=16\cdot9-12\cdot4=4\cdot5$$
$$GH=4\cdot5 \sin \theta_1=4\cdot5 \sin 13°\ 19'$$
$$=4\cdot5(0\cdot230\ 3)=1\cdot036$$
$$\angle\theta_2=\arctan \frac{GH}{HE}=\arctan \frac{1\cdot036}{51}=\arctan 0\cdot069\ 1$$
$$=3°\ 57'$$
Height of slip gauge pile$=200 \sin 3°\ 57'=200\times0\cdot068\ 9$
$$=13\cdot98$$

Answers: Slip gauge pile (first setting, about axis AB)$=46\cdot1$ mm
Slip gauge pile (second setting) $\qquad=14\cdot0$ mm

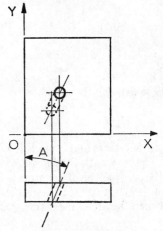

Example

In Figure 4.58, the centre-line of the hole cuts the base of the jig plate at the point (1, 1, 0), and cuts the top of the plate at the point (1·2, 1·3, 0·8). The base of the plate is therefore the xy plane through the origin. The hole is to be brought vertical on a compound sine table by first tilting by an angle A about the y-axis and then an angle B. Determine the two angles of tilt.

FIG. 4.58

$$\angle A=\arctan \frac{x_2-x_1}{z_2-z_1}=\arctan \frac{1\cdot2-1\cdot0}{0\cdot8-0}$$
$$=\arctan \frac{0\cdot2}{0\cdot8}=\arctan 0\cdot25=14°\ 2'$$

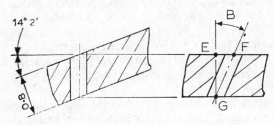

FIG. 4.59

235

After tilting by an angle A, the plate takes the position indicated in Figure 4.59. A tilt by an angle B will now bring the hole vertical.

$$EF = y_2 - y_1 = 1\cdot3 - 1\cdot0$$
$$= 0\cdot3$$

$$EG = (z_2 - z_1) \sec A$$
$$= 0\cdot8 \sec A$$
$$= 0\cdot8(1\cdot030\ 8)$$
$$= 0\cdot824\ 6$$

$$\angle B = \operatorname{arccot} \frac{EG}{EF}$$

$$= \operatorname{arccot} \frac{0\cdot8246}{0\cdot3} = \operatorname{arccot} 2\cdot749$$
$$= 20° \ 0'$$

Answers: Angle of tilt $(OY$ axis$) = 14° \ 2'$
Angle of tilt $(OX$ axis$) = 20° \ 0'$

Problems 4.6

1. A tension spring has an unladen length of 60 mm and extends for 1 mm for every 5 N of applied load. The lower attachment point has co-ordinates, in millimetres, of (10, 20, 30). The upper attachment point has co-ordinates of (22, 38, 102). Calculate the tension in the spring when it is stretched between the attachment points.

2. Taking a mast as being the z-axis with its base as the origin, a bracing wire goes from the point (14, 16, 0) m to a point on the mast 20 m above ground level. Find the length of the bracing wire and the angle that this wire makes with the horizontal.

3. During an experiment concerned with the forces acting upon a cutting tool in a turning operation, the forces acting upon the tool point in the tangential, radial and axial directions were 450 N, 200 N and 75 N respectively. Determine the magnitude of the resultant force, and the angle that this resultant makes with the horizontal plane. (The horizontal plane contains the radial and axial forces, and all three forces are mutually at right angles.)

4. A framework consists of three members of equal length in the form of a tripod. The bottom of each leg is placed at ground level at points which are the corners of an equilateral triangle having

sides of length 10 m. Each leg of the tripod has a length of 12 m. Calculate:

(a) The height of the apex of the tripod above ground level.

(b) The angle that each leg makes with the horizontal.

    (A graphical solution is not acceptable.)

(C.G.L.I.)

5. A right octagonal pyramid has a vertical height of 60 mm, the length of each side of the octagon being 20 mm. Calculate:

(a) The length of one of the eight sloping edges.

(b) The angle that a sloping edge makes with the base.

(c) The angle that a sloping triangular face makes with the base.

6. Figure 4.60 shows a framework used in a scrap yard consisting of three members in the form of a tripod. Calculate:

(a) The true length of the sloping member AD.

(b) The angle member AD makes with the horizontal.

(c) The true length of the sloping member BD.

(d) The angle member BD makes with the horizontal.

(No marks will be awarded for a graphical solution to this problem.)

(C.G.L.I.)

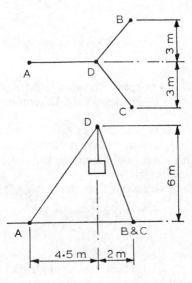

FIG. 4.60

7. During an experiment concerned with the forces on a tool point, the values of the forces F_T, F_A, and F_R shown in Figure 4.61 were 600 N, 300 N and 200 N respectively. Obtain either by calculation or with the aid of vector diagrams:
   (a) The magnitude of the resultant force.
   (b) The angle that this resultant makes with
       (i) a horizontal plane,
       (ii) the centre line of the workpiece.

(C.G.L.I.)

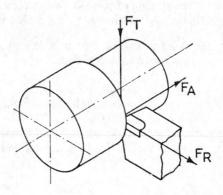

FIG. 4.61

8. (a) A link *AB* lies in space, the co-ordinates of *A* and *B* being (1, 2, 3) and (3, 5, 9) respectively. Determine the length of the link.
   (b) If the end *A* is kept in contact with the origin, but the end *B* is moved to trace out a curve on the plane $z=4$, describe the form of this curve, and determine the equation of this curve when viewed in plan.

   (A circle of radius *r* with centre at (x_1, y_1) has the equation

   $$(x-x_1)^2+(y-y_1)^2=r^2)$$

9. Three points on a plane are given by the co-ordinates (0, 0, 0), (3, 4, 0), and (5, 1, 8). Calculate the angle that this plane makes with a horizontal plane.

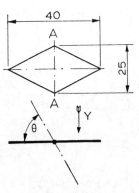

FIG. 4.62

10. Figure 4.62 shows a symmetrical diamond. Through what angle θ must it be rotated about the short diagonal AA so that a view in the direction of arrow Y shows a square? What is the length of side of the square?

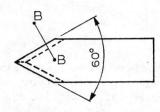

11. Figure 4.63 shows a simple form tool for cutting a vee, the tool having zero cutting rake. Calculate the vee-angle revealed by the cutting plane AA, and the actual side clearance revaled by the cutting plane BB.

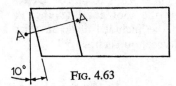

FIG. 4.63

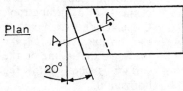

Plan

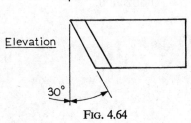

Elevation

FIG. 4.64

12. Figure 4.64 shows two views of a sloping face machined on the end of a square bar. Calculate the angle that the face makes with the base of the square bar, i.e. the angle revealed by the cutting plane AA.

239

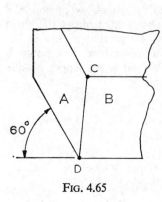

FIG. 4.65

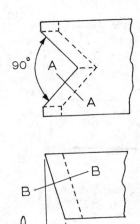

FIG. 4.66

13. Figure 4.65 shows the plan looking vertically down on two joining chamfers. Face *A* makes 45° with the horizontal. Face *B* makes 30° with the horizontal. Calculate the angle that the edge *CD* makes with the horizontal.

14. Figure 4.66 shows a form tool with zero top rake used to cut two chamfers each of 45°. The minimum clearance angle revealed by the plane *AA* is to be 10°. Determine the tool grinding angle θ and the included angle revealed by a section such as *BB*.

15. Figure 4.67 shows the basic elements of a turning tool. Calculate the true cutting rake on the section *AA*, i.e. the angle that a line on the surface makes with the horizontal.

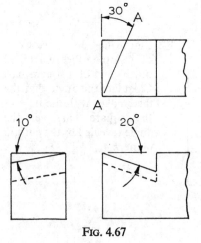

FIG. 4.67

16. A cube of side 20 mm is placed on a compound sine table, square with the axes of rotation, both centre distances of the sine setting being 100 mm. Both slip gauge piles are made 34·2 mm high, and a horizontal surface is then machined on the tilted cube so as to reveal a parallelogram, the highest corner being 20 mm above the square base. Calculate the height of the lowest corner above the square base.

17. The sloping face on the block shown in Figure 4.68 is to be machined with the aid of a compound sine table. Originally edges *DE* and *EF* are parallel with the axes of rotation. The first rotation is about an axis parallel to *EF* so as to bring *AC* horizontal. The second is then about the other axis to bring face *ABC* horizontal. Determine the heights of the slip gauge piles to be used, both sine centres being 200 mm.

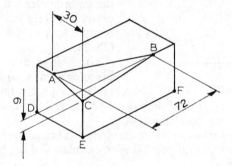

FIG. 4.68

18. In order to machine the block shown in Figure 4.69 a cube of side 50 mm is placed on a compound sine table. Originally sides *OX* and *OY* are parallel with the axes of rotation. Both sine centres are 200 mm. A first rotation is made about the axis parallel to *OX* to bring line *AB* horizontal. A second rotation is then made about the other axis to bring the sloping face *BADC* horizontal.
Calculate the height of the slip gauge piles.

241

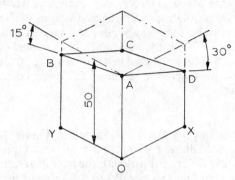

FIG. 4.69

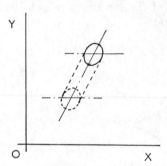

FIG. 4.70

19. Figure 4.70 shows a hole machined in a block of thickness 30 mm. Treating the base of the block as the xy plane, the centre-line of the hole cuts the base at the co-ordinates (20, 20, 0). The centre line of the hole cuts the top of the block at the co-ordinates (30, 35, 30).

The hole is drilled by setting the block on a compound sine table. Originally lines OY and OX are parallel with the axes of tilt. A first rotation takes place about the axis parallel to OX.

A second rotation about the other axis brings the hole vertical. If both sine centres are 200 mm, calculate the height of the slip gauge piles.

20. (a) Determine the co-ordinates of the intersection of the lines

$$y=2x, \quad y=5-\frac{x}{2}$$

(b) The centre line of a shaft occupies the position indicated by the line $y=2x$ in the horizontal plane $z=0$. A datum point occupies a position indicated by the co-ordinates $x=0$, $y=5$, $z=3$.

Use the result of (a) to find the shortest distance between the datum point and the centre-line of the shaft.

(C.G.L.I.)

242

Answers to problems 4.6

1. 76 N
2. 29·2 m, 43° 15′
3. 498 N at 64° 36′ to the horizontal plane
4. (*a*) 10·5 m   (*b*) 61° 15′
5. (*a*) 65·4 mm   (*b*) 66° 28′   (*c*) 68° 5′
6. (*a*) 7·5 m   (*b*) 53° 8′   (*c*) 7·0 mm   (*d*) 59° 0′
7. (*a*) 700 N   (*b*) (i) 59° 0′   (ii) 64° 37′
8. (*a*) 7   (*b*) $x^2 + y^2 = 33$
9. 66° 59′
10. 51° 19′, 17·7 mm
11. (*a*) 60° 46′   (*b*) 5° 2′
12. 61° 31′
13. 29° 54′
14. $\theta = 14° 0′$, included angle $= 91° 44′$
15. 18° 30′
16. 4·97 mm
17. 57·5 mm, 23·8 mm
18. 51·8 mm, 97·4 mm (second rotation is at 29° 9′)
19. 89·4 mm (first rotation is at 26° 34′)
    57·1 mm (second rotation is at 16° 36′)
20. (*a*) (2, 4)   (*b*) 3·74

Chapter Five

Mensuration

5.1 Surfaces and Volumes of Revolution

5.1.1 THE THEOREM OF PAPPUS (OR GULDINUS)

In article 5.6 of Book 1 it was stated that if an area moves in space so that it generates a volume, then the volume of space swept out is given by the product of the area and the distance travelled by the centroid of the area. If we consider the case of an area which is rotated about an axis for one complete revolution so as to form a complete solid of revolution, then provided that the axis does not cut the area, the theorem can be expressed with the formula

$$V = 2\pi A \bar{y}$$

where A is the area and $\bar{y}$ is the distance from the centre of the area to the axis of revolution.

Similarly, if a line is rotated about an axis for one complete revolution to form a complete surface of revolution, and the axis does not cut the line, then the surface area is given by the formula

$$A = 2\pi L \bar{y}$$

where L is the length of line and $\bar{y}$ is the distance from the centroid of the line to the axis of revolution.

In the two formulae given above, it is usual to use $\bar{y}$, as given, if the axis of revolution is horizontal, but $\bar{x}$ if the axis of revolution is vertical.

Considerable use is made of the Theorem of Pappus (or Guldinus) in determining the mass of a solid of revolution. The mass of such a solid is given by the product of its volume and the density of the material of which it is made.

Relative density is the ratio of the density of a material to the density of water. For our present purposes we can consider specific gravity to be identical to relative density, and it is immaterial which expression is used.

Density is the mass of unit volume; hence the basic SI unit would be kg/m^3. The usual unit when dimensioning engineering components is the millimetre, and the reader is reminded that $1\ m^3 = 10^9\ mm^3$. When using the metric system it is extremely convenient that the value of the relative density of a substance can, without too great an inaccuracy, be taken as equal to the value of the density of that substance in g/cm³. Multiplying the relative density by 1 000 gives the density in kg/m³. Dividing the relative density by 1 000 gives the density in g/mm³. For instance, if a particular steel had a relative density of 7·8, then that steel has a density of 7·8 g/cm³=7 800 kg/m³=0·007 8 g/mm³. The distinction between mass and weight is discussed in the companion volume, *Science for Mechanical Technicians*, Book 2. It will suffice at this juncture to state that for the accuracy desired in our present studies, the effect of gravity on a mass of one kilogramme, sometimes called a kilogramme force, can be taken as 9·81 newtons.

Let us recapitulate the Theorem of Pappus (or Guldinus) with worked examples.

Example

Obtain a formula for the volume of the frustum of a cone having a larger radius of R, a smaller radius of r, and a height of h.

The frustum is generated by one complete revolution of the shaded areas shown in Figure 5.1 about the vertical axis YY.

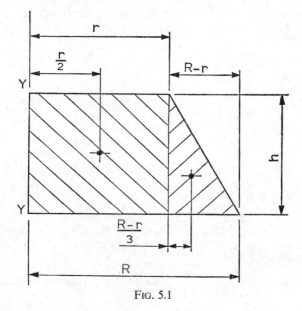

FIG. 5.1

Volume

$$=\Sigma 2\pi A\bar{x}$$

$$=2\pi(rh)\left(\frac{r}{2}\right)+2\pi\{(\tfrac{1}{2})(R-r)(h)\}\left\{r+\left(\frac{R-r}{3}\right)\right\}$$

$$=\pi r^2 h+\pi(R-r)(h)\left(\frac{R+2r}{3}\right)$$

$$=\frac{\pi h}{3}\{3r^2+(R-r)(R+2r)\}$$

$$=\frac{\pi h}{3}\{3r^2+R^2+Rr-2r^2\}$$

$$=\frac{\pi h}{3}\{R^2+Rr+r^2\}$$

Answer: Volume $=\dfrac{\pi h}{3}(R^2+Rr+r^2)$

Example

Find, in terms of the radius, the position of the centre of area of
(*a*) a quadrant of a circle,
(*b*) a quadrant fillet.

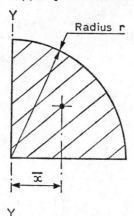

Referring to Figure 5.2, rotating the quadrant about the axis *YY* for one complete revolution generates a hemisphere.

Fig. 5 2

$$V=2\pi A\bar{x}$$
$$V=\frac{2}{3}\pi r^3,\quad A=\frac{\pi r^2}{4}.$$
$$\bar{x}=\frac{V}{2\pi A}=\frac{2\pi r^3}{3}\times\frac{1}{2\pi}\times\frac{4}{\pi r^2}=\frac{4}{3}\frac{r}{\pi}=0\cdot424r$$

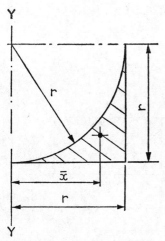

Referring to Figure 5.3, rotating the quadrant fillet about the axis YY for one revolution generates a solid of revolution, the solid being the difference between a cylinder and a hemisphere.

FIG. 5 3

Volume of the cylinder $= \pi r^2(r) = \pi r^3$

Volume of the hemisphere $= \frac{2}{3} \pi r^3$

Volume of the solid of revolution $= \pi r^3 - \frac{2}{3} \pi r^3 = \frac{\pi r^3}{3}$

Shaded area $= r^2 - \frac{\pi r^2}{4} = r^2 \left(1 - \frac{\pi}{4} \right) = 0 \cdot 214\ 6r^2$

$V = 2 \pi A \bar{x}, \quad \bar{x} = \dfrac{V}{2 \pi A} = \dfrac{\pi r^3}{3} \times \dfrac{1}{2 \pi} \times \dfrac{1}{0 \cdot 214\ 6r^2}$

$= \dfrac{r}{1 \cdot 287\ 6} = 0 \cdot 777r$ from the centre

$= 0 \cdot 223r$ from straight edges

Answers: (a) $0 \cdot 424r$ from the straight edges of the quadrant
(b) $0 \cdot 223r$ from the straight edges bounding the fillet

Example

Calculate:
(a) the mass, in kilogrammes, and
(b) the weight, in newtons
of the rope pulley shown in Figure 5.4.

247

The material has a relative density of 7·8. The centroid of a semi-circular area lies at $\frac{4r}{3\pi}$ from a diameter. One kilogramme force can be taken as 9·81 newtons, and π can be taken as $\frac{22}{7}$.

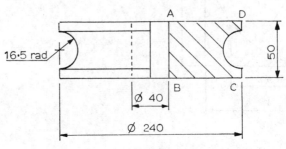

FIG. 5.4

$$\text{Area } ABCD = 50\left(\frac{240-40}{2}\right) = 50 \times 100 = 5\,000 \text{ mm}^2$$

$$\text{Distance of centroid from axis} = 20 + \frac{120-20}{2}$$

$$= 20 + 50 = 70$$

$$\text{Volume of pulley without groove} = 2\pi A\bar{x} = \frac{2 \times 22 \times 5\,000 \times 70}{7}$$

$$= 2\,200\,000 \text{ mm}^3$$

Area of a semicircle of diameter 33 mm (from tables)

$$= \frac{855\cdot3}{2} = 427\cdot65 \text{ mm}$$

Distance of centroid from diameter of semicircle

$$= \frac{4r}{3\pi} = \frac{4 \times 16\cdot5 \times 7}{3 \times 22} = 7 \text{ mm}$$

$$\text{Distance of centroid from axis} \quad = 120 - 7 = 113 \text{ mm}$$

$$\text{Volume of groove} \quad = 2\pi A\bar{x} = \frac{2 \times 22 \times 427\cdot65 \times 113}{7}$$

$$= 303\,700 \text{ mm}^2$$

$$\text{Volume of pulley} \quad = 2\,200\,000 - 303\,700$$

$$= 1\,896\,300 \text{ mm}^3 = 1\,896\,300 \times 10^{-9} \text{ m}^3$$

Relative density $=7\cdot8$ Density$=7800$ kg/m³

$\therefore$ Mass of pulley $=$ volume$\times$ density

$$=1\ 896\ 300\times10^{-9}\times7\ 800\,\frac{m^3\times kg}{m^3}$$

$$=14\cdot80\ kg$$

A mass of $14\cdot80$ kg has a weight of $14\cdot80$ kgf.

Weight of pulley in newtons$=14\cdot80\times9\cdot81$

$$=145\cdot2\ N$$

Answers: Mass of pulley $=14\cdot8$ kg

Weight of pulley$=145$ N

The working in the previous example brings into sharp focus one of the important factors when working in metric units. The usual unit for dimensioning is the millimetre. This usually results in very large values when a volume is calculated in terms of cubic millimetres, and particular care must be taken with the arithmetic. However, because a component is dimensioned in millimetres is no reason to compel us to calculate a volume in cubic millimetres. It has been pointed out that although the use of the centimetre is to be discouraged in terms of providing data, there is nothing to prevent its use during the solving of a problem. People who share this view state, quite correctly, that there is much to commend its adoption because it facilitates the arithmetic. Let us work through this problem again in terms of centimetres.

Area $ABCD$ $=5\left(\dfrac{24-4}{2}\right)=5\times10=50$ cm²

Distance of centroid from axis $=2+\dfrac{12-2}{2}=7$ cm

Volume of pulley without groove$=2\pi A\bar{x}=\dfrac{2\times22\times50\times7}{7}$

$$=2\ 200\ cm^2$$

Area of a semi-circle of diameter $3\cdot3$ cm (from tables)

$$=\frac{8\cdot553}{2}=4\cdot276\ 5$$

Distance of centroid from diameter of semicircle

$$=\frac{4r}{3\pi}=\frac{4\times1\cdot65\times7}{3\times22}=0\cdot7\ cm$$

Distance of centroid from axis $=12$ cm$-0\cdot7$ cm$=11\cdot3$ cm

Volume of groove $=2\pi A\bar{x}=\dfrac{2\times22\times4\cdot276\ 5\times11\cdot3}{7}$

$$=303\cdot7\ cm^2$$

Volume of pulley = 2 200−303·7=1 896·3 cm
Relative density = 7·8   Density=7·8 g/cm³
Mass   = volume × density=1 896·3×7·8
         = 14 800 g=14·8 kg

The question now arises as to which of the two methods is to be preferred for calculating masses. It has been suggested that the second of the two methods is better because many students will have become quite familiar with the centimetre in studies previous to technical education. However, there is no doubt that it tends to complicate fundamental principles when handling SI preferred units, and this can be distinctly dangerous in other fields of science. The author has no preference; the reader should select one method, and having selected it, keep to it.

5.1.2 THE DEVELOPMENT OF CIRCULAR BLANKS FOR DRAWN SHELLS

When a shell is produced from a circular blank as the result of a metal-forming operation such as pressworking or metal spinning, the diameter of the blank that is required can be determined approximately with the aid of the Theorem of Pappus (or Guldinus). If the metal is thin, the surface area of the blank will be approximately equal to that of the shell. If the metal is thick, a more accurate result will be obtained if the volumes of the blank and shell are equated. In the latter case, it is assumed that no thinning of the metal occurs; the thickness of the shell is assumed to be constant and equal to that of the blank.

When the volume of an engineering component has to be determined, it is often very convenient to subdivide a component of complex form into smaller sub-components whose volumes are those of simpler geometrical forms. The volume of the component is then found by summating the volumes of the various sub-components. In a similar manner, a shell of complex shape can be subdivided into simple areas of revolution or solids of revolution, and the total area or volume obtained by summation.

For the case of thin shells, where the area of the blank is equated to the area of the shell, let us assume that the shell is composed of several areas of revolution, each being generated by a line of length L whose centre of area is $\bar{x}$ from the axis of revolution. (The values of L and $\bar{x}$ may differ for each sub-component.) Generally, the area of a surface of revolution $=2\pi L\bar{x}$

$$\text{Total area of shell}=\Sigma 2\pi L\bar{x}$$

Now 2π is a constant and can be taken outside the summation sign.

Furthermore, if the circular blank has a diameter of B, its area is given by $\dfrac{\pi B^2}{4}$.

$$\therefore \quad \frac{\pi B^2}{4}=2\pi\Sigma L\bar{x}$$

whence $B^2=8\Sigma L\bar{x}$

and $\qquad B=\sqrt{(8\Sigma L\bar{x})}$

For the case of thick shells, where volumes are equated, let us assume that the shell is composed of several volumes of revolution, each being generated by an area A, the centroid being $\bar{x}$ away from the axis of revolution. (The values of A and $\bar{x}$ may differ for each sub-component.)

Then the total volume $=\Sigma 2\pi A\bar{x}=2\pi\Sigma A\bar{x}$

If the blank has a diameter of B and a thickness of t, then its volume is given by $\dfrac{\pi B^2 t}{4}$

$$\therefore \quad \frac{\pi B^2 t}{4}=2\pi\Sigma A\bar{x}$$

whence $B^2=\dfrac{8\Sigma A\bar{x}}{t}$

and $\qquad B=\sqrt{\left(\dfrac{8\Sigma A\bar{x}}{t}\right)}$

Example

Determine the diameter of the circular blank required to produce the thin flanged shell shown in Figure 5.5.

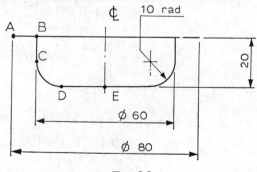

FIG. 5.5

Initially, it will be necessary to find the position of the centroid of an arc forming a quarter of a circle. In this case the centroid does not lie on the arc.

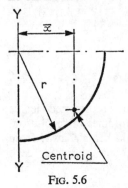

FIG. 5.6

In Figure 5.6, let the arc AB rotate for one complete revolution about the axis YY, so as to generate a hemispherical surface.

$$A = 2\pi L \bar{x}$$

$$2\pi r^2 = 2\pi \times \frac{\pi r}{2} \times \bar{x}$$

$$\bar{x} = \frac{2r}{\pi}$$

Returning now to the specific question, the axis of revolution is the centre-line of the shell.

In questions of this type, there is much to commend a tabular layout. Any calculations that may be found necessary to provide values for insertion in the table can be performed below the table.

Line	L	$\bar{x}$	$L\bar{x}$
AB	10	35	350
BC	10	30	300
CD	15·71	26·37	414·3
DE	20	10	200
		Total = $\Sigma(L\bar{x})$ =	1264·3

Length of CD $\quad = \dfrac{1}{4} \times 2\pi r = \dfrac{2 \times 22 \times 10}{4 \times 7} = \dfrac{110}{7} = 15\cdot71$

$\bar{x}$ for line CD $\quad = 20 + \dfrac{2r}{\pi} = 20 + \dfrac{2 \times 10 \times 7}{22}$

$\qquad\qquad\qquad = 20 + \dfrac{70}{11} = 20 + 6\cdot37 = 26\cdot37$

$B^2 \qquad\qquad\quad = 8\Sigma L\bar{x} = 8 \times 1264\cdot3 = 10\ 114\cdot4$

$B \qquad\qquad\quad = \sqrt{(10\ 114\cdot4)} = 100\cdot6$

Answer: Diameter of blank = 101 mm

252

Example

Calculate the diameter of a circular flat blank to produce the end-cap shown in Figure 5.7. The centre of area of a quadrant fillet can be taken as $\frac{2r}{9}$ from the bounding straight edges and the centre of area of a quadrant of a circle as $\frac{13r}{30}$ from the sides forming the right angle.

The volume is the difference between the volumes of the solids of revolution generated by rotating the shaded areas shown in Figures 5.8(a) and 5.8(b) about the lines YY.

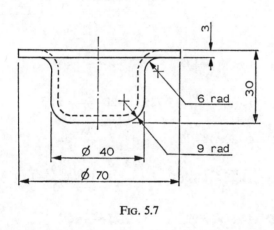

FIG. 5.7

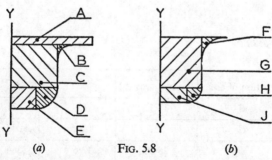

(a)   FIG. 5.8   (b)

Let us again make use of a tabular layout. We erect the table first. If it becomes necessary to make calculations to insert values in the table they can be done below the table.

Outer volume

Portion of area	Actual area A	$\bar{x}$	$A\bar{x}$
A	105	17·5	1 838
B	7·725	21·33	165
C	360	10	3 600
D	63·63	14·9	947
E	99	5·5	545
	For outer volume, $\Sigma(A\bar{x})=$		7 095

Area A $A=35\times3=105,$ $\bar{x}=\dfrac{35}{2}=17\cdot5.$

    B $A=(6)^2-\dfrac{\pi(6)^2}{4}=7\cdot725,$ $\bar{x}=20+\dfrac{2(6)}{9}=21\cdot33.$

    C $A=20\times18=360,$ $\bar{x}=\dfrac{20}{2}=10.$

    D $A=\dfrac{\pi\times9^2}{4}=63\cdot63,$ $\bar{x}=11+\dfrac{13(9)}{30}=14\cdot9.$

    E $A=11\times9=99,$ $\bar{x}=\dfrac{11}{2}=5\cdot5.$

Inner volume

Portion of area	Actual area A	$\bar{x}$	$A\bar{x}$
F	17·37	19	331
G	357	8·5	3 035
H	28·28	13·6	384
J	66	5·5	363
	For inner volume, $\Sigma(A\bar{x})=$		4 113

Area F $A=9^2-\dfrac{\pi(9^2)}{4}=81-63\cdot63=17\cdot37,$ $\bar{x}=17+\dfrac{2(9)}{9}=19.$

    G $A=21\times17=357,$ $\bar{x}=\dfrac{17}{2}=8\cdot5$

    H $A=\dfrac{\pi(6)^2}{4}=28\cdot28,$ $\bar{x}=11+\dfrac{13(6)}{30}=13\cdot6$

    J $A=11\times6=66,$ $\bar{x}=\dfrac{11}{2}=5\cdot5.$

$\Sigma(A\bar{x})$ for end cap$=\Sigma(A\bar{x})$ for outer$-\Sigma(A\bar{x})$ for inner
$$=7\,095-4\,113$$
$$=2\,982$$
$$B^2=\dfrac{8\Sigma(A\bar{x})}{t}=\dfrac{8\times2982}{3}$$
$$=\dfrac{23\,856}{3}=7\,952$$
$$B=\sqrt{7\,952}=89\cdot19$$

Answer: Diameter of blank$=89\cdot2$ mm

Problems 5.1

1. By applying the Theorem of Pappus (or Guldinus), obtain a formula for the volume of a pipe of outside diameter D mm, inside diameter d mm, and length L mm.

2. The parabolic shaded area shown in Figure 5.9 is rotated about the axis XX to produce a paraboloid of revolution. If the area of the figure is given by $\dfrac{2BH}{3}$, and the centre of area of the figure is $\dfrac{3H}{8}$ from the axis of revolution, what is the ratio of the volume of the paraboloid to the volume of the enveloping cylinder of radius H and length B?

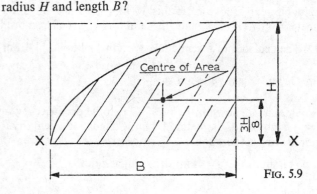

Centre of Area

FIG. 5.9

255

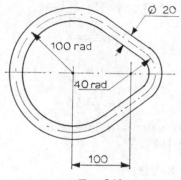

FIG. 5.10

3. The link shown in Figure 5.10 is to be manufactured from bar of diameter 20 mm, formed to shape, and the joint butt-welded. Taking the relative density as 7·8, calculate the mass of the link, in kilogrammes, to three significant figures.

4. A right cone has a base of diameter 84 mm and a vertical height of 56 mm. Calculate, using the Theorem of Pappus and taking π as $\dfrac{22}{7}$:

(a) The volume.
(b) The curved surface area.
Give the answers in millimetre units to an accuracy of three significant figures.

5. A vertical stanchion in the form of a pipe of outside diameter 200 mm is joined to a horizontal base by welding. The weld is a triangular fillet all round the outside of the pipe, the fillet being a right-angled isosceles triangle, the sides containing the right angle having a length of 15 mm. Taking π as $\dfrac{22}{7}$ calculate the amount of weld metal in mm³.

6. A semi-circular groove of radius 10 mm is turned on a bar of diameter 100 mm. Calculate the amount of metal removed in mm³. The centroid of a semicircle of radius r lies at $\dfrac{4\,r}{3\,\pi}$ from the diameter and π can be taken as $\dfrac{22}{7}$.

7. The component shown in Figure 5.11 is to be produced by upset forging from bar of diameter 20 mm. Calculate the length of bar required for the component. (The centroid of a quadrant fillet can be taken as lying $\dfrac{r}{4}$ from the straight sides.)

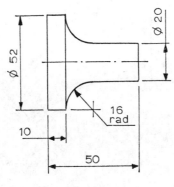

FIG. 5.11

8. Taking the relative density of a particular aluminium alloy as 2·8, calculate the mass of the casting made in that material shown in Figure 5.12. Take π as $\frac{22}{7}$, and give the answer in kg.

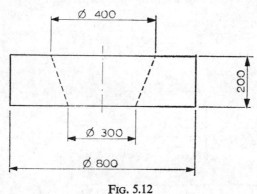

FIG. 5.12

9. Determine the mass of the symmetrical flanged pipe connector piece shown in Figure 5.13. Take $\pi = \frac{22}{7}$ and the relative density of the material as 7·8. Give the answer in kg.

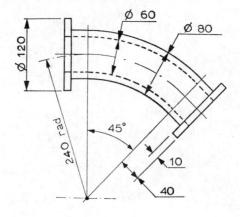

FIG. 5.13

10. Determine the mass of the forging shown in Figure 5.14. Take the relative density of the material to be 7·8, π as $\frac{22}{7}$, and assume that the centre of area of a quadrant fillet lies at $\frac{2r}{9}$ from the sides containing the right angle.

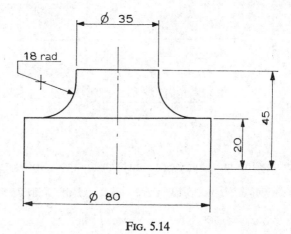

FIG. 5.14

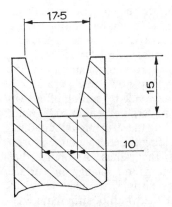

FIG. 5.15

11. The vee-groove shown in Figure 5.15 is machined around the periphery of a solid pulley of outside diameter 150 mm. Calculate the volume of metal removed in mm³.

12. A bar of diameter 80 mm and length 120 mm originally has flat ends. Calculate the percentage reduction in volume when a chamfer of dimensions 20 mm × 45° is machined around each end.

13. A curved piece of cast-iron pipe of outside diameter 80 mm and inside diameter 60 mm has its centre-line on a curve of radius 320 mm. The chordal distance between the centres of the ends is 400 mm. Taking π as $\frac{22}{7}$ and the relative density of cast-iron as 7·8, determine the mass of the pipe.

14. A tapered cored hole in a casting has a length of 80 mm. The diameter of the large end is 70 mm, and the diameter of the small end is 50 mm. The hole is machined as a taper with the larger and smaller diameters being 80 mm and 60 mm respectively, the length remaining at 80 mm. Calculate the volume of metal removed during the machining operation.

15. The bowl shown in Figure 5.16 is formed from a circular blank. Assuming that the surface area of the bowl is the same as the surface area of the flat blank, determine the blank diameter.

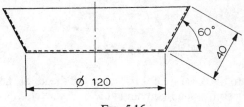

FIG. 5.16

259

Mathematics for Mechanical Technicians 2

16. (*a*) Determine, in terms of the radius, the position of the centroid of a quadrant arc from an axis of rotation, by rotating the arc about that axis so as to generate a hemispherical surface.

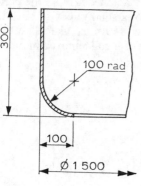

FIG. 5.17

(*b*) The portion of an aircraft engine cowling shown in Figure 5.17 is to be made by cutting off a strip of material of length 1500π mm, rolling the strip into a loop, butt-welding the ends, and then forming the radius. Assuming that there is no change in surface area during manufacture, calculate the width of strip required.

17. The shell shown in Figure 5.18 is manufactured from a circular blank. Assuming that the surface area of the blank is equal to the surface area of the shell, calculate the diameter of the blank. Take the centroid of a quadrant arc of radius r as being $\dfrac{5r}{8}$ from the radii forming the right angle.

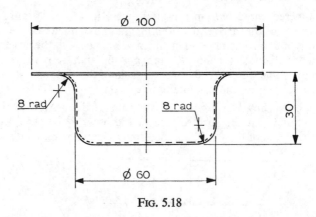

FIG. 5.18

18. In order to decrease weight in a ship bulkhead, at the same time increasing stiffness, a lightening hole of diameter D is cut in plate of thickness 10 mm. The hole is then flanged as shown in Figure

5.19. Calculate the diameter of the hole D to the nearest milli-metre. Take π as $\dfrac{22}{7}$ and approximate that the centroid of a quadrant of a circle lies at a distance of $0.4r$ from the sides forming the right angle.

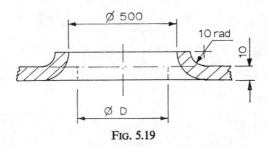

FIG. 5.19

19. The end cap shown in Figure 5.20 is made by pressing out a flat circular blank of thickness 5 mm. Taking π as $\dfrac{22}{7}$, and approximating that the centroid of a quadrant of a circle lies at a distance of $0.4r$ from the sides forming the right angle, calculate the diameter of the blank to the nearest millimetre.

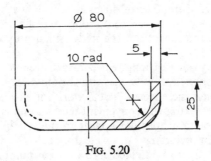

FIG. 5.20

Answers to problems 5.1

1. $2\pi\left(\dfrac{D-d}{2}\right)(L)\left(\dfrac{D+d}{4}\right) = \dfrac{\pi(D^2-d^2)L}{4}$
2. One half
3. 1·66 kg
4. (a) 103 000 mm³   (b) 9 240 mm²
5. 74 250 mm³

6. 45 200 mm³
7. 107 mm
8. 207 kg
9. 5·60 kg
10. 1·045 kg
11. 88 400 mm³
12. 13·9%
13. 7·41 kg
14. 81 700 mm³
15. 192 mm
16. (a) $\bar{x} = \dfrac{2r}{\pi}$ (b) 350 mm
17. 125 mm
18. 448 mm
19. 103 mm

5.2 Irregular Areas and Volumes

5.2.1 THE MID-ORDINATE RULE AND SIMPSON'S RULE

In article 5.3 of Book 1, the reader was introduced to a means of determining the approximate area of a figure of irregular shape by the use of the mid-ordinate rule. The figure whose area was required was divided into a number of strips of equal width by ordinates. Lengths of the mid-ordinates were found, and the area obtained by multiplying the total length of the mid-ordinates by the width of a strip.

In the majority of cases, a more accurate determination of the area of an irregular shape can be made with the aid of *Simpson's rule*. At present, this is not included in Part II work for Mechanical Technicians, but it is an extremely convenient method and is often used by engineers. Although it does not appear in the syllabus, no apology need be made for including it in this textbook.

The irregular figure is divided into an *even* number of strips of equal width, thus producing an *odd* number of ordinates. The length of each of the ordinates is then determined. If the figure is curved or pointed at its ends, the lengths of the first and last ordinates will be zero. If the width of each of the strips is w, the area is given by

$$\frac{w}{3} \left[\begin{array}{l} \text{(first+last ordinates)} \\ +4 \text{ (sum of even ordinates)} \\ +2 \text{ (sum of remaining odd ordinates)} \end{array} \right]$$

The determination of an area using Simpson's rule is aided by the use of a tabular method, and the divider and multipliers remembered by the value of $\pi (=3\cdot142)$.

Example

Sketch the area bounded by the parabola $y=16-x^2$ and the x-axis. Determine the area

        (a) by the mid-ordinate rule, and

        (b) by Simpson's rule,

        using eight strips of unit width.

If the actual area of such a parabola is $\dfrac{2BH}{3}$, comment on the accuracy of the results obtained.

The area is shown in Figure 5.21, the eight strips being indicated. The base length of the figure is 8 units, its height is 16 units.

(a) *Mid-ordinate rule*

Mid-ordinates occur at $x=-3\frac{1}{2}$, $x=-2\frac{1}{2}$ and so on, at intervals of one unit, up to $x=3\frac{1}{2}$.

If $y=16-x^2$, the heights of mid-ordinates are $3\cdot75$, $9\cdot75$, $13\cdot75$, $15\cdot75$, $15\cdot75$, $13\cdot75$, $9\cdot75$ and $3\cdot75$.

The sum of mid-ordinates$=86$ units.

        Width of one strip$=1$ unit.

        $\therefore$ Area$=86\times1=86$ square units

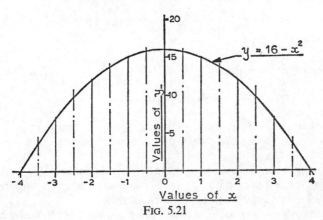

FIG. 5.21

(b) *Simpson's rule*

The ordinates occur at $x=-4$, $x=-3$, and so on, at intervals of one unit, up to $x=4$.

The heights of the nine ordinates are 0, 7, 12, 15, 16, 15, 12, 7 and 0.

We now tabulate the ordinates, in correct sequence, and an orderly table ensures that an ordinate is included once only, while vertical columns separate the ordinates into correct groups.

w	First and last	Even	Remaining odd
	0		
		7	
			12
		15	
			16
		15	
			12
		7	
	0		
1	0	44	40

Area$=\frac{1}{3}\{1(0)+4(44)+2(40)\}=\frac{256}{3}=85\frac{1}{3}$ square units

(c) *Accurate formula*

Length of base=8 units. Height=16 units.

Actual area$=\frac{2(8)(16)}{3}=85\frac{1}{3}$ square units

Answers: (a) By mid-ordinate rule, area=86 square units
(b) By Simpson's rule, area=$85\frac{1}{3}$ square units

The mid-ordinate rule is apparently slightly inaccurate; but for this particular question it appears that Simpson's rule is not approximate when applied to a parabola, it is accurate.

(*Note: Simpson's rule is deduced using calculus, by assuming that the points on the ends of the ordinates are joined by parabolic curves. This is why Simpson's rule, in the majority of cases, tends to be more accurate. The mid-ordinate rule is an approximation based on the ends of ordinates being joined by straight lines. In general, an irregular*

*figure is bounded by curves, and parabolic curves joining ends of ordi-
nates are much more likely to produce a closer approximation to the
profile of an irregular figure.*)

5.2.2 THE DETERMINATION OF APPROXIMATE VOLUMES FOR SOLIDS OF IRREGULAR SHAPE

In the previous articles we have been dealing with irregular areas,
and determining the approximate magnitudes of these areas with the
aid of ordinates and mid-ordinates. The same principles apply to
solids of irregular shapes, but in this latter case we have to consider
areas of cross-sections instead of lengths of lines.

When applying the mid-ordinate rule we divide the solid into sections, each of constant width. We then establish areas at the middle
of each section. The approximate volume is then given by multiplying
the sum of all these 'mid cross-sectional areas' by the constant width
of a section.

When using Simpson's rule the tabular layout can be used, but the
values in that table are now cross-sectional areas instead of ordinates.

Example

A barrel has a height of 2 m, its diameters at invervals of 0·5 m
being given by:

Position	Base	0·5	1·0	1·5	Top
Diameter	1·5 m	1·8 m	2·0 m	1·8 m	1·5 m

Calculate the capacity of the barrel in litres. A litre is a cubic deci-
metre. Take π as $\frac{22}{7}$.

To facilitate calculations we will leave π as a constant multiplier.

Area of each end $= \frac{\pi D^2}{4} = \frac{\pi \times 1\cdot5 \times 1\cdot5}{4} = \frac{2\cdot25\pi}{4} = 0\cdot562\ 5\pi$

Area at 0·5 and 1·5 $= \frac{\pi \times 1\cdot8 \times 1\cdot8}{4} = \frac{3\cdot24\pi}{4} = 0\cdot81\pi$

Area at centre $= \frac{\pi \times 2 \times 2}{4} = \pi$

h	Areas		
	First and last	Even	Remaining odd
	$0.562\,5\pi$		
		0.81π	
			π
		0.81π	
	$0.562\,5\pi$		
0.5	1.125π	1.62π	π

$$V = \frac{0.5}{3}\left\{1(1.125\,\pi) + 4(1.62\,\pi) + 2(\pi)\right\}$$

$$= \frac{0.5}{3}\left\{1.125\,\pi + 6.48\,\pi + 2\,\pi\right\}$$

$$= \frac{0.5}{3} \times 9.605\,\pi = \frac{0.5 \times 9.605 \times 22}{3 \times 7}$$

$$= \frac{105.655}{21} = 5.031 \text{ m}^3$$

1 m³ = 1 000 dm³, there are 1 000 litres in a cubic metre.
∴ Capacity = 5·031 × 1 000 = 5 031 litres

Answer: Capacity = 5 030 litres

A very useful application of Simpson's rule occurs when an area has flat ends (or a solid has flat ends) and when the length between those ends is small relative to the area. In this case it is only necessary to consider three ordinates, the two ends and the central ordinate. If the figure has a length of L, the distance between the ordinates is $\frac{L}{2}$. The sum of the first and last ordinates is $H_1 + H_3$. There is one even ordinate, H_2. There are no 'remaining odd ordinates'.

Applying Simpson's rule, we get

$$\text{approximate area} = \frac{h}{3} \left\{ \begin{array}{l} \text{(first and last ordinates)} \\ +4 \text{ (sum of even ordinates)} \\ +2 \text{ (sum of remaining odd ordinates)} \end{array} \right\}$$

$$= \frac{L}{2 \times 3} \left\{ H_1 + H_3 + 4(H_2) + 2(0) \right\}$$

or
$$A = \frac{L}{6} \left(H_1 + 4H_2 + H_3 \right)$$

Let us apply the modified rule to a solid.

Example

Using the modified rule, find the volume of a frustum of a cone having radii of R and r separated by a height of h.

Writing the trapezoidal rule for volume as

$$V = \frac{h}{6} \left(A_1 + 4A_2 + A_3 \right)$$

$$A_1 = \pi R^2 \quad A_3 = \pi r^2$$

Radius at mid-height $= \dfrac{R+r}{2}$

$$A_2 = \pi \left(\frac{R+r}{2} \right)^2 = \frac{\pi}{4} \left(R^2 + 2Rr + r^2 \right)$$

Then
$$V = \frac{h}{6} \left\{ \pi R^2 + \frac{4 \times \pi}{4} (R^2 + 2Rr + r^2) + \pi r^2 \right\}$$

$$= \frac{h}{6} \left\{ \pi R^2 + \pi R^2 + 2\pi Rr + \pi r^2 + \pi r^2 \right\}$$

$$= \frac{h}{6} \left\{ 2\pi R^2 + 2\pi Rr + 2\pi r^2 \right\}$$

whence
$$V = \frac{\pi h}{3} \left(R^2 + Rr + r^2 \right)$$

Answer: $V = \dfrac{\pi h}{3} \left(R^2 + Rr + r^2 \right)$

5.2.3 THE PLANIMETER

A planimeter is an instrument for measuring the area inside a closed plane curve. There are many different forms of the instrument, the most common being 'wheel and tracer' planimeters, typical being

Amsler's planimeter. Included in the design of such a planimeter is a movable point which traces the contour of the enclosed area, and a wheel which registers the number of revolutions in a complete circuit of the curve. The arrangements of the tracer and directions of motion of the wheel are made so that the area depends upon the dimensions of the instrument and the number of revolutions of the wheel.

The distance between the tracer and the centre of the wheel is fixed for a particular determination, and when the tracer moves around the curve, the wheel registers an amount of turning proportional to the enclosed area. It is usual practice to first calibrate the planimeter by the use of squared paper, and then to determine the actual area being measured by proportion.

Problems 5.2

1. A body is acted upon by a variable force. If d is the distance from datum in metres, the magnitude of the force F newtons is given by $F=100 \sin (10d°)$. The body moves a distance of 8 m. Treating the work diagram as four strips of width 2 m, calculate the values of F when $d=1$ m, 3 m, 5 m, and 7 m, and use the mid-ordinate rule to find the work done in joules.

2. Figure 5.22 shows a work diagram. The pressure is given in units of 10^6 N/m² and the volume in units of m³. Using the mid-ordinate rule with 5 strips, calculate the amount of work represented by the diagram in kilojoules.

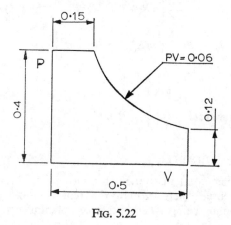

Fig. 5.22

3. The velocity v, in metres per second, is noted t seconds after a body starts from rest, producing the following data:

v	0	10	20	29	36	41	44
t	0	1	2	3	4	5	6

Determine with the aid of Simpson's rule, the distance travelled during the six seconds.

4. A shaft was subjected to a variable torque, giving the following data:

Angle turned (radians)	0	$\dfrac{\pi}{3}$	$\dfrac{2\pi}{3}$	π	$\dfrac{4\pi}{3}$	$\dfrac{5\pi}{3}$	2π
Torque (Nm)	0	50	86·6	100	86·6	50	0

Use Simpson's rule to find the work done, in joules, during the 2π radians which were turned.

5. Sketch a semicircle of radius 100 mm. Erect ordinates at intervals of 20 mm and their mid-ordinates.
   (*a*) Calculate the lengths of the mid-ordinates.
   (*b*) Determine the area of the semicircle by the mid-ordinate rule.
   (*c*) Calculate the lengths of the ordinates.
   (*d*) Determine the area of the semicircle by Simpson's rule.
   (*e*) Determine the percentage of inaccuracy of each of the methods, giving the answers to two significant figures, taking π as 3·1416.

6. A river of width 20 m is measured for depth at intervals of 2 m across its width, producing the following data:

Distance from bank (m)	0	2	4	6	8	10	12	14	16	18	20
Depth (m)	0	1·8	2·6	3·0	3·4	4·8	5·4	6·0	5·4	3·2	0

Find the cross-sectional area of flow:

(*a*) By using ordinates at intervals of 4 m, so that alternate values such as 1·8, 3·0, 4·8, etc., become mid-ordinates, and applying the mid-ordinate rule.

(*b*) By using all the data given and applying Simpson's rule.

7. A segment of radius 50 mm has a chord of length 80 mm. Calculate the height of ordinates at intervals of 10 mm along the chord and use Simpson's rule to determine the area of the segment.

8. A lake is used as a reservoir. To calculate the storage capacity, imaginary parallel vertical sections through the water produced the following data:

Distance from shore (m)	0	5	10	15	20	25	30
Cross-sectional area (m²)	0	23	57	58	41	23	0

Calculate with the aid of Simpson's rule, the approximate storage capacity in cubic metres.

9. An ingot of aluminium alloy has the form of the frustum of a square pyramid. The square faces have sides of length 80 mm and 40 mm, the distance between the square faces being 50 mm. The alloy has a relative density of 2·8. Calculate its mass, in grammes, using the modified Simpson's rule.

10. Figure 5.23 shows a wire drawing die made of cemented carbide, the width of the die being 15 mm.

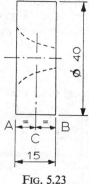

FIG. 5.23

The aperture cross-sectional areas at *A*, *C*, and *B* are 80 mm², 40 mm², and 20 mm² respectively. The carbide has a relative density of 6. Determine the mass of the die in grammes. Use the modified Simpson's rule and take π as $\frac{22}{7}$.

11. A work diagram for one stroke was obtained from the cylinder of an internal combustion engine. The vertical ordinate represented pressure to a scale of 1 mm = 50 000 N/m². The horizontal ordinate represented the stroke volume to a scale of 1 mm = 0·002 m³.
    (*a*) What amount of work, in joules, is represented by one square millimetre of the work diagram?
    The area of the diagram was established with a planimeter, which was adjusted so that one revolution of the wheel represented an area of 100 mm². The commencing datum on the wheel was 0·015 rev, the final datum 0·890 rev.
    (*b*) Determine:
        (i) the indicated work done, per stroke, in joules
        (ii) the indicated power, in kilowatts, if there are 5 strokes per second.

12. The equation of a modified curve of normal distribution can be taken as
$$y = e^{-\left(\frac{x^2}{2}\right)}$$
    (*a*) Find the heights of the ordinates at *x*=0, *x*=0·5, and *x*=1·0.
    (*b*) Use the modified Simpson's rule to find the area under the curve between *x*=0 and *x*=1·0.

Answers to problems 5.2

1. 17·36 N, 50·00 N, 76·60 N, 93·97 N; 476 J
2. 134 kJ
3. 159 m
4. 400 J
5. (*a*) 43·59, 71·41, 86·60, 95·39, 99·50, 99·50, 95·39, 86·60, 71·41, 43·59
   (*b*) 15 859·6 mm²
   (*c*) 0, 60·00, 80·00, 91·65, 97·98, 100·00, 97·98, 91·65, 80·00, 60·00, 0
   (*d*) 15 500·8 mm²

(e) Mid-ordinate rule, $+1\cdot0\%$
Simpson's rule, $-1\cdot3\%$
6. (a) 75·2 m²   (b) 72·5 m²
7. 0, 10·00, 15·83, 18·99, 20·00, 18·99, 15·83, 10·00, 0; 1 120 mm²
8. 1020 m³
9. 187 000 mm³
10. 109 grammes
11. (a) 100 J   (b) (i) 8750 J   (ii) 43·75 kW
12. (a) 1·000, 0·883, 0·606   (b) 0·856

5.3 Sectors and Segments of Circles

5.3.1 MENSURATION OF SECTORS AND SEGMENTS

The area of a sector of a circle of radius r is given by the formula $\dfrac{r^2\theta}{2}$, where θ is the sector angle expressed in radians. The length of the circular arc of the sector is given by $r\theta$ if θ is again measured in radians. There are 2π radians in one complete revolution, hence 1 radian $=\dfrac{360°}{2\pi}=57\cdot3°$ very nearly. If the angle θ is expressed in degrees, then the area is given by $\dfrac{\theta}{360}(\pi r^2)$ and the length of arc by $\dfrac{\theta}{360}(2\pi r)$.

For the segment of the circle shown shaded in Figure 5.24, the area is given by $\dfrac{r^2}{2}$ (θ in radians$-\sin\theta$).

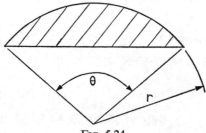

Fig. 5.24

The relation between the height h, the length of chord w, and the radius r, can be deduced from the property of intersecting chords in a circle.

272

Referring to Figure 5.25,

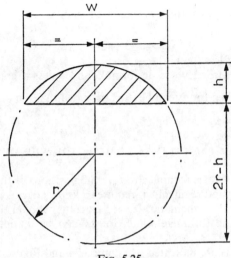

FIG. 5.25

$$\left(\frac{w}{2}\right)\left(\frac{w}{2}\right)=h(2r-h)$$

$$\frac{w^2}{4}=2rh-h^2$$

This equation can be manipulated to give a formula for r.

$$\frac{w^2}{4}+h^2=2rh$$

$$8rh=w^2+4h^2$$

$$r=\frac{w^2+4h^2}{8h}$$

The reader is warned not to adopt certain approximate formulae for the area of a segment unless he is completely aware of their limits of accuracy. These formulae are often used when the chord length w and the segment height h are known.

If h and w only are known, the formula

$$A=\frac{4h^2}{3}\sqrt{\left(\frac{w^2}{4h^2}+0{\cdot}392\right)}$$

gives a value for the area which is within $0{\cdot}1\%$ of the true value provided that the implied angle θ does not exceed 150°. If the $\dfrac{w}{h}$ ratio is greater than 3, then the approximate formula

$$A = \frac{2wh}{3} + \frac{h^3}{2w}$$

has an error of less than 0·1 %.

This is an extremely simple formula and unless a high degree of accuracy is called for, it can be used provided that the $\dfrac{w}{h}$ ratio is first established to be greater than 3.

5.3.2 THE CENTRE OF AREA OF A SECTOR AND OF A SEGMENT

In order to deduce formulae to give the positions of the centres of area of sectors and segments, it requires a knowledge of a very interesting branch of mathematics termed calculus. Should the positions be required, the formulae which follow can be accepted without proof.

The positions are indicated in Figure 5.26 and Figure 5.27.

Sector of a circle

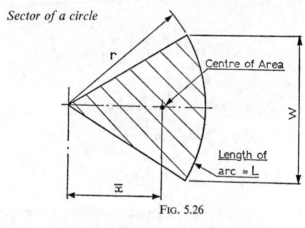

FIG. 5.26

$$\bar{x} = \frac{2rw}{3L} = \frac{r^2w}{3A},$$

A being the area

For the particular case of the sector being one-quarter of a circle, $\bar{x} = 0.6r$, very nearly.

For the particular case of the sector being one-sixth of a circle, $\bar{x} = 0.637r$, very nearly.

Segment of a circle

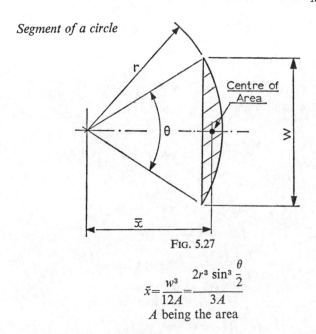

FIG. 5.27

$$\bar{x}=\frac{w^3}{12A}=\frac{2r^3 \sin^3 \frac{\theta}{2}}{3A}$$

A being the area

The centroid of a circular arc

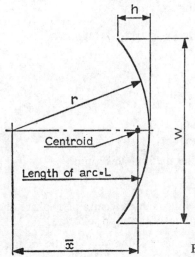

FIG. 5.28

The position is indicated in Figure 5.28, and once more the formula must be accepted without proof.

$$\bar{x}=\frac{rw}{L}=\frac{w(w^2+4h^2)}{8Lh}$$

If the arc is one-quarter of a circle, $\bar{x}=0\cdot9r$, very nearly.

If the arc is one-sixth of a circle, $\bar{x}=0\cdot955r$, very nearly.

Example

A segment of a circle has a chord length w of 10 mm and a height h

275

of 1 mm. Determine the area of the segment, to three significant figures:

(a) Using an accurate formula.

(b) Using the approximate formula $A=\dfrac{2wh}{3}+\dfrac{h^3}{2w}$

Let θ be the implied angle of the segment.

(a) $\qquad\qquad A=\dfrac{r^2}{2}\ (\theta\ \text{in radians}-\sin\theta)$

$$r=\frac{w^2+4h^2}{8h}=\frac{10^2+4(1)}{8}=\frac{104}{8}=13$$

$$\sin\frac{\theta}{2}=\frac{w}{2r}=\frac{10}{26}$$

$$\therefore\ \operatorname{cosec}\frac{\theta}{2}=\frac{26}{10}=2\cdot6$$

$$\frac{\theta}{2}=22°\ 37'\quad\theta=45°\ 14'$$

$$\theta\ \text{in radians}=0\cdot789\ 5$$
$$\sin\theta=0\cdot710\ 0$$

$$A=\frac{r^2}{2}\ (\theta\ \text{in radians}-\sin\theta)$$

$$=\frac{169}{2}\ (0\cdot789\ 5-0\cdot710\ 0)$$

$$=84\cdot5\ (0\cdot079\ 5)=6\cdot718\ \text{mm}^2$$

(b) $\qquad\qquad A=\dfrac{2wh}{3}+\dfrac{h^3}{2w}$

$$=\frac{(2)(10)(1)}{3}+\frac{1}{20}$$

$$=6\cdot667+0\cdot05$$

$$=6\cdot717\ \text{mm}^2$$

Answer: Area, by either method$=6\cdot72\ \text{mm}^2$

Example

A hole of diameter 6 mm passes through the centre of a sphere of diameter 10 mm. Calculate the volume of the hoop so formed.

An approximate formula can be used if the $\dfrac{\text{chord}}{\text{height}}$ ratio of the implied segment is greater than 3. Take $\pi=\dfrac{22}{7}$.

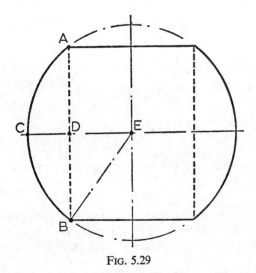

FIG. 5.29

Referring to Figure 5.29,

$$BE = \text{radius of sphere} = 5$$
$$DE = \text{radius of hole} = 3$$
$$BD = \sqrt{(5^2 - 3^2)} = \sqrt{16} = 4$$

Chord length w of segment $= 2(BD) = 8$
$$CD = CE - DE = 5 - 3 = 2.$$
Height h of segment $= 2$.

The $\dfrac{w}{h}$ ratio is greater than 3, hence the approximate formula can be used. The error in the area will be less than 0.1%

$$A = \frac{2wh}{3} + \frac{h^3}{2w} = \frac{2(8)(2)}{3} + \frac{2^3}{16}$$

$$= \frac{32}{3} + \frac{1}{2}$$

$$= \frac{67}{6}$$

The centroid of the segment lies at $\dfrac{w^3}{12A}$ from the axis of revolution (see Figure 5.27).

$$\bar{x}=\frac{8^3}{12\times\dfrac{67}{6}}=\frac{256}{67}$$

$$V=2\pi A\bar{x}$$

$$=\frac{44}{7}\times\frac{67}{6}\times\frac{256}{67}$$

$$=\frac{44\times128}{21}=\frac{5632}{21}=268\cdot2 \text{ mm}^3$$

Answer: Volume of hoop=268 mm³

Example

An extruded section has the form of the minor segment of a circle of radius 17 mm. The chord of the segment is of length 16 mm. The section is extruded from a billet of diameter 17·5 mm and length 80 mm.

Calculate the length of section extruded from the billet.

Take π as $\dfrac{22}{7}$, assume that there is no loss of volume during extrusion, and if the $\dfrac{\text{chord}}{\text{height}}$ ratio of the segment is over 3, an approximate formula for the area of the segment can be used.

$$8rh=w^2+4h^2 \text{ (see section 5.3.1)}$$
$$8\,(17)h=(16)^2+4h^2$$
$$136h=256+4h^2$$
$$4h^2-136h+256=0$$
$$h^2-34h+64=0$$
$$(h-32)(h-2)=0$$

∴ $h=2$ (the value $h=32$ applies to the major segment)

$\dfrac{w}{h}=\dfrac{\text{chord}}{\text{height}}$ ratio$=\dfrac{16}{2}=8$, hence an approximate formula can be used.

$$A=\frac{2wh}{3}+\frac{h^3}{2w}$$

$$=\frac{2(16)(2)}{3}+\frac{2^3}{32}$$

$$=21\cdot33+0\cdot25$$

$$=21\cdot58 \text{ mm}^2$$

Volume of section=volume of billet

Let length of section be L

$$21 \cdot 58 \times L = \frac{22}{7} \times \frac{70}{4} \times \frac{70}{4} \times \frac{80}{4}$$

$$21 \cdot 58 \; L = 19\,250$$

$$L = \frac{19\,250}{21 \cdot 58} = 892 \cdot 1$$

Answer: Length of section $= 892$ mm

Problems 5.3

1. An approximate formula sometimes used for the area of certain segments is

$$A = \frac{4h^2}{3} \sqrt{\left(\frac{w^2}{4h^2} + 0 \cdot 392 \right)}$$

where w is the length of the chord and h is the height of the segment.

Apply this formula to find the area of the minor segment of a circle of radius 41 mm, the height of the segment being 32 mm. Determine also the area using an accurate formula. (Use four-figure tables for the calculations.)

2. A formula for the area of a segment of a circle of radius r, the ends of the chord subtending an angle of θ is

$$A = \frac{r^2}{2} \; (\theta \text{ in radians} - \sin \theta).$$

If the length of arc is L, the height of the segment is h, and the length of chord is w, deduce another formula for the area of a segment in terms of r, L, h, and w, using the identity $\sin \theta = 2 \sin \frac{\theta}{2} \cos \frac{\theta}{2}$.

3. An approximate formula sometimes used for finding the area of a segment is $\frac{2wh}{3} + \frac{h^3}{2w}$, where w is the length of the chord and h is the height of the segment. This formula should only be adopted if the $\frac{w}{h}$ ratio is greater than 3. Obtain an indication of its inaccuracy by considering a semicircle to be a segment and determine the percentage error to one significant figure, if the approximate formula is mistakenly used.

4. A cylinder of aluminium alloy has a diameter of 100 mm and a length of 200 mm. A flat of width 40 mm is machined along the whole length.
Calculate:
(*a*) The depth of cut.
(*b*) The mass of metal removed, in grammes.
Take the relative density of the aluminium alloy as 2·8. An approximate formula for the area of a segment can be used if desired.

5. A bar of diameter 34 mm and length 80 mm has a slot machined of width 16 mm along its length. The depth at the side of the slot is 8 mm. Calculate the volume of metal removed in mm³.

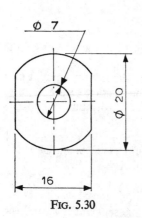

6. The special washer shown in Figure 5.30 is cut from strip of width 24 mm. The progression per washer is 18 mm. What percentage of material of the strip is used for the washers? An approximate formula for the area of a segment can be used and π can be taken as $\frac{22}{7}$.

Fig. 5.30

7. Figure 5.31 shows an extruded section. Calculate the length of this section, in millimetres, that can be extruded from a slug of diameter 28 mm and length 100 mm.

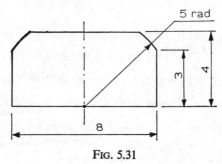

Fig. 5.31

8. A container in the form of a barrel has flat ends of diameter 1·2 m and the length between the ends is 2·4 m. The greatest diameter, at the centre, is 2·4 m. If the cross-section of the curved portion is a circular arc, calculate the capacity of the barrel, in litres. One cubic metre = 1000 litres, and adopt an approximate formula for the area of a segment. If L is the length of chord of a segment and A is its area, the centroid lies at $\dfrac{L^3}{12A}$ from the centre of the circular arc.

Answers to problems 5.3

1. Approximate value 1909 mm², accurate value 1908 mm².
2. $A = \dfrac{rL - wr + wh}{2}$
3. 0·8 % too large
4. (a) 4·17 mm   (b) 62·89 g
5. 12 000 mm³
6. 56·3 %
7. 1 980 mm
8. 8 060 litres
   (The segment has an area of 1·005 m², its centroid lying 0·846 2 m from the axis)